jumbo
Bible
crossword
collection
volume 3

BARBOUR
PUBLISHING, INC.
Uhrichsville, Ohio

© MCMXCIX by Barbour Publishing, Inc.

ISBN 1-57748-610-2

Published by Barbour Publishing, Inc., P.O. Box 719, Uhrichsville, Ohio 44683
http://www.barbourbooks.com

 Member of the
Evangelical Christian
Publishers Association

Printed in the United States of America.

jumbo Bible crossword collection

volume 3

PUZZLE 1

ACROSS

1. "Abraham built an ____"
   (Gen. 22:9)
5. "After these ____" (Gen. 22:1)
10. Public transportation
12. Needed for a shower
13. "Where is the lamb for a ____
    offering?" (Gen. 22:7)
14. Irish freedom fighters, abbr.
16. Peter said, "____ , we have left
    all" (Mark 10:28)
17. Male pronoun
18. "____ took all the silver"
    (1 Kings 15:18)
19. Study for an exam
21. Exclamation
22. Asian beast of burden
24. Concern
26. Isaac's replacement
    (Gen. 22:13)
28. First person pronoun
29. Place where Mary and Joseph
    found no room
30. Preposition that indicates
    belonging
32. Where Abraham went to
    sacrifice Isaac (Gen. 22:2)
34. He "laid the wood ____ order"
    (Gen. 22:9)
37. "God will ____" (Gen. 22:8)
39. "I and the lad will ____ yonder"
    (Gen. 22:5)
40. Company, abbr.
41. The opposite of followed
42. Irish county, abbr.
43. Lemon thirst quencher
44. Elongated fish
46. "Abraham and the ____ went
    together" (Gen. 22:5)
48. Adjective suffix indicating
    nationality or "somewhat"

49. Simile preposition
50. "Abraham rose up ____"
    (Gen. 22:3)
51. Abraham took three ____ to
    reach the mountain (Gen. 22:4)

DOWN

2. The kind of job your car needs
3. "God tested ____"
   (Gen. 22:1 NIV)
4. What a baseball player wants
5. Where the ram was caught
   (Gen. 22:13)
6. Abraham's son
7. Negative
8. Guy's date
9. Voiced
11. "None can ____ his hand"
    (Dan. 4:35)
15. Transportation on tracks, abbr.
17. The story's main character
20. Northeastern state
21. Either
23. Sky fellow, abbr.
25. Nurses, abbr.
27. Where Abraham was told to go
    (Gen. 22:2)
31. ____ up, excited
33. "The ____ of the Lord called
    unto him" (Gen. 22:11)
35. A swollen mass of tissue
36. The ____ was laid on the altar
    (Gen. 22:9)
37. "Abraham. . .saw the ____ afar
    off" (Gen. 22:4)
38. "Abraham lifted up his ____"
    (Gen. 22:4)
40. School group
42. "Pharaoh. . .sought to ____
    Moses" (Exod. 2:15)
45. Inquiring noise

4

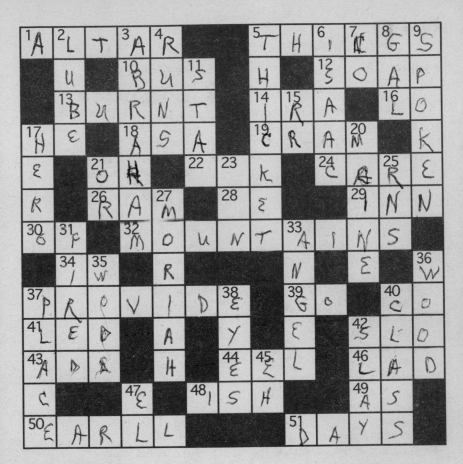

47. Overhead train
    by Elizabeth B. Smith

ACROSS

1. Moses's brother
5. People who make cloth by inter-lacing threads
11. Possible undergraduate degree for a minister, abbr.
12. Not yes
13. Do not ____ to the words of the prophecy (Rev. 22:18)
14. Black sticky substance
15. Infant
17. ____ of the Chaldees
18. Preposition that indicates location
20. Burnt offering for peace to the Lord (Exod. 24:5)
22. Aromatic substances (Exod. 25:6)
25. Sympathetic noise
26. Hole
27. Name for Mother
28. "____ a child is known by his doings" (Prov. 20:11)
30. Control
32. Something given to God
34. The color of the Tabernacle's ram skins (Exod. 25:5)
35. The language of Cervantes, abbr.
36. Head
38. The beings whose wings cover the mercy seat (Exod. 25:20)
43. Address abbreviation
45. Opposite of off
46. Selenium, chem. symbol
47. Eleven, Rom. num.
48. Ancient
49. Metal taken as a Tabernacle offering (Exod. 25:3)
51. Why Jesus died
52. Place near Bethel (Gen. 13:3 NIV)
53. Young adult, abbr.
54. Greatest Christian virtue
55. Fabric dyed blue, purple, and scarlet for the Tabernacle (Exod. 25:4)
56. Silver, chem. symbol
57. The priest who took care of Hannah's son Samuel

DOWN

1. Short for Abigail
2. Woman's name
3. Stone worn on Aaron's shoulders (Exod. 28:9, 12)
4. A denial
5. Armed conflict
6. Edward, for short
7. Adjust
8. Alien from space, abbr.
9. "Let us run with patience the ____ that is set before us" (Heb. 12:1)
10. Jr.'s father
16. Kind of tie
17. Not, prefix
19. Note on the scale
21. "The Lord shall reign for ____ " (Exod. 15:18)
22. "Trees of the wood ____ out" (1 Chron. 16:33)
23. "Enter. . .into his ____ with praise" (Ps. 100:4)
24. "Thy ____ will I establish" (Ps. 89:4)
25. American Academy of Family Physicians, abbr.
26. Writing instrument
27. The man God sent to deliver the Israelites from the Egyptians
29. Contender
31. Shelter from the wind

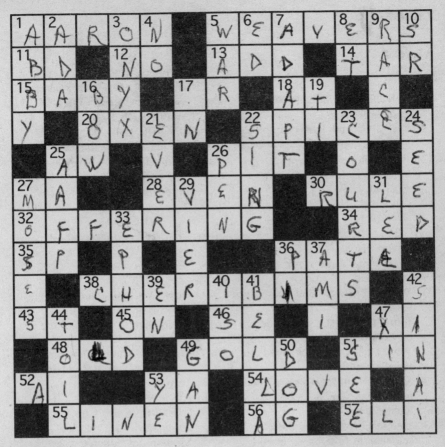

A	A	R	O	N		W	E	A	V	E	R	S
B	D		N	O		A	D	D		T	A	R
B	A	B	Y			R		A	T		C	
Y		O	X	E	N		S	P	I	C	E	S
	A	W		V		P	I	T		O		E
M	A		E	V	E	R	N		R	U	L	E
O	F	F	R	I	N	G			R	E	D	
S	P	P	E					P	A	T	E	
E		C	H	E	R	I	B	U	M	S		S
S	T		E	I	B			I		X	A	
	O	A	D	G	O	L	D		S	I	N	A
A	I		Y	A			L	O	V	E		A
	L	I	N	E	N		A	G		E	L	I

Across / Down clues:

33. Jewish priest's outer vestment
36. Greek letter
37. Friend, Fr.
39. Printer's measure, approximately half of an em
40. United Service Organizations, abbr.
41. Beautiful, Ital.
42. Mountain where Moses talked with God
44. "They _____ not, neither do they spin" (Matt. 6:28)
47. Greek letter
49. Past tense of gin

50. "A _____ returneth to his vomit" (Prov. 26:11)
51. "That we may _____ and believe" (Mark 15:32)
53. Old-fashioned you

7

ACROSS

1. Biblical river
6. Longest book in the Bible
11. Female friends, Fr.
12. "There is death in the ____" (2 Kings 4:40)
13. Where those who are alive will meet the Lord when He comes again (1 Thess. 4:17)
14. "He esteemeth ____ as straw" (Job 41:27)
15. "She. . .hid them with the ____ of flax" (Josh. 2:6)
16. Ceremonial form of prayer
19. Asian tree
20. When you'll get there, more or less, abbr.
22. John the Baptist's was made of camel hair (Matt. 3:4)
25. What a baby needs changed
28. Hesitant syllable
29. Jonathan shot this to warn David not to return to Saul's house
32. Route, abbr.
33. Joseph's brothers had these searched to find his silver cup
36. The eleventh letter of the Hebrew alphabet
37. Exclamation of surprise and triumph
38. God sent Jonah to warn this city
40. The wise men
41. Put off till a later time
42. Exist
43. Article that precedes a vowel
44. Firstborn son of Isaac and Rebecca
45. Chum
46. Severely
49. Bitter water was turned to this at Marah
50. Abraham's father

DOWN

1. Man charged to keep Paul and Silas safe in prison (Acts 16:23)
2. Sixth king of Israel (1 Kings 16:16)
3. Violent public disturbance
4. Small silver coin of ancient Rome
5. Preposition used in a simile
6. "We are the clay, and thou our ____" (Isa. 64:8)
7. "The Lord. . .purposed it to ____ the pride" (Isa. 23:9)
8. "Cast alive into a ____ of fire" (Rev. 19:20)
9. How God first watered the earth
10. Twelfth-grader, abbr.
12. Addendum at the end of the letter, abbr.
17. Told by Elisha to wash himself seven times in the River Jordan
18. Yelp
21. Albert's nickname
23. One of the Spirit's fruit, a lowly spirit
24. Modern-day country where Noah's Ark is rumored to be
26. Spinning toy
27. Son of Kishi (1 Chron. 6:44)
30. Cheer
31. Ezekiel saw this in his visions
32. Sixth book of the New Testament
34. Apple drink
35. Psalm word
39. Burial chamber
42. "Valley of ____" (Ps. 84:6)
46. Masculine pronoun
47. Preposition indicating location
48. King James Version of you

1 J	2 O	3 R	4 D	5 A	N	■	6 P	7 S	A	8 L	9 M	10 S
11 A	M	I	A	S	■	12 P	O	T	■	13 A	I	R
14 I	R	O	R	■	15 S	T	A	L	K	S	■	
16 L	I	T	A	17 N	18 Y	■	19 T	I	■	20 E	T	21 A
E	■	22 R	A	I	M	23 M	E	N	24 T	■	■	L
R	25 D	I	A	P	E	R	■	U	26 T	■		
■	27 E	28	M	■	E	29 A	R	30 R	O	31 W		
32 R	T	33 S	A	34 C	K	35 S	■	36 K	H	P		
37 O	H	38 N	I	N	E	V	39 E	H				
40 M	A	G	I	41 D	E	L	A	Y	42 B	E		
43 A	N	44 T	S	A	U	45 P	A	L				
N	46 H	47 A	R	S	E	L	48 Y	C				
49 S	W	E	E	T	■	50 T	E	A				

ACROSS

1. Father of the Chosen People (Gen. 12:1–3)
8. Prophet who tore his cloak into twelve pieces (1 Kings 11:30)
13. Sheep's noise
14. Old Testament prophet, between Amos and Jonah
17. Brief letter
18. Samuel's mentor
19. The rock city of Idumaea (Isa. 16:1)
20. No-good fellow
22. Lions failed to harm him
23. Third longest book of prophecy in the Old Testament
24. Northern central state, abbr.
25. Drill instructor, abbr.
26. King of Israel (1 Kings 16:16)
27. Jacob's son (Gen. 30:10–11)
28. Belonging to a son of Aaron (1 Chron. 24:1)
32. This animal alive is better than a dead lion (Eccles. 9:4)
33. Belonging to the man who shot Jehoram through the heart (2 Kings 9:24)
35. Nehemiah's priest and scribe
39. Eliasaph was the son of this man (Num. 7:42)
41. A servant in the house of Saul (2 Sam. 9:2)
44. "All they that hate me love ____" (Prov. 8:36)
46. Asian woman's garment
47. Abraham's son
48. "Cursed is the ____ who. . . sacrifices a blemished animal to the Lord" (Mal. 1:14 NIV)
50. This place in Moab was ruined in the night (Isa. 15:1)
51. "____! The gate to the nations is broken" (Ezek. 26:2 NIV)
52. The judge and prophet who established the kingship in Israel (1 Sam. 8:21–22)
53. His wife became a pillar of salt
54. The Lord showed him a plumbline

56. Chemical symbol for argon
57. "Prophet of the Temple" and a colleague of Zechariah (Ezra 5:1)
59. "The name of the wicked shall ____" (Prov. 10:7)
61. Needed for a photograph
64. Unit of dry measurement, abbr.
65. Moses successor (Num. 27:18–23)
68. One of the twelve spies, the only one left alive in the desert with Joshua (Num. 26:65)
70. Exist
72. Cast a ballot
73. Sleuth, abbr.
74. "I will spread my ____ upon them" (Hos. 7:12)
75. David's father

DOWN

1. In bed
2. The mercenary prophet (Num. 22:5–7)
3. "I will ____ bread from heaven" (Exod. 16:4)
4. Prophet who married Gomer
5. Killed by his brother
6. Last book of the Old Testament, abbr.
7. Joshua sent men there from Jericho (Josh. 7:2)
8. King of Judah at 22 years old who reigned for only a year (2 Kings 8:26)
9. Opposite of out
10. He was 8 years old when he became king and he reigned for 31 years (2 Kings 22:1)
11. Preposition
12. State of everlasting separation from God
15. Israel's poet king
16. Did perfectly on a test
21. Eastern seaboard state
24. "The ____ of sin is death" (Rom. 6:23)
26. Son of Boaz (Ruth 4:21)
27. Appeared to Abraham when he was 99 years old (Gen. 17:1)

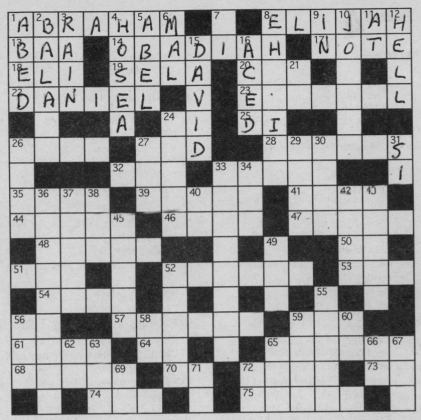

29. Ezekiel's father (Ezek. 1:3)
30. Egyptian goddess
31. Juan's yes
33. The weeping prophet
34. Word said by Christ on the cross (Matt. 27:46)
36. Second from the last book of the Old Testament
37. The son of Shema and the father of Jorkoam (1 Chron. 2:43)
38. Consumed
40. United Airlines, abbr.
42. Ahab served this god (1 Kings 16:31)
43. Supported Moses' hands in battle (Exod. 17:8–13)
45. "A ____ word stirs up anger" (Prov. 15:1 NIV)
49. King Darius threw Daniel here (Dan. 6:16)

52. The youngest son of Hiel of Bethel, who lost his life when the gates of Jericho were set up (1 Kings 16:34)
55. The man to whom God gave the Ten Commandments
56. American Football Conference, abbr.
58. Fifth month of the Jewish year
59. Decays
60. Chemical symbol for thorium
62. Lending library, abbr.
63. "I will make you fishers of ____" (Matt. 4:19)
65. Joseph for short
66. The opposite of down
67. To trouble, afflict
69. Chemical symbol for beryllium
71. Estimated position, abbr.
72. Video jockey, abbr.
by Michael J. Landi

11

PUZZLE 5

ACROSS

1. "Give me this ____" (John 4:15)
5. "____ of false prophets" (Matt. 7:15)
10. Jacque's friend
11. Noncommissioned officer, abbr.
12. Angry
14. "Behold the ____ of God" (John 1:29)
16. Small child
17. "Set your affection on things above, not on things on the ____" (Col. 3:2)
20. "Cleanse your ____" (James 4:8)
24. Dessert
25. "Ye have not because ye ____ not" (James 4:2)
26. "Set thy ____ among the stars" (Obad. 1:4)
27. New England state, abbr.
28. Abram's nephew
30. The son of Peleth (Num. 16:1)
31. "God gave the ____" (1 Cor. 3:6)
34. Ruth's second husband (Ruth 4:13)
35. Masculine pronoun
36. "At thy word I will let down the ____" (Luke 5:5)
37. "Every ____ shall see him" (Rev. 1:7)
39. Summer beverage
40. Alternating current, abbr.
41. "The ____ of those things is death" (Rom. 6:21)
44. Spoken
46. "____ thy foot against a stone" (Matt. 4:6)
48. God gave Joshua the victory over ____ (Josh. 8:1)
50. "Clothed in pure and white ____" (Rev. 15:6)
51. Nicodemus was a ____ of the Jews (John 3:1)
53. Alcoholic beverage
54. The Creator
55. "There is none good but ____" (Mark 10:18)

DOWN

1. "We ____ by faith" (2 Cor. 5:7)
2. Japanese pearl diver
3. "Grace to help in ____ of need" (Heb. 4:16)
4. Nurse, abbr.
5. "____ young men, and maidens" (Ps. 148:12)
6. "None is able to ____ thee" (2 Chron. 20:6)
7. Relating or resembling, suffix
8. "Who giveth ____ upon the earth" (Job 5:10)
9. And, Lat.
13. Elevated trains
15. To immerse or dip in water
18. Smallest state, abbr.
19. "A ____ of babes" (Rom. 2:20)
21. Largest state, abbr.
22. Dead letter office, abbr.
23. Genus, comb. form
25. Score an A
26. "These were more ____ than those in Thessalonica" (Acts 17:11)
28. "If thou ____ this man go" (John 19:12)
29. "False ____ among you" (2 Pet. 2:1)
32. Regarding, abbr.
33. The ____ is the word of God (Luke 8:11)
38. "Teach the ____ women" (Titus 2:4)

39. Louisiana's neighbor, abbr.
40. Preposition
42. "She put her hand to the ____"
    (Judg. 5:26)
43. "Jesus saith unto them, Come
    and ____." (John 21:12)
45. "Paul the ____" (Philem. 9)
47. "____ to keep you from falling"
    (Jude 24)
49. Male sibling, for short
50. City in California, abbr.
52. International peace-keeping
    organization, abbr.
    by Carole Stengel

PUZZLE 6

ACROSS

1. "Receive his mark in his ____, or in his hand" (Rev. 14:9)
7. "If the foot shall say, Because I am not the ____, I am not of the body" (1 Cor. 12:15)
10. Imperial Chemical Industries, abbr.
11. "In the day thou wast born thy ____ was not cut" (Ezek. 16:4)
12. Bird's beak
13. "Let ____ esteem other better than themselves" (Phil. 2:3)
14. Speed measurement, abbr.
15. Car fuel
16. Peruvian beast of burden
18. The letter that follows "em"
20. East Indies, abbr.
21. Either
22. "Fall by the ____ of the sword" (Luke 21:24)
24. Activity or movement
26. Preposition
27. Fifteen, Rom. num.
28. Wing of a building
29. "I am escaped with the skin of my ____" (Job 19:20)
32. The letter that precedes "em"
34. "A man's pride shall bring him ____" (Prov. 29:23)
36. "The government shall be upon his ____" (Isa. 9:6)
40. Midwest state, abbr.
41. Negative
43. Last, prefix
44. Violent group
45. Sticky
46. "God. . .spake in time ____ unto the fathers by the prophets" (Heb. 1:1)
49. First person plural pronoun
50. Female, suffix
51. Sheep's noise
52. And so on, Lat. abbr.
53. Verb of being
54. "The ____ of every man is Christ" (1 Cor. 11:3)

DOWN

1. "Jesus. . .with his ____ wrote on the ground" (John 8:6)
2. The Atlantic or Pacific
3. "The Lord God. . .took one of his ____ , and closed up the flesh" (Gen. 2:21)
4. "Thou shalt bruise his ____ " (Gen. 3:15)
5. "Immediately his feet and ____ bones received strength" (Acts 3:7 O.E. spelling)
6. Flower
7. Fifth letter of the Hebrew alphabet
8. Soul, Lat.
9. Remove horns
17. The widow's ____
19. Edward, for short
21. Kind of tea
22. "Having ____, see ye not?" (Mark 8:18)
23. Used-to-be, prefix
25. "Love worketh no ____ to his neighbour" (Rom 13:10)
26. Exist
29. "The ____ is a little member" (James 3:5)
30. "Take of his blood. . .upon the ____ of their right hand" (Exod. 29:20)
31. "____, is the Lord of Hosts" (Isa. 6:3)
32. Word reviser, abbr.

14

33. "They brake not his ____"
    (John 19:33)
35. First person plural pronoun
37. Arizona's neighbor, abbr.
38. "Only her ____ moved, but her
    voice was not heard"
    (1 Sam. 1:13)
39. Rodent
42. To drive out
47. The remains of burned wood
48. "With the ____ bone of an
    ass . . . have I slain a thousand
    men" (Judg. 15:16)
50. Printer's measure

51. Minister's undergraduate
    degree, abbr.

ACROSS

1. Cut
7. "He fell into a ____"
   (Acts 10:10)
13. Declares
14. "The son of Geber, in ____-gilead" (1 Kings 4:13)
15. Jesus' birthplace
17. Exist
19. The number of commandments God gave Moses
20. "____, every one that thirsteth" (Isa. 55:1)
22. Animal that Christ rode on Palm Sunday
24. Depend on others' money
26. "Whether it be good or ____" (2 Cor. 5:10)
27. Activity
29. "Then an ____ cried aloud" (Dan. 3:4)
31. Pertaining to air, prefix
32. "God hath given ____ unto your brethren" (Josh. 22:4)
33. Hastens
35. "The seed is ____ under their clods" (Joel 1:17)
37. Vigor
38. "____ died without children" (1 Chron. 2:30)
40. When you think you'll get there, abbr.
41. Three feet, abbr.
43. Relative, abbr.
45. Part of the blood that carries iron, abbr.
46. "The Lord fulfil all thy ____" (Ps. 20:5)
50. "This Agar is Mount Sinai in ____" (Gal. 4:25)

52. "We have had ____ to eat" (2 Chron. 31:10)
55. "The ____ is not dead, but sleepeth" (Mark 5:39)
56. "Thou shalt utterly ____ it" (Deut. 7:26)

DOWN

1. Verb of being
2. The Bible's new covenant, abbr.
3. Taxi
4. Article
5. Place
6. Mehir was the father of ____ (1 Chron. 4:11)
7. "He made a ____ about the altar" (1 Kings 18:32)
8. Cheer
9. "Surely I come quickly. ____" (Rev. 22:20)
10. Name, Fr.
11. Massachusetts' neighbor
12. Questioning noise
16. Man's name
17. Sheep noise
18. "There ____ not a man of them" (1 Sam. 30:17)
20. "I will save her that ____" (Zeph. 3:19)
21. "The ____ number of them is to be redeemed" (Num. 3:48)
23. Sharply inclined
24. Emotions
25. "They should not return to ____" (Matt. 2:12)
26. Sew quickly
28. Anger
30. Return, abbr.
33. "Who came in privily to ____ out our liberty" (Gal. 2:4)
34. Appearing in consecutive parts

35. "They ____ upon the Lord God of their fathers" (2 Chron. 13:18)
36. Seize for arrest
39. "I will ____ you go"(Exod. 8:28)
42. "Their ____ shall not become garments" (Isa. 59:6)
44. Nautical mile
46. Girl's nickname
47. "____ them about thy neck" (Prov. 6:21)
48. "The Lord our God is____ Lord" (Mark 12:29)
49. "If any man will ____ thee at the law" (Matt. 5:40)
50. Commercial, abbr.
51. Radium, chem. symbol
53. Organization for young females, abbr.
54. Altitude, abbr.

by Evelyn M. Boyington

ACROSS

1. "I am the ____ ____ ____,
   and the lily of the valleys"
   (Song of Sol. 2:1) (3 words)
9. Not out
10. Timid
11. On or about, abbr.
12. "I am the ____ ____, and know
    my sheep" (John 10:14)
    (2 words)
17. Immerse briefly in water
18. Central state, Des Moines is the
    capital, abbr.
20. "I am the way, ____ ____, and
    the life" (John 14:6) (2 words)
24. "Behold the ____ of God"
    (John 1:29)
26. Extraterrestial, abbr.
27. Suffix
28. "____, every one that thirsteth"
    (Isa. 55:1)
29. Two, Rom. num.
31. "The ____ ____ ____ is Lord
    even of the sabbath" (Matt. 12:8)
    (3 words)
34. "We have not ____ this power"
    (1 Cor. 9:12)
37. Network, especially of blood
    vessels
38. Learning disabled, abbr.
39. "Jesus Christ, the ____ ____
    ____" (Mark 1:1) (3 words)
42. Certified Public Accountant,
    abbr.
43. Containing oxygen, prefix
44. Dorothy's state, abbr.
45. Head nurse, abbr.
46. "Lest I ____ you in pieces"
    (Ps. 50:22)
48. "The Spirit of God descending
    like a ____" (Matt. 3:16)
51. Took a chair

53. "I am the ____" (John 14:6)
54. "I am. . .the bright and ____
    ____" (Rev. 22:16) (2 words)

DOWN

1. "An advocate with the Father,
   Jesus Christ the ____"
   (1 John 2:1)
2. "Who built ____, and Lod"
   (1 Chron. 8:12)
3. Compose, var. form
4. Follicle stimulating hormone,
   abbr.
5. Feminine pronoun
6. Hypothesis, abbr.
7. "Let her be as the loving hind
   and pleasant ____" (Prov. 5:19)
8. Paddle
13. Poem
14. Nimble
15. Masculine pronoun
16. "His eyes were ____, so that he
    could not see" (Gen. 27:1)
19. "According to his ____ mercy"
    (1 Pet. 1:3)
21. Altitude, abbr.
22. Thorough, nonstandard spelling
23. Sharpened
24. "I am the bread of ____"
    (John 6:35)
25. Direct toward a target
30. Understanding
32. Writings that contain the old
    covenant, abbr.
33. "I am ____ and Omega"
    (Rev. 1:8)
35. "They were ____ afraid"
    (Mark 9:6)
36. "I am the ____:. . .if any man
    enter in, he shall be saved"
    (John 10:9)

40. Effects, abbr.
41. "Emmanuel, which being interpreted is, _____ with us" (Matt. 1:23)
44. "I will give unto thee the _____ of the kingdom" (Matt. 16:19)
46. Nashville's state, abbr.
47. "Why make ye this _____, and weep" (Mark 5:39)
49. "I seek not mine _____ will, but the will of the Father" (John 5:30)
50. Vagrancy, abbr.
51. Large body of water

52. Nurse, abbr.

PUZZLE 9

ACROSS

1. "A ____ that needeth not to be ashamed" (2 Tim. 2:15)
6. "The word of God. . .is sharper than any twoedged ____" (Heb. 4:12)
10. Friend, Fr.
11. When you will arrive, approximately, abbr.
12. In favor of
13. Belonging to God's chose nation
15. Young lady, Fr., abbr.
17. Man's name
19. Sons of Judah, Er and ____ (Gen. 46:12)
21. Edward, for short
23. Chinese dynasty
24. Firstborn son of Judah (Gen. 38:2–3)
27. Primps
29. "____ not yourselves" (Rom. 12:19)
31. "When the morning stars ____" (Job 38:7)
32. "Jesus thou ____ of God" (Matt. 8:29)
33. Letter before "em"
34. Teletypewriter, abbr.
35. In order that
37. Small particle
39. Translation, abbr.
41. Son of Adam
43. Prophet during David's reign
46. Masculine article, Fr.
47. Indicate agreement with a movement of the head
48. "These ____ Milcah did bear" (Gen. 22:23)
50. Letter after "em"
52. Preposition
53. "Lion will not ____ himself" (Isa. 31:4)
55. Sea lettuce
57. "____ obtained favor" (Esther 2:15)
58. Moisten

DOWN

1. "As ____ as snow" (Rev. 1:14)
2. "A ____ thing" (Dan. 2:11)
3. Department store chain
4. Appearance
5. Sea monster of loch
6. America's uncle
7. "____ the ears, but he heareth not" (Isa. 42:20)
8. Transportation on tracks, abbr.
9. "Let us not be weary in well ____" (Gal 6:9)
14. "____ my people go" (Exod. 5:1)
16. Brief periods of time
18. Hills
20. Response, abbr.
22. "I. . .beheld your ____, I found an altar with this inscription, TO THE UNKNOWN GOD" (Acts 17:23)
25. City in Nevada
26. "Delivered when she was past ____" (Heb. 11:11)
28. "Take it, and ____ it up" (Rev. 10:9)
29. Josaphat's father (Matt. 1:8)
30. Building wing
35. To stow, especially in a ship's hold
36. Exclamation
38. St. Paul is the capital of this state, abbr.
39. Not that

40. "The heathen _____" (Ps. 46:6)
42. Masculine article, Sp.
44. "Lest he _____ my soul like a lion" (Ps. 7:2)
45. New England state, abbr.
47. "As it was in the days of _____, so shall it be also in the days of the Son of man" (Luke 17:26)
49. Stomach, for short
51. Girl's name
53. Syllable of satisfaction
54. Exist
56. Low pressure, abbr.

by Cheryl Keiser

ACROSS

1. "Divided the light from the ____" (Gen. 1:4)
8. "He causeth his wind to ____" (Ps. 147:18)
12. Indiana State University, abbr.
13. Angers
14. "Sat upon ____ of them" (Acts 2:3)
15. Village, abbr.
16. "The earth brought forth ____" (Gen. 1:12)
18. Nazareth College and Academy, abbr.
19. Chemical suffix
20. Eastern seaboard state
21. "Being understood by the things that are made, even his ____ power" (Rom. 1:20)
25. Iron, chem. symbol
26. 9th through 12th grades, abbr.
27. "Let my people ____" (Exod. 5:1)
28. "Voice ____ like the sea" (Jer. 6:23 NAS)
30. "And darkness was upon the face of the ____" (Gen. 1:2)
32. "In the beginning ____" (Gen. 1:1)
34. Son of Peleg (Gen. 11:18)
35. "God called the light ____" (Gen. 1:5)
36. "Yielding ____ after his kind" (Gen. 1:12)
37. "____ I have done this" (Ps. 7:3)
39. Fifty-four, Rom. num.
40. "Thou mayest freely ____" (Gen. 2:16)
41. "She took some and ____ it" (Gen. 3:6 NIV)
42. Articles

44. "____ that may fly above the earth" (Gen. 1:20)
47. "Thou shalt ____ eat of it" (Gen. 2:17)
48. "Let there be ____ in the firmament" (Gen. 1:14)
50. "Planted a garden in the ____" (Gen. 2:8 NIV)
52. Fellow of Entomology Society, abbr.
53. American Association of University Professors, abbr.
55. "The ____ was without form" (Gen. 1:2)
56. "And the ____ yielding fruit" (Gen. 1:12)

DOWN

1. "God ____ the light from the darkness" (Gen. 1:4)
2. "I will now turn ____, and see" (Exod. 3:3)
3. "The greater light to ____ the day" (Gen. 1:16)
4. "And the darkness he called ____" (Gen. 1:5)
5. "A people that do ____ in their heart" (Ps. 95:10)
6. "Have dominion over the fish of the ____" (Gen. 1:26)
7. Selective Service System, abbr.
8. "Let there ____ light" (Gen. 1:3)
9. "Let the dry ____ appear" (Gen. 1:9)
10. Ozark Christian College, abbr.
11. "God created great ____" (Gen. 1:21)
17. "I saw a ____ fall from heaven" (Rev. 9:1)
21. Catch sight of
22. "Any taste in the white of an ____" (Job 6:6)

23. Rest, as a bird
24. "And the ____ God planted" (Gen. 2:8)
25. "And the ____ of righteousness is sown in peace" (James 3:18)
26. "Thus the ____ and the earth were finished" (Gen. 2:1)
29. Of age, Lat. abbr.
31. Revise
33. Dover's state, abbr.
38. "The God which ____ me all my life" (Gen. 48:15)
39. "The moving creature that hath ____" (Gen. 1:20)
40. Suffix meaning to the utmost degree

41. "Thou shalt make an ____" (Exod. 30:1)
43. "Why beholdest thou the ____" (Matt. 7:3)
44. "____ which we did eat in Egypt" (Num. 11:5)
45. King of Bashan (Num. 21:33)
46. "Said unto the woman, ____ is this?" (Gen. 3:13)
48. "____ there be light" (Gen. 1:3)
49. "If any man will ____ thee" (Matt. 5:40)
51. Preposition
52. Romance language, abbr.
54. Sweaty class
by Rebecca Souder

PUZZLE 11

ACROSS

1. "There was a marriage in ____ of Galilee" (John 2:1)
5. Headwear
8. "When they saw the ____, they rejoiced" (Matt. 2:10)
12. Son of Jerameel (1 Chron. 2:25)
13. "If we confess ____ sins" (1 John 1:9)
14. "Her ____ shall be holiness to the Lord" (Isa. 23:18)
15. Mexican money
16. Suffix meaning "process or function"
17. "For I have slain ____ ____" (Gen. 4:23) (2 words)
18. "Thou hast made us to drink the wine of ____" (Ps. 60:3)
21. "The archers ____ him" (1 Sam. 31:3)
22. Shoe width
23. "It shall be health to thy ____" (Prov. 3:8)
26. Girl's name
27. "That I may ____ Christ" (Phil. 3:8)
30. "It shall be a statute for ____" (Lev. 23:31)
31. "Samuel arose, and ____ him up from Gilgal" (1 Sam. 13:15)
32. Son of Zerah (1 Chron. 2:6)
33. Money owed the government
34. "____ also the Jairite was a chief ruler about David" (2 Sam. 20:26)
35. "Thou shalt call his name ____: for he shall save his people from their sins" (Matt. 1:21)
36. Onassis
37. "Babylon is taken, ____ is confounded" (Jer. 50:2)

38. "To ____ of goods, or to imprisonment" (Ezra 7:26)
44. "There was also ____ ____ for the tribe of Manasseh" (Josh. 17:1) (2 words)
45. Place for experiments
46. "Strain at a ____" (Matt. 23:24)
48. Belonging to me
49. Compass point
50. Prefix for half
51. Not rich
52. Of the, Sp.
53. Very, Fr.

DOWN

1. Police officer (slang)
2. Vicinity
3. Scottish lake
4. "There arose ____ generation after them" (Judg. 2:10)
5. "____ it all joy" (James 1:2)
6. Comb. form for ear
7. "Now therefore ____ yourselves before the Lord" (1 Sam. 10:19)
8. "How long will you turn my glory into ____?" (Ps. 4:2)
9. "My ____ is at hand" (Mt. 26:18)
10. Brother of Uz (1 Chron. 1:42)
11. "A great and strong wind ____ the mountains" (1 Kings 19:11)
19. "They. . .their lamps, and took no ____ with them" (Matt. 25:3)
20. "Even as a ____ gathereth her chickens" (Matt. 23:37)
23. "For he shall pluck my feet out of the ____" (Ps. 25:15)
24. "And the king of Assyria brought men from Babylon. . . and from ____" (2 Kings 17:24)
25. "For they ____ you with their

wiles" (Num. 25:18)
26. Auto club, abbr.
27. "And the child _____ cured" (Matt. 17:18)
28. First son of Caleb (1 Chron. 4:15)
29. Naval Air Station, abbr.
31. "The rams . . .are ringstraked. . . and _____" (Gen. 31:12)
32. "But his _____ is in the law of the Lord" (Ps. 1:2)
34. A son of Bela (1 Chron. 7:7)
35. Type of airplane
36. "They returned from searching of the land _____ forty days" (Num. 13:25)
37. "And the beginning of his [Nimrod's] kingdom was _____" (Gen. 10:10)
38. "I will _____ against thee" (Isa. 29:3)
39. Miscellaneous mixture
40. Something forbidden
41. "Sweet _____ from a far country" (Jer. 6:20)
42. Latin prefix meaning "burden"
43. "Ye might have life through his _____" (John 20:31)
47. Poetic contraction for "it is"

by Janet W. Adkins

ACROSS

1. Christian disciple from Joppa who was known for her charity (Acts 9:36–43)
6. Resurrection day
10. Sixth Jewish month (Neh. 6:15)
11. Jesus did not give this to Pilate (John 19:9)
12. In the direction of
13. Derisive wit that attacks evil
15. A priest placed blood on the tips of these (Lev. 14:14)
18. Dog noise
19. Laughter noise
20. "The valley of the shadow of ____" (Ps. 23:4)
21. Live
22. Noah's boat
24. What John did to the little book given to him by the angel (Rev. 10:10)
25. Eagle (Lev. 11:18)
27. The son of Ikkesh (2 Sam. 23:26)
28. Expressing gratitude
31. Ceremonial act
32. "Wilt thou break a ____ driven to and fro?" (Job 13:25)
33. In order that
35. Up to now
36. "May be able to comprehend with all saints what is the ____, and length, and depth, and height" (Eph. 3:18)
39. "This is the ____ which the Lord hath made" (Ps. 118:24)
41. Absence or closure of a natural body passage
44. "I shall ____ thee wisdom" (Job 33:33)
46. The Lord makes us do this in green pastures
48. To act properly
50. "____ Lord God! behold, thou hast made the heaven and earth" (Jer. 32:17)
51. "They sought to ____ hold on him" (Mark 12:12)
52. Edward, for short
53. One does this on the seventh day of the week
54. Feminine pronoun

DOWN

1. Dover is the capital of this state, abbr.
2. Old Latin, abbr.
3. Moabite woman from whom Christ was descended
4. Jesus ascended up to heaven in one of these
5. A day of rest and worship
6. Curved shape
7. Gone
8. Animal or plant bristle
9. Voyage
14. Son of Salah and grandson of Shem (Gen. 10:24)
15. "The child Jesus ____ behind in Jerusalem" (Luke 2:43)
16. "His ____ was locusts" (Matt. 3:4)
17. "For every one that ____ shall be cut off" (Zech. 5:3)
19. Esau was, but Jacob wasn't
21. Pleads
23. Part of the children of Zebulun's inheritance (Josh. 19:15–16)
25. "Covet earnestly the best ____" (1 Cor. 12:31)
26. Opposite of out

29. "The day of the Lord is ____" (Obad. 1:15)
30. Location of the water of Meribah (Num. 27:14)
34. Amorite king (Deut. 31:4)
37. Contests of speed
38. "The mountains and the ____ shall break forth before you into singing" (Isa. 55:12)
40. Paul continued a ____ and a half at Corinth (Acts 18:11)
42. The father of Rizpah, Saul's concubine (2 Sam. 3:7)
43. President Lincoln, for short
45. Address abbreviation
47. "Mine ____ affecteth mine heart" (Lam. 3:51)
49. Edwin for short
50. In this way
by Janet W. Adkins

ACROSS

1. King of Judah (Isa. 38:1)
7. Son of Jacob
10. Four, Rom. num.
11. While in Antioch, this man predicted a famine (Acts 11:27–28)
12. "At Antioch there were prophets and teachers: Barnabas, Simeon. . . , Lucius of Cyrene, ____ and Saul" (Acts 13:1 NIV)
14. This king destroyed and burned an idol his mother had made (1 Kings 15:13)
16. Don't fight like a man beating this (1 Cor. 9:26)
17. For example, Lat. abbr.
18. Ancestor of Saul and the son of Benjamin (1 Sam. 9:1)
20. God's name for Himself, I ____
21. "Will your ____ talk reduce men to silence?" (Job 11:3 NIV)
23. "A man of ____ spirit gains honor" (Prov. 29:23 NIV)
25. Cathode, abbr.
27. Southern state, abbr.
28. "The ____ shall eat straw like the ox" (Isa. 11:7)
30. Pertaining to urinary tract, prefix
31. "The body is a ____, though it is made up of many parts" (1 Cor. 12:12 NIV)
32. The man who lost both his inheritance and his blessing to his brother (Gen. 27:30–40)
33. Succeeded Ahaziah as king (2 Kings 1:17 NIV)
35. Nautical measure of speed, abbr.
36. Harry's nickname
38. First month of autumn, abbr.
40. One of the border towns of the children of Naphtali (Josh. 19:32–33)
43. "Their feet ____ into sin" (Isa. 59:7 NIV)
45. Article
46. Belonging to a priest in Midian who had seven daughters (Exod. 2:11–3:1)

49. "The ____ is already at the root" (Matt. 3:10 NIV)
50. Alternate spelling for 15 down
51. Greek word for "my God" (Matt. 27:46 NIV)
53. Shipbuilder and zookeeper
55. A prophet and book of the Old Testament
56. Dorm helper, abbr.
57. Collection of sayings
59. New Testament prophetess (Luke 2:36)
60. "Cancel any ____ your brother owes" (Deut. 15:3 NIV)
62. Old Testament book that follows Ezra
65. "Better a ____ of vegetables where there is love" (Prov. 15:17 NIV)
67. "Let the dead ____ their dead" (Luke 9:60)
68. A book of the Penteteuch, abbr.
70. This man lived and died, but he was never born
72. "____, follow me" (Matt. 4:19 NIV)
73. This man disagreed with a great fish
74. A son of Noah (Gen. 5:32)

DOWN

1. Prophet of Judah and book of the Old Testament
2. King who went into the citadel of the palace and set it on fire, dying there (1 Kings 16:18)
3. Peron's first name
4. "Let us make man in our ____" (Gen. 1:26)
5. False prophet who took the yoke off Jeremiah's neck and broke it (Jer. 28:10)
6. Sent to David to rebuke him and expose his sin (2 Sam. 12:1–10)
7. Father of all who play the harp or the flute (Gen. 4:21)
8. America, abbr.
9. Amnon was killed by him for raping Tamar (2 Sam. 13:1–29)
13. Girl's name
15. Youngest of the Little Women

19. "Ye know neither the day nor the ____" (Matt. 25:13)
22. A Reubenite who was swallowed up by the earth (Num. 16:27–32)
24. A gentle answer turns this away (Prov. 15:1)
26. The daughter of Phanuel (Luke 2:36)
28. Library science, abbr.
29. Old uncial, abbr.
32. The man who went to heaven in a fiery chariot
33. Nebat's son (2 Chron. 10:15)
34. Great work
37. Be, first person singular, present tense
39. Giant killed by David
41. Defendant's adversary, abbr.
42. Article
44. Esther and Mordecai's enemy
47. Printer's measure

48. Father of Abraham (Gen. 11:27)
51. An elder who prophesied with Medad (Num. 11:26)
52. Globe
53. Book of the Old Testament that follows Micah
54. "Give bread unto thine ____" (Judg. 8:6)
55. One of the Gospels, abbr.
58. Mountain where Moses died
61. Son of Baasha (1 Kings 16:8)
63. Before, poetic
64. Past
66. "Take him to the . . .doorpost and pierce his ____ with an awl" (Exod. 21:6 NIV)
68. Father, dial Brit
69. Used to indicate ordinal numbers
71. Common graduate degree, abbr.
   by Elizabeth B. Smith

ACROSS

1. "I ____ not want" (Ps. 23:1)
6. "The sucking child shall play on the hole of the ____ " (Isa. 11:8)
9. Father of Hophni and Phinehas (1 Sam. 2:27, 34)
10. "Lie down in green ____ " (Ps. 23:2)
14. "Then I will ____ your flesh" (Judg. 8:7)
16. "____ the people together" (Deut. 33:17)
17. Mother, for short
19. Sandwich shops
21. Maiden name
22. "I will fear no ____ " (Ps. 23:4)
24. "All the days of my ____ " (Ps. 23:6)
26. "He will not ____ thee" (Deut. 31:8)
28. "Thy rod and thy staff they____ me" (Ps. 23:4)
31. "Thou preparest a ____ before me" (Ps. 23:5)
34. Yukon Front, abbr.
35. Mined matter
37. "Even unto the ____ of the jubile" (Lev. 27:18)
38. "Lord, be not ____ from me" (Ps. 35:22)
40. What?
42. "Thy ____ and thy staff" (Ps. 23:4)
44. "Valley of the shadow of ____ " (Ps. 23:4)
46. "None that doeth good, no not ____ " (Ps. 14:3)
47. Maryland's neighbor to the south, abbr.
49. Flightless bird

51. "In ____ time Christ died for the ungodly" (Rom. 5:6)
54. "To lie down in ____ pastures" (Ps. 23:2)
57. Assistant, abbr.
59. Not Jr.
60. Edible root
61. Inhabitant

DOWN

2. "____ maketh me to lie down" (Ps. 23:2)
3. Height, abbr.
4. "____ down in green pastures" (Ps. 23:2)
5. Organization for veterans, abbr.
6. Preposition indicating when or where
7. "I. . .will ____ with him, and he with me" (Rev. 3:20)
8. Fruit
10. "Thou ____ a table before me" (Ps. 23:5)
11. "Beside the ____ waters" (Ps. 23:2)
12. Wind direction
13. "The Lord is my ____ "(Ps. 23:1)
15. In the year of our Lord, Lat. abbr.
17. "____ shall follow me"(Ps. 23:6)
18. Audio-visual, abbr.
20. Yes, Sp.
23. "____ ____ hath sent me unto you" (Exod. 3:14) (2 words)
25. "____ their skin from off them" (Mic. 3:3)
26. "Fear no evil: ____ thou art with me" (Ps. 23:4)
27. "God saw that ____ was good" (Gen. 1:10)

Down / Across clues:

29. Not on
30. "Dwell in the house of the Lord _____ _____" (Ps. 23:6) (2 words)
32. "The well. . .is between Kadesh and _____" (Gen. 16:14)
33. Southeast Asian
36. Myself
39. Paid announcement
41. "I will dwell in the _____ of the Lord" (Ps. 23:6)
43. Medium, abbr.
45. "Annointest my _____ with oil" (Ps. 23:5)
48. "Thou _____ with me" (Ps. 23:4)

50. Social worker's graduate degree
52. "_____ not vain repetitions" (Matt. 6:7)
53. "Do not _____, my beloved brethren" (James 1:16)
55. Apiece, abbr.
56. "I will fear _____ evil" (Ps. 23:4)
58. Thallium, chem. symbol

by Elizabeth B. Smith

ACROSS

1. "Ye are the _____ of the earth"
   (Matt. 5:13)
5. Peter healed this man who
   had been bedridden with
   palsy for eight years
   (Acts 9:33–34)
9. "I am _____ your pillows"
   (Ezek. 13:20)
10. "_____, I am with you alway"
    (Matt. 28:20)
11. Og's bed was made of this
    (Deut. 3:11)
12. Set apart for worship
16. Edward's nickname
17. A camel has one
18. Quality, suffix
19. "It shall return, and shall be
    eaten: as a _____ tree" (Isa. 6:13)
21. Presently
23. "Strain at a gnat, and swallow a
    _____" (Matt. 23:24)
26. "Go to the _____, thou sluggard"
    (Prov. 6:6)
27. Noah's son
28. "Listen, O _____, unto me"
    (Isa. 49:1)
31. A magistrate of ancient Rome
33. A case for holding small articles
34. The second note of the musical
    scale
36. Nickel, chem. symbol
37. "That we may _____ our hearts,
    unto wisdom" (Ps. 90:12)
38. "I will _____ thee and teach thee"
    (Ps. 32:8)
41. Not off
42. Winged mammal
43. Kentucky's neighbor, abbr.
44. "The twenty-four _____ fall down
    before him" (Rev. 4:10 NIV)

48. "Rejoice not against me, O mine
    _____" (Mic. 7:8)
50. Step
51. I
52. "Lips of wise _____ knowledge"
    (Prov. 15:7)

DOWN

1. "Salute every _____ in Christ"
   (Phil. 4:21)
2. "_____ with thine adversary"
   (Matt. 5:25)
3. John sent his Revelation to this
   church in Asia Minor (Rev. 1:11)
4. "_____. . .that may abide the fire"
   (Num. 31:22–23)
5. "And hereby we know that we
   are of the truth, and shall _____
   our hearts before him"
   (1 John 3:19)
6. Where Samson lived after he
   slaughtered the Philistines
   (Judg. 15:8, 11)
7. "He that hath an _____, let him
   hear" (Rev. 2:7)
8. Paul wrote one of his epistles to
   these people
13. Compound, abbr.
14. Seventh letter of the Greek
    alphabet
15. Succession of rulers from the
    same descent
20. "Kings of the earth shall. . .
    _____" (Rev. 18:9)
22. Activated
24. Spring-flowering bush with
    fragrant blossoms
25. Twelfth letter of the alphabet
27. "The Son of man shall be
    betrayed unto the chief priests
    and unto the _____" (Matt. 20:18)

29. Groups of seven
30. Elongated fish
32. Soiled
35. The father of Ahira (Num. 1:15)
39. "And there shall come forth a rod out of the _____ of Jesse" (Isa. 11:1)
40. Not, prefix
41. Either
45. "One went out into the field to gather herbs,. . .and gathered thereof wild gourds his _____ full" (2 Kings 4:39)
46. What would happen to Adam and Eve if they ate the forbidden fruit
47. "The wayfaring men. . .shall not _____" (Isa. 35:8)
49. "Come unto _____, all ye that labour" (Matt. 11:28)
50. Silicon, chem. symbol

PUZZLE 16

ACROSS

1. "A stormy wind shall ____ it" (Ezek. 13:11)
5. "Jonah was gone down ____ the sides of the ship" (Jon. 1:5)
9. Ration
12. "My cup runneth ____" (Ps. 23:5)
13. "Every one had ____ faces" (Ezek. 1:6)
14. "A vineyard of ____ wine" (Isa. 27:2)
15. Prevent
17. To be announced, abbr.
18. "Nathan the prophet and Shimei, and ____" (1 Kings 1:8)
19. "Prince of the power of the ____" (Eph. 2:2)
21. "Neither will I ____ an offering at your hand" (Mal. 1:10)
23. "Those virgins arose, and ____ their lamps" (Matt. 25:7)
27. "The ____ was come to the place of the arrow" (1 Sam. 20:37)
28. Charged particles
29. The disciple who denied Christ
31. Interrogatory syllable
33. "I have stretched out my hand, and no ____ regarded" (Prov. 1:24)
34. "Number all the firstborn of the ____" (Num. 3:40)
35. Fruit drink
36. "The children of Gad called the altar ____" (Josh. 22:34)
37. "But ye are a chosen generation, a ____ priesthood" (1 Pet. 2:9)
38. Colored layer of the eye
39. "A third part shall be at the gate of ____" (2 Kings 11:6)
40. December 31
42. "They shall take up a lamentation for thee, and ____ over thee" (Ezek. 27:32)
45. Cup
46. "____, even the ancient high places are our's in possession" (Ezek. 36:2)
47. Anger
49. "____, Mahalaleel, Jered" (1 Chron. 1:2)
53. "Bring unto thee pure ____ olive beaten for the light" (Lev. 24:2)
54. "I went down into the garden of ____ to see the fruits of the valley" (Song of Sol. 6:11)
56. "He went into a city called ____" (Luke 7:11)
57. Sun, Sp.
58. Equipment
59. "And came to the strong hold of ____" (2 Sam. 24:7)

DOWN

1. "Thy ____ and thy staff they comfort me" (Ps. 23:4)
2. "The serpent beguiled ____" (2 Cor. 11:3)
3. "The fishes that are taken in an evil ____" (Eccles. 9:12)
4. "The diviners. . .have told false ____" (Zech. 10:2)
5. "____ they shall enter into my rest" (Heb. 4:3)
6. "____ by might, nor by power" (Zech. 4:6)
7. Large wind instrument
8. "Unto them were committed the ____ of God" (Rom. 3:2)
9. "Cause me to understand wherein I have ____" (Job 6:24)
10. "____ thou not silence" (Ps. 83:1)
11. Blue-pencil
16. Edge
20. "I will ____ it" (Philem. 19)
22. Auto
23. "I set him a ____" (Neh. 2:6)
24. "Whither have ye made a ____ to day" (1 Sam. 27:10)
25. "There was no room for them in the ____" (Luke 2:7)
26. "Thou shalt no ____ to offer the first of thy ripe fruits" (Exod. 22:29)

30. "Ziph, and ____, and Bealoth" (Josh. 15:24)
31. First garden
32. "Hairs of your ____ are all numbered" (Luke 12:7)
34. "Thou shalt seek me in the ____" (Job 7:21)
35. Latin expression of greeting
37. "Ye tithe mint and ____ and all manner of herbs" (Luke 11:42)
38. "The king's commandment was ____" (Dan. 3:22)
39. "I am ____ and despised" (Ps. 119:141)
41. Diving bird
42. East Asian country

43. "Uzzah and ____, the sons of Abinadab" (2 Sam. 6:3)
44. "That was the ____ Light" (John 1:9)
48. Approximate time of arrival, abbr.
50. "I tell you ____; but rather division" (Luke 12:51)
51. "Meet the Lord in the ____" (1 Thess. 4:17)
52. Compass point
55. Twelfth-grader, abbr.
by Evelyn M. Boyington

PUZZLE 17

ACROSS

1. To damage
4. "And Saul ____ unto David" (1 Sam. 17:37)
8. Cushions
12. "Blessed ____ the meek" (Matt. 5:5)
13. Son of Helem (1 Chron. 7:35)
14. Operatic solo
15. ____ ____ Goliath (2 words)
17. Genuine
18. Genesis garden
19. ____ ____ of Two Cities (2 words)
20. "The wine ____ ____" (Ps. 75:8) (2 words)
22. Man of brave deeds
24. Female rabbits
25. Sealing wax
29. Epoch
30. Member of the nobility
31. Anger
32. "Making a noise with psalteries ____ ____" (1 Chron. 15:28) (2 words)
34. "They ____ not the bones till the morrow" (Zeph. 3:3)
35. "The ____ are a people not strong" (Prov. 30:25)
36. "Yet offend in one ____" (James 2:10)
37. "The ____ of his fire shall not shine" (Job 18:5)
40. "____! for that day is great" (Jer. 30:7)
41. "The ____ of the Lord was with him" (Luke 1:66)
42. David's friend
46. Father of Shammah (2 Sam. 23:11)
47. Son of Jerahmeel (1 Chron. 2:25)
48. Female sheep
49. "Thou shalt not build it of ____ stone" (Exod. 20:25)
50. Wagers
51. Fourth letter of the alphabet

DOWN

1. "Lo, ye see the man is ____" (1 Sam. 21:14)
2. Son of Jether (1 Chron. 7:38)
3. Pastor's title
4. Having walls
5. "There was ____ ____ sent from God" (John 1:6) (2 words)
6. "There was no room for them in the ____" (Luke 2:7)
7. Father
8. "And he was in the hinder ____ ____ the ship" (Mark 4:38) (2 words)
9. Length x width
10. Knob
11. Garage ____
16. The ____ of March
19. Son of Dishan (1 Chron. 1:42)
20. Thought
21. "As ____ as I had eaten it, my belly was bitter" (Rev. 10:10)
22. "We hanged our ____ upon the willows" (Ps. 137:2)
23. Greek god of love
25. "For we know in ____" (1 Cor. 13:9)
26. "He said, It is ____" (John 19:30)
27. Teheran's country
28. Salamander
30. "Behold, I stood upon the ____ of the river" (Gen. 41:17)

33. "_____ not your hearts" (Heb. 3:8)
34. "He shall bring a she _____ of the first year for a sin offering" (Num. 15:27)
36. Schemes
37. Middle eastern ruler
38. Book leaf
39. "_____ _____ heart also will I give you" (Ezek. 36:26) (2 words)
40. "Casting _____ _____ into the sea" (Mark 1:16) (2 words)
42. Old Testament book
43. Metal-bearing rock
44. "Stand in _____, and sin not" (Ps. 4:4)
45. Born, Fr.

by Elaine Okupski

PUZZLE 18

ACROSS

1. "Give ear, O _____ of Israel" (Ps. 80:1)
8. Animal fat
11. "And now abideth faith, _____, charity" (1 Cor. 13:13)
12. "Every _____ shall be filled, and every mountain and hill shall be brought low" (Luke 3:5)
14. Gold, chem. symbol
15. Revise
17. Direction
18. Dental surgeon, abbr.
19. "Make the _____ for fire" (Ezek. 24:9)
20. Advantage, resource
22. Over (poetic)
24. Father
26. What the doctor wants you to say when you open your mouth
27. "To him. . .who liveth for _____" (Rev. 4:9)
30. "They shall fall, and _____ rise" (Amos 8:14)
33. Abijam's son (1 Kings 15:8)
34. Foreign
36. A cereal grain
37. Three letters of Latin anagram for Christ
38. Chemical warfare, abbr.
39. Old Testament, abbr.
40. Longing
42. Land measurement
44. Larger, abbr.
46. "The four and twenty elders, which sat before God on their _____" (Rev. 11:16)
48. A snake-shaped fish
49. "The veil of the temple was _____ in the midst" (Luke 23:45)
51. Paul was a _____-maker

53. Building wing
54. "What then? are we _____ than they?" (Rom. 3:9)
56. "He shall suck the poison of _____" (Job 20:16)
58. Exclamation of disgust
59. "Cattle shall feed in large _____" (Isa. 30:23)

DOWN

1. "Put your trust in my _____" (Judg. 9:15)
2. "Peace be to thine _____" (1 Sam. 25:6)
3. Estimated position, abbr.
4. Chick's sound
5. "Turn ye from your _____ ways" (Ezek. 33:11)
6. Scored
7. 550, Rom. num.
8. Part of an eye or a camera
9. Affirmative votes
10. "Deliver our lives from _____" (Josh. 2:13)
13. "Narrow is the way, which _____ unto life" (Matt. 7:14)
16. "Pharisee besought him to _____" (Luke 11:37)
21. "He that hath an _____, let him hear" (Rev. 2:7)
23. "Elias verily cometh first, and _____ all things" (Mark 9:12)
25. "I am the God of Bethel, where thou _____ the pillar" (Gen. 31:13)
28. Very large
29. Color again
31. Passport
32. European Community, abbr.
33. Alcoholics Anonymous, abbr.
35. Inhabits

36. "Hurt not the wine and the
    ____" (Rev. 6:6)
38. Crawls
41. "Take, ____; this is my body"
    (Matt. 26:26)
43. Common Era, abbr.
45. Gregory, for short
46. "There is but a ____ between me
    and death" (1 Sam. 20:3)
47. Tin, chem. symbol
50. New Testament, abbr.
52. Black sticky material
54. Abbreviation for a dry measure
55. Royal Academy, abbr.
57. Direction

PUZZLE 19

ACROSS

1. Detestable, disgusting (Prov. 3:32)
8. Dishonest person, a cheat (Isa. 32:5)
12. A unit of measure, just less than two quarts (2 Kings 6:25 KJV)
13. "Also the ____ and the bear will graze" (Isa. 11:7)
15. The Peach state, abbr.
16. Sharp instrument (Josh. 5:2–3)
18. Passover (Acts 12:4 KJV)
21. Allow (Ps. 119:10)
23. The Lord turned this river into blood using Moses' staff (Exod. 7:20–21)
25. The body of writing that describes the new covenant between God and man, abbr.
26. "Speaking out arrogant words of ____" (2 Pet. 2:18)
27. Book of the Apocrypha
28. Often a symbol of refreshment and blessing in the dry summers of Palestine (Deut. 32:2)
29. "As far as the east is from the ____" (Ps. 103:12)
31. An image of a false god (Exod. 20:4)
32. Hebrew word for house; also second letter of the Hebrew alphabet
33. Unit of weight, abbr.
34. "The Word of God enlightens the ____" (Ps. 19:8)
35. "And takes a cypress or an ____" (Isa. 44:14)
36. The oldest son of Elpaal, a Benjamite (1 Chron. 8:12)
38. Piece of clothing to wear on the upper body
40. David's book of poetry, abbr.
41. "Do not ____ meaningless repetition" (Matt. 6:7)
42. "Surely in a night, ____ of Moab is devastated and ruined" (Isa. 15:1)
43. Amos denounces Israel for its use of this (Amos 3:15 & 6:4)
44. A trap (Ps. 140:5 KJV)
46. Grandfather of the prophet Zechariah (Zech. 1:1, 7)
48. Grandson of Boaz, father of David (Ruth 4:22)
49. "Altars to ____ were built in Palestine, thanks to Jezebel and Athalia" (1 Kings 16:31–32)
52. An Israelite who took a garment, silver, and gold from the spoil at Jericho (Josh. 7:21)
53. "____ them around your neck" (Prov. 6:21)
56. Health Management Organization, abbr.
57. "Reduced Sodom and Gomorrah to ____" (2 Pet. 2:6)
58. ____ Nebo, abbr.
59. Roman colony (Acts 16:8)
61. Preposition that indicates position
62. We are this through Christ (Gal. 4:1)
64. "Received the linen ____" (2 Chron. 1:16 KJV)
65. "God shall ____ to him the plagues" (Rev. 22:18)
66. Imitate
68. "____ to speak" (James 1:19)
70. Isaiah compared Israel's despoiling to robbing one of these (Isa. 10:14)
71. Second son of Noah (Gen. 5:32)
72. Deception took its first hold on humanity here
73. Do not let this go down on your anger (Eph. 4:26)

DOWN

1. "See fit to ____ God" (Rom. 1:28)
2. A Levite who sealed the covenant (Neh. 10:13)
3. A camel driver, keeper of King David's camels (1 Chron. 27:30)
4. "He casts forth his ____ as fragments" (Ps. 147:17)
5. "The city of the God ____-Amon" (Nah. 3:8)
6. "Stand in ____ of him" (Ps. 33:8)
7. Longing, intense desire (Matt. 5:28)
9. "The cities of ____" (Josh. 13:21)
10. Area in Palestine (Isa. 9:1)
11. Paul restored his life after he fell out of a window (Acts 20:9)
14. Disclosure of something previously unknown (Gal. 1:12)

17. Shackles for the feet (Prov. 7:22)
19. One who usurps Christ's name (1 John 2:22)
20. "But whenever ____ flesh appears on him, he shall be unclean" (Lev. 13:14)
22. And, Lat.
24. "Shall be ____ to separate us from the love of God" (Rom. 8:39)
28. "God may open up to us a ____ for the Word" (Col. 4:3)
30. Grow less
37. Custodian of royal harems (Dan. 1:3–18)
38. Continent in the southern hemisphere, abbr.
39. A chamber for deceased bodies (Matt. 27:60)
40. The Great Sphinx stands guard over this
45. Person from a non-Jewish nation (Matt. 6:7)

47. Divine nature (Col. 2:9)
48. With Jesus at the transfiguration (Matt. 17:1–8)
50. Exclamation of satisfaction
51. The capital city of Great Britain
52. Led the singing and sounded the cymbol; credited to him (Ps. 50 & 78–83)
54. "Watchful" (Num. 26:36)
55. "One ____ disobedience" (Rom. 5:19)
60. A prince known as a raven of the Midianites; was beheaded (Judg. 7:24–25)
63. Jacob used this to change the color of Laban's goats (Gen. 30:37–41)
65. This animal saw an angel (Num. 22:23)
66. Preposition used in similes
67. Electrical engineer, abbr.
69. Ourselves (NASB)

by Michael J. Landi

41

ACROSS

1. God told Adam and Eve to be fruitful and ____ (Gen. 1:22)
8. Without, Fr.
12. What Samuel does to Saul to show he'll be Israel's king
13. Clothing that covers the back
14. The prodigal son almost ate their food (Luke 15:16)
15. "____ not at all; neither by heaven; for it is God's throne" (Matt. 5:34)
17. A metal burned by fire (Num. 31:22–23)
18. Eleven, Rom. num.
20. "I am Alpha and the Omega, beginning and the ____" (Rev. 22:13)
21. Ma's husband
22. To trap
24. Gideon saw men lapping water like this animal (Judg. 7:5)
26. Address abbreviation
27. A rough rock where the eagle dwells (Job 39:27–28)
29. At the end of the world we will hear about these and rumors of these (Matt. 24:6)
32. Large feline
34. Dover is the capital of this state, abbr.
35. A soft, lustrous fabric made by worms
38. Hebrew custom of allowing the poor to follow the reapers and gather grain
40. Jesus said not to speak these kind of words (Matt. 12:36)
41. The initials of the man who came up with the theory of relativity

42. After eight days, Jesus was circumcised and ____ (Luke 2:21)
45. Negative
46. Tensile strength, abbr.
47. To direct the course
48. Gideon hoped this would be wet, then dry
50. Exclamation of surprise
51. A name for Mother
52. Ourselves
53. Homonym of sew
54. A tall pasture grass
56. A printer's measure
57. A Levitical city in the hill country of Judah (Josh. 15:51)
58. Briefly lowers the head

DOWN

1. Ruler, lord, teacher (Matt. 8:19)
2. To reverse the winding
3. When you wear the armor of God, you should have your ____ girt with truth (Eph. 6:14)
4. A soft metal
5. Not exact
6. Two cups, abbr.
7. Life support system, abbr.
8. "Yea, though I walk through the valley of the ____ of death" (Ps. 23:4)
9. Jesus spoke of the fowls of the ____ (Matt. 6:26)
10. Not rated, abbr.
11. Produces hot, moist air
13. "God. . .shall ____ his angel" (Gen. 24:7)
16. Us
19. Supply with water by artificial means
23. If we wait upon the Lord, we will mount up with wings like these birds

25. Seventh son of Jacob, firstborn of Zilpah (Gen. 30:11)
28. Word to make a horse turn to the right
30. What Christ did for us
31. Everything
33. "The Son of man came. . .to give his life a _____" (Matt. 20:28)
35. Marked by sin
36. "Little children, keep yourselves from _____" (1 John 5:21)
37. City in south Judah, conquered by Joshua in the northern campaign (Josh. 12:22)
39. Prophet during the reigns of David and Solomon

43. Myself
44. Persian coins (Ezra 2:69)
49. The sound of a dove
54. The opposite of stop
55. The article that precedes words beginning with a vowel

43

PUZZLE 21

ACROSS

1. Greek letter used for the ratio of a circle's circumference to its diameter
3. Undergraduate degree, abbr.
5. David was king in ____ (2 Sam. 2:11)
9. Raises up
11. Organization for African Unity, abbr.
13. In regards to, abbr.
14. He made a vow with David (1 Sam. 18:3)
18. Girl's name
20. Stomach muscle, for short
21. A small building
22. Compass point
23. Jesse's youngest son (1 Sam. 16:11)
25. Regret
27. "If the Syrians be ____ strong for me" (2 Sam. 10:11)
28. Sense of who you are
29. Champion of the Philistines (1 Sam. 17:4)
31. Lieutenant, abbr.
32. The opposite of down
34. Six, Rom. num.
36. David used this to kill Goliath (1 Sam. 17:50)
39. Amount, abbr.
41. Woman's name
43. David's elder brother (1 Sam. 17:28)
44. A characteristic of David (1 Sam. 16:18)
47. "Drunk neither wine ____ strong drink" (1 Sam. 1:15)
49. A type of tree
50. Masculine article, Fr.
52. "Are not his sisters ____ with ___?" (Mark 6:3)

53. His mother was Bathsheba (2 Sam. 12:24)
54. Resident, abbr.

DOWN

1. Nob was their city (1 Sam. 22:11)
2. That is, Lat. abbr.
3. Priests gave David hallowed ____ (1 Sam. 21:4)
4. Simile preposition
6. Period of time
7. Sheep's cries
8. A Moabite woman who was an ancestress of David and Jesus
10. "Thou ____ a virtuous woman" (Ruth 3:11)
12. The opposite of out
14. Saul threw it at David (1 Sam. 18:11)
15. Japanese sash
16. Not there
17. David escaped to this man's cave (1 Sam. 22:1)
19. "Herod. . .slew all the children. . . from ____ years old and under" (Matt. 2:16)
24. Wheeless vehicle
26. Electronic funds transfer, abbr.
28. That woman
30. Egg, prefix
33. David wrote many of these
35. David was in a ____ with Saul (1 Sam. 24:3)
37. "David made haste to ____ away" (1 Sam. 23:26)
38. "It was impossible for God to ____" (Heb. 6:18)
39. The captain of Saul's host (1 Sam. 14:50)

40. Sown among the wheat
    (Matt. 13:25)
42. Dekaliter, abbr.
45. "By him were ____ things
    created" (Col. 1:16)
46. New, recent, comb. form
48. Precious metal
51. "My word hath ____ place in
    you" (John 8:37)
    by Elizabeth B. Smith

ACROSS

1. "Blessed is the man that ____ not in the counsel of the ungodly" (Ps. 1:1)
7. "The ungodly shall not ____ in the judgment" (Ps. 1:5)
11. "Christ is the ____ of the church" (Eph. 5:23)
12. "Be like a tree planted by the ____ of water" (Ps. 1:3)
13. "A word spoken in ____ season, how good is it!" (Prov. 15:23)
14. Nest of an eagle or hawk
15. Preposition: toward
17. "Eyes have they, but they ____ not" (Ps. 115:5)
18. Took food
19. "All we like ____ have gone astray" (Isa. 53:6)
21. William, abbr.
22. Church, abbr.
23. Californian city, abbr.
24. "Nor ____ in the seat of the scornful" (Ps. 1:1)
27. Revise
29. It's capital is Indianapolis, abbr.
30. English Version, abbr.
31. Morning, abbr.
32. Vesicular exanthema, abbr.
33. Conjunction
34. "His ____ also shall not wither" (Ps. 1:3)
35. Elevated railroad
37. Alvin and Alan
38. Material at the bottom of the page, abbr.
40. "The Lord knoweth the way of the ____" (Ps. 1:6)
44. A cart for hire in India
45. National Guard, abbr.
47. Word to begin a question

48. To begin on a journey (2 words)
51. A telephone company, abbr.
52. "A tree. . .that bringeth forth his ____ in his season" (Ps. 1:3)

DOWN

1. "____ he doeth shall prosper" (Ps. 1:3)
2. Initials of the man who wrote the equation $E = MC2$
3. "His delight is in the ____ of the Lord" (Ps. 1:2)
4. Boxing term, knocked down, abbr.
5. "I am the ____ vine" (John 15:1)
6. Go quickly
7. "Nor sitteth in the ____ of the scornful" (Ps. 1:1)
8. "And he shall be like a ____ " (Ps. 1:3)
9. Airport surveillance radar, abbr.
10. "Whatsoever he ____ shall prosper" (Ps. 1:3)
13. Department, abbr.
16. Exclamation of surprise
17. "We shall all stand before the judgment ____ of Christ" (Rom. 14:10)
18. Amount, abbr.
20. "Therefore, ____ said unto Samuel, Go, lie down" (1 Sam. 3:9)
21. "The ____ driveth away" (Ps. 1:4)
22. "The godly are not so: but are like the ____" (Ps. 1:4)
24. "Nor standeth in the way of ____" (Ps. 1:1)
25. Gives a report
26. The nights before

28. "His _____ is in the law of the Lord" (Ps. 1:2)
36. Cozy talk
37. Gold, chemical symbol
39. "In his law doth he meditate day and _____" (Ps. 1:2)
41. Indian riverbank steps
42. Translation, abbr.
43. Public crier's word
45. Neither
46. Russian chief intelligence directorate, abbr.
47. Northwestern state, abbr.
49. Following, abbr.
50. Seventh note on the musical scale

ACROSS

1. Fiddling emperor
5. New Testament book
9. Noah's vessel
12. Dismounted
13. "For many _____ false witness against him" (Mark 14:56)
14. Gardening tool
15. "He shall not come _____ to offer the bread of his God" (Lev. 21:21)
16. "Every beast, every _____ thing, and every fowl" (Gen. 8:19)
18. Leah's second son (Gen. 30:12–13)
20. Actor James _____ Jones
21. "Then he that had received the five talents went and _____ with the same" (Matt. 25:16)
23. "There met him ten men that were lepers, which stood _____ off" (Luke 17:12)
27. Get a perfect score on a test
29. Result of sunbathing
30. "And Jacob _____ away unawares to Laban" (Gen. 31:20)
31. _____-man, scary childhood character
33. Son of Dishon (Gen. 36:26)
34. Rhythm and _____
35. "T" in PTL
36. Newsman Koppel
37. "My couch shall _____ my complaint" (Job 7:13)
38. Height of Noah's ark in cubits (Gen. 6:15)
40. Eastern garment
42. "And over the course of the second month was _____ an Ahohite" (1 Chron. 27:4)

45. "This is the token of the _____ which I have established" (Gen. 9:17)
49. Sudden attack
50. "And all went to be taxed, every _____ into his own city" (Luke 2:3)
51. Popular brand of sneakers
52. Biblical city
53. "But _____ unto you, scribes and Pharisees, hypocrites!" (Matt. 23:13)
54. "I am the Lord, and there is none _____" (Isa. 45:5)
55. Being, Lat.

DOWN

1. Common nickname for Grandmother
2. Belonging to inventor Whitney
3. "I am not come to call the _____, but sinners" (Matt. 9:13)
4. "The name of the one was Orpah, and the name of the _____ Ruth" (Ruth 1:4)
5. Beginning of the alphabet
6. To sway wildly
7. "Every place that the sole of your foot shall _____ upon" (Josh. 1:3)
8. Prophet
9. Son of Abdiel (1 Chron. 5:15)
10. Actor/director Howard
11. Small cask
17. "And thou shalt make a _____ of pure gold" (Exod. 28:36)
19. Gives a grade
22. "For this is the _____ of the Lord God of hosts" (Jer. 46:10)

24. "I will cause it to rain upon the earth ____ ____" (Gen. 7:4) (2 words)
25. Wings
26. "A time to ____, and a time to sew" (Eccles. 3:7)
27. Abbot, Fr.
28. Soft drink
30. Scrap of pottery
32. "Silly" birds
33. Greek letter
35. Calls to mind
38. Pathway
39. Rich cake

41. Actress Bancroft
43. Haughty conduct
44. Thought, Fr.
45. Milk provider
46. Biblical plain (Neh. 6:2)
47. Type of neckline
48. Golf peg
by Elaine Okupski

ACROSS

1. "The gold of ____"
   (1 Chron. 29:4)
5. "Four men. . .____ in the. . .fire"
   (Dan. 3:25)
10. Sweaty class, abbr.
11. Shining circle indicating holiness
13. "What ye hear in the ____"
    (Matt. 10:27)
14. "He shewed himself alive after
    his ____" (Acts 1:3)
16. Period of time
17. Land where Cain lived after he
    killed Abel (Gen. 4:16)
18. South American language, abbr.
20. ____ sold his birthright
    (Heb. 12:16)
22. "I will ____ the loving-
    kindnesses of the Lord"
    (Isa. 63:7)
26. It is, contr.
28. Do again, prefix
29. Pimple
31. "____ by the Holy Ghost"
    (Rom. 15:16)
36. "To whom shall we ____?"
    (John 6:68)
37. Astronomical unit, abbr.
38. Adam and Eve's third son
    (Gen. 4:25)
40. "I. . .will ____ thee with my
    hand while I pass by"
    (Exod. 33:22)
44. Third Gospel, abbr.
45. "The ____ of the just is as the
    shining light" (Prov. 4:18)
47. Parentless child
48. Standard temperature and
    pressure, abbr.
49. Myself
50. "The ____ of all them that
    believe" (Rom. 4:11)

53. "It pleased the Lord to ____
    him" (Isa. 53:10)
56. Continent in the southern
    hemisphere, abbr.
57. Executive order, abbr.
59. Soviet Socialist Republic, abbr.
60. "Thy faithfulness shalt thou
    ____ in the very heavens"
    (Ps. 89:2)

DOWN

1. "____ not the widow, nor the
   fatherless" (Zech. 7:10)
2. Pod vegetable
3. Jesus Savior of Mankind, Lat.
   abbr.
4. "The ____ is over and gone"
   (Song of Sol. 2:11)
5. His name shall be called ____
   (Isa. 9:6)
6. "As ye have done it unto one of
   the ____ of these" (Matt. 25:40)
7. Cathode, Gk. abbr.
8. Anger
9. "The ____ tidings of the
   kingdom of God" (Luke 8:1)
12. Frame for weaving
15. "Stood a Lamb as it had been
    ____" (Rev. 5:6)
19. Preachy, Brit.
21. Universal time, coordinated,
    abbr.
23. Not elsewhere indicated, abbr.
24. Dorothy's imaginary land
25. "If a man walk in the ____, he
    stumbleth" (John 11:10)
27. Address abbreviation
30. Preposition
32. People who love and worship
33. Des Moines is the capital of this
    state, abbr.
34. Einsteinium, chem. symbol

35. "The _____ saith, It is not in me" (Job 28:14)

by Carole Stengel

39. Adhesive strip
40. Used for grooming the hair
41. Replaces the president in case of sickness or death, abbr.
42. Questioning word
43. "In the third day he will _____ us up" (Hos. 6:2)
46. Greeting
48. Thrust a knife
51. A king (1 Kings 15:8)
52. Dweller, abbr.
54. Abram's birth place (Gen. 11:28)
55. Plural suffix
58. Exclamation

ACROSS

1. A Roman centurion (Acts 10:1)
7. The disciple that walked on water
11. We worship _____ God
12. Dutch, abbr.
13. Modern day Persia
15. "So that Christ's power may _____ on me" (2 Cor. 12:9)
17. "Mock him and spit on him, flog him and _____ him" (Mark 10:34)
19. Store
20. Maritime province, abbr.
21. Tint
23. Possessing height
25. Peter's original name
27. "Keep on praying for all the _____" (Eph. 6:18)
30. "I will send fire on _____" (Ezek. 39:6)
32. Neptunium, chem symbol
33. Laughter sound
34. Large green moth
36. Forward a letter
38. Preposition
39. Imaginary land where the Emerald City is
40. A synagogue ruler who was beaten (Acts 18:17)
42. A king of Judah (1 Kings 15:16)
44. Greek letter used for the ratio of a circle's circumference to its diameter
45. The disciple standing with Jesus' mother at the crucifixion (John 19:26)
46. He was called a Levi (Mark 2:14)
48. United Kingdom, abbr.
49. Indianapolis's state, abbr.
51. Worried expression (2 words)
53. Roman emperor who issued a decree for a census to be taken (Luke 2:1)
58. Each, abbr.
59. Letter that precedes em
61. Article that precedes a vowel
62. Northwestern state, abbr.
64. "God _____ His love among us" (1 John 4:9)
68. The brother of Jesus (Gal. 1:19)
70. Indefinite article
71. The peach state, abbr.
72. New Testament prophetess
74. "Asahel was as light of foot as a wild _____" (2 Sam. 2:18 KJV)
75. Relative by marriage
78. Distress signal
79. One of the twelve disciples (Matt. 10:3)

DOWN

1. Sore bumps on the toes
2. Runaway slave (Philem. 10)
3. Dweller, abbr.
4. Nickname for Edward
5. Paul's companion in Rome (2 Tim. 4:11)
6. Paul's companion during his second missionary journey (Acts 15:22, 40)
7. Jesus asked him, "Where shall we buy bread for these people?" (John 6:5)
8. Disciple from Lystra who traveled with Paul (Acts 16:1)
9. Period of time
10. "Lips that speak knowledge are a _____ jewel" (Prov. 20:15)
14. New covenant writings, abbr.
16. Doubted the resurrection (John 20:24–26)
18. Lieutenant, abbr.
22. Woman's name
24. Alights
26. Rich man from Arimathea (Matt. 27:57)
28. Salvation Army, abbr.
29. This man was raised from the dead
31. Magical inhabitant of a bottle
35. Norman's nickname
37. Northeastern area of the US, abbr.
38. Ruptured

39. Old style, abbr.
41. Coworker with Paul (2 Cor. 2:13)
42. One of the first disciples (John 1:35–42)
43. High priest during the time of Jesus (Matt. 26:3)
45. Christ's betrayer
47. Warrant officer, abbr.
50. Name unknown, abbr.
52. Male pronoun
54. If a man does this of the world, he forfeits his own soul (Matt. 16:26)
55. International peace-keeping organization, abbr.
56. Son of Nachor, father of Abraham (Luke 3:34 KJV)

57. "A longing fulfilled is _____ to the soul" (Prov. 13:19)
60. Lower limb
63. Preposition
65. Bright circle indicating saintliness
66. His sons were Shammai and Jada and his mother was Atarah (1 Chron. 2:26–28)
67. God created _____ and night
69. Morocco, abbr.
73. Negative
75. Input/output
76. National League, abbr.
77. Ourselves

NIV
by Michael J. Landi

PUZZLE 26

ACROSS

1. "The children of Gad called the altar ____" (Josh. 22:34)
3. "I have trusted also in the Lord; therefore I shall not ____" (Ps. 26:1)
7. A son of Zibeon (1 Chron. 1:40)
10. "The seed is ____ under their clods" (Joel 1:17)
12. "They ____ hands on them" (Acts 4:3)
14. "They are all ____ as an oven" (Hos. 7:7)
15. "Few there be that ____ it" (Matt. 7:14)
16. "Broughtest [Abram] forth out of ____ of the Chaldees" (Neh. 9:7)
17. "They left their father Zebedee in the ____" (Mark 1:20)
19. "Praise the Lord, all ye Gentiles; and ____ him" (Rom. 15:11)
20. "This man, after he had offered ____ sacrifice for sins for ever" (Heb. 10:12)
21. "I am as one mocked of ____ neighbour" (Job 12:4)
22. "The earth was without form, and ____" (Gen. 1:2)
23. "How ____ a man then understand?" (Prov. 20:24)
24. "He said, ____ is finished" (John 19:30)
25. Wail
26. "Turned from ____ eastward toward the sunrising"(Josh. 19:12)
28. "____, and all hills, fruitful trees, and all cedars" (Ps. 148:9)
30. "Round about the throne were four and twenty ____" (Rev. 4:4)
32. "____ it in a book" (Isa. 30:8)
33. "So ____, being many, are one body in Christ" (Rom. 12:5)
34. Metal
35. "In ____ and caves of the earth" (Heb. 11:38)
36. "When Jesus ____ finished these parables, he departed"(Matt. 13:53)
37. "Is ____ sick among you?" (James 5:14)
38. "I will put my hook in thy ____ " (2 Kings 19:28)
39. "Let me ____ through thy land" (Deut. 2:27)
40. "Where ____ God my Maker?" (Job 35:10)
41. "The ____ are a people not strong" (Prov. 30:25)
42. "Rabbi, thou ____ the Son of God" (John 1:49)
43. "I saw, and behold a ____ in the midst of the earth" (Dan. 4:10)
44. Something that wipes away
47. "Sallu, ____, Hilkiah, Jedaiah" (Neh. 12:7)
48. "Thou shall not ____ to offer the first of thy ripe fruits" (Exod. 22:29)
49. Sodium, chem. symbol

DOWN

1. A son of Judah (1 Chron. 2:3)
2. "If thou ____ these things" (John 7:4)
3. "All iniquity shall ____ her mouth" (Ps. 107:42)
4. "And God said, ____ there be light" (Gen. 1:3)
5. "I shall never be ____ adversity" (Ps. 10:6)
6. "Achim begat ____" (Matt. 1:14)
7. Help
8. According to Freud, the selfish part of the self
9. "Turn aside, sit down ____" (Ruth 4:1)
11. "Lo ____, we have searched it" (Job 5:27)
13. "Rejoice ____ be glad in thee" (Ps. 70:4)
15. "I will send ____ into their hearts" (Lev. 26:36)
16. "Bakbukiah and ____, their brethren" (Neh. 12:9)
17. Recoils
18. "The archers ____ him" (1 Sam. 31:3)

19. "The _____ which is lent to the Lord" (1 Sam. 2:20)
20. "Wherein shall go no galley with _____" (Isa. 33:21)
22. You, Fr.
23. "The sweet _____ from a far country" (Jer. 6:20)
25. "Why beholdest thou the _____ that is in thy brother's eye?" (Luke 6:41)
26. Takes a chair
27. "To every man according to his _____" (Rom. 2:6)
28. Joseph's wife
29. Perfect excellence
31. Long periods of time
33. "The Lord _____ not in the wind" (1 Kings 19:11)
35. "She _____ on her lovers" (Ezek. 23:5)

36. Head coverings
37. "The children of Benjamin. . . dwelt at Michmash and _____" (Neh. 11:31)
38. Compass point
39. "_____ for the peace of Jerusalem" (Ps. 122:6)
41. "The _____ of the covenant" (Heb. 9:4)
42. "The sons of Jether, Jephunneh, and Pispah, and _____" (1 Chron. 7:38)
43. "I will be _____ him a Father" (Heb. 1:5)
44. Letter that precedes em
45. Letter that follows em
46. Egyptian sun god

by Evelyn M. Boyington

Puzzle 27

ACROSS

1. "____ the lilies" (Matt. 6:28)
8. Woody Guthrie's son
11. Ann, Russ.
12. Moses' brother
13. Indianapolis' state, abbr.
14. Roman Catholic, abbr.
15. "They ____ unto them" (Exod. 12:36)
17. Bean curd
19. Apiece
21. Sews quickly
23. Turns away from sin
25. House of Lords, abbr.
26. The writings that contain the new covenant, abbr.
28. "Hole of the ____" (Isa. 11:8)
29. Nickel, chem. symbol
30. High male voices
34. "Every ____ of doctrine" (Eph. 4:14)
36. "He took. . .the ____ out of the house" (2 Chron. 33:15)
37. Three, prefix
38. More, suffix
39. "Pure ____ of water of life" (Rev. 22:1)
41. Overeaters Anonymous, abbr.
42. New England state, Concord is the capital, abbr.
44. Evergreen
45. Perform
46. Caleb's brother (Josh. 15:17)
50. "He riseth. . .and took a ____" (John 13:4)
52. Grievance
54. Metal thread
55. "Get thee hence, ____" (Matt. 4:10)
56. The meal's last course

DOWN

1. Joseph's profession (Mark 6:3)
2. One time
3. The Empire State, abbr.
4. Girl's name, for short
5. Bilhah's son (Gen. 35:25)
6. "They work, and ____" (2 Thess. 3:12)
7. Railed transportation, abbr.
8. Small insects
9. Throw out the ____
10. Burden
16. Chinese ruler
18. Son of Shemaiah (1 Chron. 26:7)
20. Rural route, abbr.
21. Noblemen, below a baron and above a knight, abbr.
22. Snake
24. Not applicable, abbr.
27. Tellurium, chem. symbol
31. Modern Bible translation, abbr.
32. Poem
33. Sea level, abbr.
34. "____ of heaven" (Mal. 3:10)
35. Small drip
37. Black sticky substance
40. Within, prefix
41. "Cake of ____ bread" (Exod. 29:23)
43. Howard, for short
44. Womanly, abbr.
46. Officers of the Guard, abbr.
47. Head covering
48. National Vision Associates, abbr.
49. Man's name
51. To make a mistake
53. Born, Fr.

ACROSS

1. Fellow
5. Halfway, prefix
8. Charles, for short
12. Aircraft, prefix
13. Summer, Fr.
14. Alley Oop's girlfriend
15. "And he beat down the tower of Penuel, and ____ the men of the city" (Judg. 8:17)
16. Resident, abbr.
17. "Shall ____ words have an end?" (Job 16:3)
18. "We are troubled on every ____ ... we are ____" (2 Cor. 4:8) (2 words)
21. To make free of
22. Boy's name
23. "The ____ and flags shall wither" (Isa. 19:6)
26. Belonging to the author of much of the New Testament (2 words)
30. Referring to the nose, prefix
31. "Let me ____ the death of the righteous" (Num. 23:10)
32. Belonging to the National Security Agency, abbr.
33. Stutter
35. Sticks with a knife
36. Adjective suffix
37. Weep
38. "That the ____ ____ might through the thanksgiving of many redound to the glory of God" (2 Cor. 4:15)
45. Elbow-shaped pasta, for short
46. "But let your communication be, ____" (Matt. 5:37)
47. "____ that great city, that was clothed in fine linen" (Rev. 18:16)
48. ____ Domini

49. "Of ____, the family of the Erites" (Num. 26:16)
50. "But this woman since the time I came in hath not ceased to ____ my feet" (Luke 7:45)
51. Chinese food
52. Noise
53. Feminine name ending

DOWN

1. One of the Mamas and the Papas
2. Sun, prefix
3. "They bring thee ____ ____ heifer without spot" (Num. 19:2) (2 words)
4. "Far above all principality, and ____, and might, and ____" (Eph. 1:21) (2 words)
5. "The sons of Ezra were, Jether, and ____" (1 Chron. 4:17)
6. Roman road
7. "Hath done ____ unto the Spirit of grace" (Heb. 10:29)
8. "My ____ they ____, although I was an husband unto them" (Jer. 31:32)
9. Deception
10. "A strong delusion, that they should believe ____ ____" (2 Thess. 2:11)
11. "Though the number of the children of Israel be as the ____ of the sea" (Rom. 9:27)
19. Greek letters used for the ratio of a circle's circumference to its diameter
20. What you lose when you stand
23. Drs.' assistants
24. "Therefore, the children of Israel ____ not of the sinew which shrank" (Gen. 32:32)
25. That, Sp.

26. "And he answered. . .I go, _____: and went not" (Matt. 21:30)
27. Abbreviation for America
28. Where scientists work
29. Selective Service System, abbr.
31. "I made haste, and _____ not to keep thy commandments" (Ps. 119:60)
34. "I said of laughter, it is _____" (Eccles. 2:2)
35. Soak
37. "I will _____ all my raiment" (Isa. 63:3)
38. "Balak the king of Moab hath brought me from _____" (Num. 23:7)

39. "Thou hast smitten all mine enemies upon the cheek _____" (Ps. 3:7)
40. "Bakbukiah and _____ . . .were over against them in the watches" (Neh. 12:9)
41. "Salathiel, which was the son of _____" (Luke 3:27)
42. Got down from
43. "Have ye not _____ out the priests of the Lord" (2 Chron. 13:9)
44. To be, Lat.
by Janet W. Adkins

ACROSS

1. Lot was told to go to the ____ (Gen. 19:17)
7. "There was no harm in the ____" (2 Kings 4:41)
9. Yes, Sp.
10. How many daughters Lot had (Gen. 19:8)
11. Who came to Lot (Gen. 19:1)
14. "He. . .did ____ unleavened bread" (Gen. 19:3)
16. "Bring them out ____ the place" (Gen. 19:12)
17. Dessert
18. Informed on a person
21. "The Lord ____ upon Sodom and upon Gomorrah" (Gen. 19:24)
24. "This ____ fellow came in to sojourn" (Gen. 19:9)
25. Abraham's nephew (Gen. 12:5)
27. Pittsburg's state, abbr.
28. In the year of our Lord, Lat. abbr.
29. One of the cities destroyed by God (Gen. 19:24)
32. Large vase
33. Farrow's first name
34. "Is there any taste in the white of an ____?" (Job 6:6)
35. "I cannot escape to the mountain, lest. . .I ____" (Gen. 19:19)
37. Held up Moses' hands (Exod. 17:12)
39. Lot was told to ____ (Gen. 19:17)
41. "Lot ____ out at the door" (Gen. 19:6)
43. Continent in the northern hemisphere, abbr.
44. Masculine pronoun
45. Corrida cheer

46. "Then said I, ____, I come" (Ps. 40:7)
48. "Their sin ____ very grievous" (Gen. 18:20)
50. "Now, this ____ is near" (Gen. 19:20)
51. "He overthrew ____ cities" (Gen. 19:25)

DOWN

1. They compassed Lot's house (Gen. 19:4)
2. "Neither shall ye ____ enchantment" (Lev. 19:26)
3. Nothing
4. "There came two angels to Sodom ____ even" (Gen. 19:1)
5. ____ Jima
6. "____ man hath seen God" (John 1:18)
7. "God destroyed the cities of the ____" (Gen. 19:29)
8. Golf peg
11. "They. . .brought them forth ____" (Gen. 19:17)
12. "Lot sat in the ____ of Sodom" (Gen. 19:1)
13. Another city destroyed by God
14. Bits per inch, abbr.
15. "They shall ____ the way of the Lord" (Gen. 18:19)
19. "Lot went out. . .____ shut the door" (Gen. 19:6)
20. Bashemath was her daughter (Gen. 26:34)
22. "God remembered ____" (Gen. 19:29)
23. They escaped with Lot (Gen. 19:16)
26. Thomas, for short
29. "He pressed upon them ____" (Gen. 19:3)

30. Japanese unit of distance
31. "Take. . .thy daughters, which are ____" (Gen. 19:15)
32. Unemployment insurance, abbr.
35. Female deer
36. Male adults
38. "Lot. . .rose ____ to meet them" (Gen. 19:1)
40. "She became a pillar of ____" (Gen. 19:26)
41. A woman in the army, abbr.
42. "I will ____ overthrow this city" (Gen. 19:21)
47. "____, let me escape" (Gen. 19:20)
48. Island, abbr.

49. Southeast, abbr.

by Elizabeth B. Smith

ACROSS

1. "They had ordained them elders in every ____" (Acts 14:23)
6. "Better is a dry ____, and quietness therewith, than an house full of sacrifices with strife" (Prov. 17:1)
11. "It is a ____ thing that the king requireth" (Dan. 2:11)
12. North central state whose capital is Madison, abbr.
13. J, K, L, __, __, __
14. American traitor, Benedict ____
15. Strange
16. South American language, abbr.
17. Do, ____, mi
18. Carpet
19. Hawaiian standard time, abbr.
20. "____ out heaven with the span" (Isa. 40:12)
22. "How long. . .____ thou be quiet?" (Jer. 47:6)
23. Assigned a monetary punishment
26. "They make a noise like a ____" (Ps. 59:6)
27. Curt
30. Do over, prefix
32. "Jesus, when he had cried again with a loud voice, yielded up the ____" (Matt. 27:50)
35. Exist
36. Adam's wife
38. "To him that overcometh will I give to eat of the ____ of life" (Rev. 2:7)
39. To arrange or plan
40. Help
41. This man had 454 descendents who escaped captivity in Babylon (Ezra 2:15)
44. Tender loving care, abbr.

45. "Wherefore come out from among them, and be ye ____" (2 Cor. 6:17)
46. Note of debt
48. Son of Judah (Gen. 38:4)
49. "And David was the ____ [son of Jesse]" (1 Sam. 17:14)
50. Degrees, suffix

DOWN

1. Smash
2. "____ and psalteries for singers" (2 Chron. 9:11)
3. Vase
4. Unidentified virus, prefix
5. "None of these things are ____ from him" (Acts 26:26)
6. Megawatts, abbr.
7. Kind of bread that Moses put in Aaron's hands for a wave offering to the Lord (Lev. 8:26–27)
8. Campfire treat made from graham cracker, marshmallow, and chocolate
9. Lasts
10. "We have both straw and provender enough, and room to ____ in" (Gen. 24:25)
17. "Though [your sins] be ____ like crimson, they shall be as wool" (Isa. 1:18)
20. "According to the working of his ____ power" (Eph. 1:19)
21. Nervous
23. Haze
24. What a spider spins
25. "I rejoiced ____" (3 John 3)
28. "A ____ shall be saved" (Rom. 9:27)
29. "The brightness of his glory, and the ____ image of his person" (Heb. 1:3)

Down / Across clues:

31. "The tree of knowledge of good and ____" (Gen. 2:9)
33. Either
34. Kettle
37. European Defense Community, abbr.
42. "Sons of ____" (Gen. 46:23)
43. Modern Persia
45. "If any man will____ thee at the law, and take away thy coat, let him have thy cloke also" (Matt. 5:40)
46. The opposite of out
47. King of Bashan (Josh. 13:12)

by Cheryl Keiser

ACROSS

1. Thrives
8. Boy's name, var. form
11. Played again
12. Set in
14. Two, Rom. num.
15. God told Moses His name was I ____
16. Overdose, abbr.
17. Milligram, abbr.
18. "Destroy. . .the ____" (Deut. 20:17)
20. Carrot family herb
23. Public transportation
24. Number of lepers that Christ healed
25. Charged particle
27. Christ is the Alpha and ____
29. And, Lat.
30. By the grace of God, Lat. abbr.
31. Preposition
32. Pull
33. Long walk
36. Tin container
37. Mr., Sp. abbr.
39. "The Lord will not ____ his people" (1 Sam. 12:22)
41. The self, according to Freud
43. "____, every one that thirsteth" (Isa. 55:1)
45. Sixteenth letter of Greek alphabet (plural)
47. Preposition
48. Aaron's son (Exod. 6:25)
51. Childrens Bible club
53. Potato state
54. "____ my steps in thy word" (Ps. 119:133)
56. Russian ruler
57. "Take up thy ____, and go" (Matt. 9:6)
58. Church education, abbr.

DOWN

1. Monkey, for example
2. "Thy God ____!" (Isa. 52:7)
3. Either
4. Bags
5. IOU, in other words, abbr.
6. City in Zebulun (1 Chron. 6:77)
7. Tin, chemical symbol
8. Middle
9. Preposition
10. Feline's foot (2 words)
13. Paris university
15. Support organization for addicts, abbr.
19. African fly that spreads disease
21. Not out
22. Sea duck with soft feathers
26. King of Bashan (1 Kings 4:19)
28. Mythological snake-haired woman
31. "Howl, O ye ____ of Bashan" (Zech. 11:2)
34. "____ it be thou, bid me come" (Matt. 14:28)
35. Belonging to the leader of a rebellion against Moses (Num. 16)
36. Egyptian city
38. Arab chief
40. Fashionable resort
42. Belonging to one of the sons of Judah (Num. 26:19)
44. "The dragon, that ____ serpent" (Rev. 20:2)
46. Filled with wonder
49. "Let us ____, and be merry" (Luke 15:23)
50. Animals, scientific suffix
51. Lemon beverage
52. Clinton's state, abbr.
55. Rubidium, chem. symbol

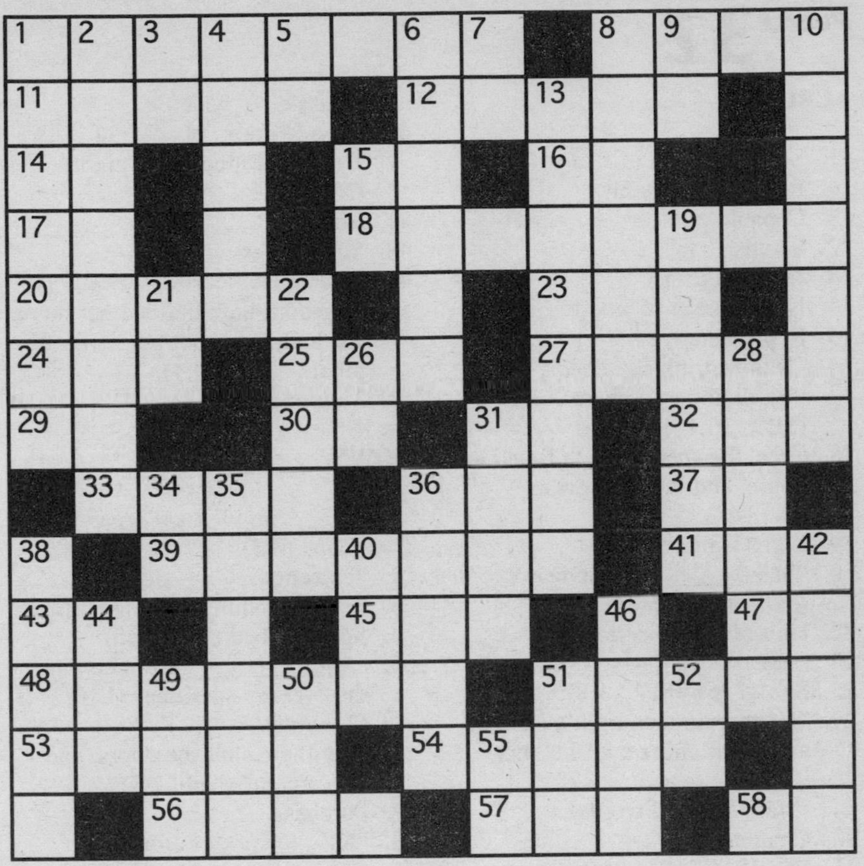

ACROSS

1. Son of Abijam (1 Kings 15:8)
4. Pull against the bit
8. Capable
12. Scottish cap
13. Jacob's brother
14. Narrow strip of wood
15. Representative
17. "If they drink any deadly thing, it shall not ____ them" (Mark 16:18)
18. "Yea, the sparrow hath found an house, and the swallow a ____" (Ps. 84:3)
19. Large water birds
20. "Stand ____ ____, and sin not" (Ps. 4:4) (2 words)
22. Unit of hay or cotton
24. Fathers
25. Son of Asa (Matt. 1:8)
29. "Neither do men light a candle, and put it under a bushel, but ____ ____ candlestick" (Matt. 5:15) (2 words)
30. Challenged
31. Period of time
32. "The ____ is worthy of his hire" (Luke 10:7)
34. Irish girl's name
35. Thomas Hardy heroine
36. "And if someone wants to sue you and take away your tunic, let him have your ____ as well" (Matt. 5:40 NIV)
37. "And four wagons and ____ oxen he gave unto the sons of Merari" (Num. 7:8)
40. Slipped
41. "Then Jacob ____ his clothes" (Gen. 37:34 NIV)
42. Old Testament book named for the Jewish leader who supervised the rebuilding of Jerusalem's wall
46. "The children of ____ of Hezekiah, ninety and eight" (Neh. 7:21)
47. Region
48. Strong brew
49. Announces
50. "Wisdom hath builded her house, she hath ____ out her seven pillars" (Prov. 9:1)
51. Title of respect

DOWN

1. "I ____ no pleasant bread" (Dan. 10:3)
2. Texas hero, ____ Houston
3. Son of Aram (Matt. 1:4)
4. Son of Obed (Matt. 1:5)
5. "And ____ ____ astonied until the evening sacrifice" (Ezra 9:4) (2 words)
6. "Let them shut the doors, and ____ them" (Neh. 7:3)
7. Purchase
8. "As ____ ____ before her shearers is dumb" (Isa. 53:7) (2 words)
9. "And thou shalt make a veil of ____, and purple, and scarlet" (Exod. 26:31)
10. Swedish man's name
11. Diminutive suffix
16. Stitches
19. "I was ____ when they said unto me, Let us go into the house of the Lord" (Ps. 122:1)
20. False god
21. Grandmother
22. Drills
23. Anna's tribe (Luke 2:36)
25. Containers
26. Herod's wife (Mark 6:19)
27. Operatic solo

28. Armored vehicle
30. Song for two voices
33. "If ____ be partakers of this power over you, are not we rather?" (1 Cor. 9:12)
34. "And they came to ____, where were twelve wells of water" (Exod. 15:27)
36. "Create in me a ____ heart, O God" (Ps. 51:10)
37. Greek letters
38. An infinitesimal amount, a jot
39. "The beauty of old men is the ____ head" (Prov. 20:29)
40. "I will ____ thee the bride" (Rev. 21:9)
42. Nope
43. Before
44. Boxer Mohammed ____
45. "Go to the ant, thou sluggard; consider ____ ways" (Prov. 6:6)

by Elaine Okupski

ACROSS

1. "He that loveth his _____ abideth in the light" (1 John 2:10)
6. "They. . .spake _____ one to another" (Mal. 3:16)
10. Anger
12. When you'll get to your destination, more or less, abbr.
13. "The _____ of the Lord. . .run to and fro" (Zech. 4:10)
16. "Let _____ the rich man glory in his riches" (Jer. 9:23)
17. Classifies
18. "We are the people of his pasture, and the sheep of his _____" (Ps. 95:7)
20. Dormitory helper, abbr.
21. "_____ is the fulfilling of the law" (Rom. 13:10)
22. "Love worketh _____ ill to his neighbour" (Rom. 13:10)
23. Plural suffix
25. Month, abbr.
26. "Good _____ from a far country" (Prov. 25:25)
28. Article that precedes a vowel
29. "Jesus saith unto them, Come and _____" (John 21:12)
31. "Do not your _____ before men" (Matt. 6:1)
32. "The first covenant had. . .a worldly _____" (Heb. 9:1)
38. "For the wrath is come upon them to the _____"(1 Thess. 2:16)
41. Swine
42. Preposition
43. Noah's vessel
44. Assist
46. "He hath a great _____ for you" (Col. 4:13)
47. Nathan, for short
49. Tell an untruth

51. "The light of the body is the _____" (Luke 11:34)
53. And, Lat.
54. "A woman hath a familiar spirit at _____" (1 Sam. 28:7)
55. Extraterrestrial, abbr.

DOWN

1. "_____ are the meek" (Matt. 5:5)
2. "By so much was Jesus made a surety of a better _____" (Heb. 7:22)
3. Head nurse, abbr.
4. Make a mistake
5. Radium, chem. symbol
6. Old English, abbr.
7. Number of commandments God gave to Moses
8. European Theater of Operations, abbr.
9. "The Lord is high above all _____" (Ps. 113:4)
11. "O _____, where is thy victory?" (1 Cor. 15:55)
14. Year old, abbr.
15. "Do not _____, my beloved brethren" (James 1:16)
18. "_____ thy father and thy mother" (Exod. 20:12)
19. "A _____ commandment I give unto you" (John 13:34)
22. "Father, glorify thy _____" (John 12:28)
24. Sister, abbr.
27. Simon _____
30. Nothing
33. New England state, abbr.
34. "Ye are the _____ of the living God" (2 Cor. 6:16)
35. "They were all _____ at the mighty power of God" (Luke 9:43)

36. "I am the _____ of Sharon"
    (Song of Sol. 2:1)
37. Backbone
39. "We spend our years as a _____
    that is told" (Ps. 90:9)
40. Trapshooting
45. Narrow fish
48. A unit of value in Laos
50. Not out
52. "_____ shall be as gods"
    (Gen. 3:5)
    by Carole Stengel

ACROSS

1. First book of the Bible
5. Jesus sat silent before this man (Matt. 27:11–14)
11. Cuckoo
12. David wrote most of this book, abbr.
14. "Everyone will be salted with ____" (Mark 9:49)
15. Appliance and electronics company, abbr.
16. Old Testament prophet
19. "Whoever loses his life for me will ____ it" (Matt. 16:25)
21. "Thou anointest my head with ____" (Ps. 23:5 KJV)
22. Name unknown, abbr.
23. He accused Paul of being out of his mind (Acts 26:24–25)
25. In the year of our Lord, Lat. abbr.
26. Letter's afterword
28. "He maketh me to ____ down in green pastures" (Ps. 23:2 KJV)
30. "____ is light" (1 John 1:5)
32. He was stoned to death after preaching to the Sanhedrin (Acts 7:59)
33. Beg
35. Printer's measure
36. Preposition
38. Greek for "my master" (Matt. 23:7)
41. "____ whatever gift he has received to serve others" (1 Pet. 4:10)
42. ____, so, la, ti, do
43. College English Association, abbr.
44. This beast spoke in a man's voice (2 Pet. 2:16 KJV)
46. Part of the high priest's breastplate (Exod. 28:30)
48. Exclamation
49. Ruthenium, chem. symbol
50. Leafy dish
51. Also known as Barsabbas (Acts 1:23)
53. The swallow had one for herself (Ps. 84:3)
56. Truckload, abbr.

58. Strategic Defense Initiative, abbr.
59. When Paul left Greece heading for Syria by way of Macedonia, he was accompanied by this Ephesian Christian (Acts 21:29)
62. Master of Arts in Teaching, abbr.
64. Undergraduate degree, abbr.
66. The man whose face was on the denarius (Matt. 22:20–21)
68. "For though I am ____ from you in body" (Col. 2:5)
71. Body of water
73. Born to Adam and Eve after the death of Abel (Gen. 4:25)
75. Visualize
78. America's abbreviation
79. A messenger of the church and companion of Paul (Phil. 2:25)

DOWN

1. One of the chief Philistine cities (Josh. 15:47)
2. Compass points
3. Secret disciple (John 3:1)
4. Twirl
6. "____ any of you lacks wisdom, he should ask God" (James 1:5)
7. "I will give you the crown of ____" (Rev. 2:10)
8. Seized by the crowd at Ephesus (Acts 19:29)
9. "I think it is right to refresh your memory as long as I live in the ____ of this body" (2 Pet. 1:13)
10. An Israelite
13. This man spoke slander about the Lord's disciples (Acts 9:1)
17. Brief greeting
18. Father of James (Matt. 10:3)
20. "____ down deep and laid the foundation of rock" (Luke 6:48)
23. Paul had a trial before him (Acts 24:1–4)
24. Fa, ____, la, ti, do
25. Consumed
27. Placed
29. Innings pitched, abbr.
31. "Isn't this the cup my master ____ from and also uses for divination?" (Gen. 44:5)

34. Dictionary of American English, abbr.
37. Paul was trained under him (Acts 22:3)
39. A blind beggar (Mark 10:46)
40. Companion of Paul who sold his property and gave to the apostles (Acts 4:36–37)
42. Dirt
45. Susan, for short
47. Egyptian sun god
48. Breakfast beverage, for short
52. Northwest state whose capital is Pierre
54. Address abbreviation
55. "I am the ____ vine, and my Father is the gardener" (John 15:1)
57. "Made him to ____ honey out of the rock" (Deut. 32:13 KJV)

60. "If a blind man leads a blind man, both will fall into a ____" (Matt. 15:14)
61. Self-addressed envelope, abbr.
63. ____ and crafts
65. Mr. Lincoln
67. Social Security, abbr.
69. "You shall ____ greater things than that" (John 1:50)
70. Gun organization, abbr.
72. Shakespeare's Much ____ About Nothing
74. He saw Noah's nakedness (Gen. 9:20–27)
76. Fifth day of the week, abbr.
77. Nebo, for example, abbr. (NIV)

by Michael J. Landi

71

ACROSS

1. "We should be made ____ "
   (Titus 3:7)
5. "Now I have prepared. . .for the house of my God. . .all manner of precious stones, and ____ stones in abundance"
   (1 Chron. 29:2)
10. Each, abbr.
11. "I entreat thee also, true ____ fellow, help those women"
    (Phil. 4:3)
14. Federal Aviation Agency, abbr.
15. "This ____ said, I am able"
    (Matt. 26:61)
17. Laughter sound
18. "A meat offering baken in a ____ " (Lev. 2:5)
20. Unit of verse measurement
22. District of Colombia, abbr.
23. Letter after em
24. Timothy, for short
25. Hare
27. Railway, abbr.
28. Do, ____, mi
29. Kilogram, abbr.
30. "This ____ the day which the Lord hath made" (Ps. 118:24)
31. "All things ____ together for good to them that love God"
    (Rom. 8:28)
32. The self, according to Freud
34. Common Era, abbr.
36. Louise, for short
37. Matured
38. Springfield's state, abbr.
39. "A time to weep, and a time to ____ " (Eccles. 3:4)
41. Pierre's state
42. Paid, abbr.
43. Capital of Tibet

46. "I, John. . .was in the ____ that is called Patmos" (Rev. 1:9)
48. "As many as they found, both ____ and good" (Matt. 22:10)
50. "My fellow ____ in Christ Jesus" (Philem. 23)
52. "Thou shalt not muzzle the ____ when he treadeth out the corn"
    (Deut. 25:4)
53. Gym class, abbr.
55. Iridium, chem. symbol
56. To-do
57. Joined himself to a ____ of that country (Luke 15:15)

DOWN

1. But are ____ of your joy
   (2 Cor. 1:24)
2. 10 across
3. A type of grain
4. "Send to you Epaphroditus, my brother. . .and fellow ____ "
   (Phil. 2:25)
6. Air Force, abbr.
7. "Joshua saved ____ the harlot alive" (Josh. 6:25)
8. Sheep's sound
9. Command
12. Kiloliter, abbr.
13. End of month, abbr.
15. Footnote, abbr.
16. "These only are my fellow ____ unto the kingdom of God"
    (Col. 4:11)
19. "Lest at ____ time thou dash thy foot against a stone" (Matt. 4:6)
21. Tattered
22. "And the ____ were called Christians first in Antioch"
    (Acts 11:26)
24. "Emptied her pitcher into the

____ " (Gen. 24:20)

26. Two, prefix
31. "They _____ have repented long ago" (Matt. 11:21)
33. Exclamation of pain
35. "The four and twenty _____. . . fell down and worshiped God" (Rev. 19:4)
36. Californian city, abbr.
39. Work
40. Sound of laughter
44. South America's language, abbr.
45. Western state, abbr.
46. Independent Order of Foresters, abbr.
47. A blunt nose
49. "Now also the _____ is laid unto the root of the trees (Matt. 3:10)
51. Anger
53. Greek letter used for the ratio of a circle's circumference to its diameter
54. And, Lat.

ACROSS

1. "With the ____ angels"
   (Mark 8:38)
3. "The Holy ____ shall teach you"
   (Luke 12:12)
7. "They went. . .from ____. . .into
   Canaan" (Gen. 11:31)
8. A short laugh
9. Moses and ____ went before
   Pharaoh (Exod. 5:1)
10. "____ is the way, which leadeth
    unto life" (Matt. 7:14)
12. Des Moines' state, abbr.
14. One of the twelve tribes
    (Num. 1:38)
15. David reigned there (2 Sam. 2:1)
16. Substantive, abbr.
18. "The ____ of thy life shall be
    many" (Prov. 4:10)
20. Northeastern area of the U.S.,
    abbr.
21. Earned runs, abbr.
23. "Mine ____ is as nothing before
    thee" (Ps. 39:5)
24. "Our ____ is grown up"
    (Ezra 9:6)
29. Graduate degree, abbr.
31. A poem
32. Some were clay and some iron
    (Dan. 2:42)
34. "These are the ____ covenants"
    (Gal. 4:24)
36. "Being reviled, ____ bless"
    (1 Cor. 4:12)
38. "God saw that ____ was good"
    (Gen. 1:10)
39. An unclean thing (Lev. 11:29)
41. Santa Fe's state, abbr.
42. A city belonging to the tribe of
    Naphtali (Josh. 19:38–39)
44. A mongrel

47. "By faith they passed through
    the ____ sea" (Heb. 11:29)
49. Warrant officer, abbr.
50. News agency, abbr.

DOWN

1. "With his ____ spread up to
   heaven" (1 Kings 8:54)
2. "Confess that Jesus Christ is
   ____" (Phil. 2:11)
3. Guaranteed annual wage, abbr.
4. "Perform unto the Lord thine
   ____" (Matt. 5:33)
5. Salvation Army, abbr.
6. "Deliver me out of all ____"
   (1 Sam. 26:24)
7. The joining of two or more
   things into one
8. "Provide things ____ in the
   sight of all men"
   (Rom. 12:17)
11. Man's name, for short
13. Over again
17. "Abraham ____ Isaac"
    (Gen. 25:19)
19. "A bruised ____ shall he not
    break" (Matt. 12:20)
22. Do, ____, mi
23. I ____. God's name given to
    Moses
25. "I am the ____ and the offspring
    of David" (Rev. 22:16)
26. "He revealeth his ____ unto his
    servants" (Amos 3:7)
27. "____ I opened my mouth"
    (Ezek. 3:2)
28. Stitches
30. "One ____ or one tittle shall in
    no wise pass from the law"
    (Matt. 5:18)

33. "When we shall _____ him"
    (Isa. 53:2)
35. "If any _____ have children"
    (1 Tim. 5:4)
37. "The noise of a _____, and the
    noise of the rattling of the
    wheels" (Nah. 3:2)
40. Zaccur's father (Neh. 3:2)
43. "To be sin for us, who knew
    _____ sin" (2 Cor. 5:21)
44. Pa's wife
45. "He was taken _____; and a cloud
    received him out of their sight"
    (Acts 1:9)

46. "Given _____ hospitality"
    (Rom. 12:13)
48. "Without me ye can _____
    nothing" (John 15:5)
    by Carole Stengel

ACROSS

1. Formal request for one's presence
9. Preposition
11. Sodium, chem. symbol
12. Nickel, chem. symbol
13. Man's name
14. "____ it with thy might" (Eccles. 9:10)
15. "The Lord knoweth the ____ of the wise" (1 Cor. 3:20)
18. "____ hath he quickened" (Eph. 2:1)
19. Worries
20. Belonging to
22. Nurse, abbr.
23. Belonging to Judah's firstborn (Num. 26:19)
24. The Anointed One
26. Frigid
29. Indefinite article
30. Flightless bird
32. "For God ____ loved the world" (John 3:16)
33. Concept
36. Twelfth-grader, abbr.
37. Frightened
39. Article that precedes a vowel
40. "Phebe our ____" (Rom. 16:1)
43. Anger
44. Floss
47. "That have the rule ____ you" (Heb. 13:17)
50. Atomic energy, abbr.
52. Not, prefix
53. "Ye might have life through his ____" (John 20:31)
54. Shut noisily
55. Bristle
56. "Is my hand shortened at all, that it cannot ____?" (Isa. 50:2)
57. Light wood

DOWN

1. "Who also maketh ____ for us" (Rom. 8:34)
2. Slang negative
3. Accustomed to something unpleasant
4. Big cat
5. Small children
6. "Groweth of ____ own" (Lev. 25:5)
7. Writings that Jews and Christians have in common, abbr.
8. "I will fear ____ evil" (Ps. 23:4)
9. Smells
10. Spring of water
16. Preposition
17. Altitudes, abbr.
20. Exclamation
21. Scared, for short
24. Group of singers
25. India, abbr.
27. Son of Becher (1 Chron. 7:8)
28. Lutetium, chem. symbol
31. Someone who takes advantage
32. Southern continent, abbr.
34. Apiece, abbr.
35. Feelers
38. Wrinkle
41. Exhausted
42. Trite
45. "A ____ without blemish" (1 Pet. 1:19)
46. Promises
48. Various, abbr.
49. Suffix
51. Shade tree
by Cheryl Keiser

Puzzle 38

ACROSS

1. Division of opposing parties
5. "____ thy way unto the Lord" (Ps. 37:5)
8. Exclamation
9. Small amount
10. "____ my Father's house are many mansions" (John 14:2)
11. "Jesus saith unto them, Come and ____" (John 21:12)
12. Nativity set
15. Indianapolis's state, abbr.
16. Where Goliath was from (2 Sam. 21:22)
17. Social equal
19. Overdose, abbr.
20. New Testament book that follows Galatians, abbr.
21. Isaiah's father (Isa. 1:1)
23. Exclamation of satisfaction
25. Sound used to attract attention
27. Rachel's handmaid given to Jacob to bear a son (Gen. 30:3)
29. "____ is a rewarder of them that diligently seek him" (Heb. 11:6)
30. "____ ye therefore, and teach all nations" (Matt. 28:19)
31. Lower limb
33. Legendary bird of prey
36. Line, abbr.
37. Time past
38. Office of Technology Assessment
39. Cow's noise
40. Dover's state, abbr.
41. "Thy word have I ____ in mine heart" (Ps. 119:11)
43. "There shall in no wise enter into it any thing that defileth, neither whatsoever worketh ____" (Rev. 21:27)
47. "Why beholdest thou the ____ that is in thy brother's eye?" (Luke 6:41)
49. Where Job lived (Job 1:1)
50. High ranking Turkish official
51. "He planteth an ____, and the rain doth nourish it" (Isa. 44:14)
52. Man who died after he had deceived the apostles (Acts 5:1–5)

DOWN

1. Father of Israelite spy (Num. 13:10)
2. Lower part of the face
3. Yes, Sp.
4. Land that lies ten miles east of Beer-sheba (Neh. 11:26)
5. Hidden store
6. The Philistines put five golden ____ in the Ark of the Covenant as a trepass offering when they returned it (1 Sam. 6:4)
7. To stick, adhere
13. Hebrew unit of measure (Exod. 16:36)
14. More, suffix
16. Leave
18. Steal
21. Solomon planted these trees in terraces up to the temple (2 Chron. 9:11)
22. City of David (2 Chron. 5:2)
24. Circle of light
26. Herod's wife and sister-in-law (Luke 3:19)
28. Not him
32. Elisha's servant (2 Kings 4:12)
34. Begins with Genesis and ends with Malachi, abbr.

35. Pertaining to the body
36. Unwilling
37. Arab country
40. "My meat is to _____ the will of him that sent me" (John 4:34)
42. Pronoun for a thing
44. "_____ still, and know that I am God" (Ps. 46:10)
45. Joshua's father (Josh. 1:1)
46. King of Bashan (1 Kings 4:19)
47. Mother
48. Old style, abbr.

PUZZLE 39

ACROSS

1. "____ and see" (John 1:39)
5. Town near Bethel (Josh. 7:2)
6. "Them that ____ in riches" (Mark 10:24)
11. Valley near Jerusalem (Josh. 15:8)
13. "____ is he" (Rom. 14:22)
14. Aluminum, chem. symbol
15. Nashville's state, abbr.
16. "I am the ____" (John 14:6)
18. "Trees of the Lord are full of ____" (Ps. 104:16)
19. Large stringed instruments
21. Do, ____, mi
22. "We beheld his ____" (John 1:14)
24. "Like a refiner's ____" (Mal. 3:2)
26. East Indies, abbr.
27. "Whosoever ____ in him should not perish" (John 3:16)
31. "A great ____ dragon" (Rev. 12:3)
33. "Unto the ____ of the earth" (Acts 13:47)
34. Resound
35. "The ____ of death is sin" (1 Cor. 15:56)
37. "To sit up ____" (Ps. 127:2)
38. "When ____ the king had heard these things, he was troubled" (Matt. 2:3)
40. "Naphtali is a ____ let loose" (Gen. 49:21)
43. Calendar numbers
46. Victory in Europe, abbr.
47. "He was ____ the world" (John 1:10)
49. Accomplish

52. "He ____, and denied not" (John 1:20)
56. "Made it a ____ of thieves" (Matt. 21:13)
57. "No man hath ____" (John 3:13)
58. Road, abbr.

DOWN

1. "Poured out the ____ money" (John 2:15)
2. "Took no ____ with them" (Matt. 25:3)
3. St. Paul's state, abbr.
4. "He cannot ____ into the kingdom of God" (John 3:5)
5. "I ____ the living bread" (John 6:51)
6. "Father, glorify ____ name" (John 12:28)
7. Egyptian sun god
8. ____ and downs
9. "He that ____ his rod" (Prov. 13:24)
10. Kind, variety
12. "Glory as of the ____ ____ of the Father"(John 1:14) (2 words)
16. "The ____ was made by him" (John 1:10)
17. "Love one another, ____ I have loved you" (John 15:12)
19. Company, abbr.
20. "Go thy way; thy son ____" (John 4:50)
23. "As much as ____ in you" (Rom. 12:18)
24. Iron, chem. symbol
25. "As many as ____ him, to them gave he power" (John 1:12)
28. Printer's measure

29. "I. . .was in the _____ that is called Patmos" (Rev. 1:9)
30. "_____ fast that which is good" (1 Thess. 5:21)
32. "Jesus Christ, Who _____ for us" (1 Thess. 5:9–10)
36. Gun lobbyists, abbr.
39. Eastern seaboard state, abbr.
41. "_____ man spake like this" (John 7:46)
42. Type style
44. Correspondence enclosure, abbr.
45. Doctorate degree, abbr.

48. Negative votes
50. Committee for Economic Development, abbr.
51. "To this _____ I was born" (John 18:37)
53. State where man first flew, abbr.
54. Far East, abbr.
55. Northwest state, abbr.

by Rebecca Souder

PUZZLE 40

ACROSS

1. "Ye tithe _____ and rue and all manner of herbs" (Luke 11:42)
4. "But the _____ are beaten out with a staff" (Isa. 28:27)
9. Sound of hesitation
10. "I will sing of the mercies of the Lord for _____" (Ps. 89:1)
13. Poem
14. "Then took Mary a pound of ointment of _____" (John 12:3)
17. Royal Air Force, abbr.
18. African antelope
20. "All thy garments smell of myrrh, and _____" (Ps. 45:8)
22. "I will give unto thee the _____ of the kingdom of heaven" (Matt. 16:19)
23. "I. . .brought thee out of _____ of the Chaldees" (Gen. 15:7)
24. Republic of Rwanda, abbr.
25. "They slew the kings of Midian . . .namely, _____" (Num. 31:8)
27. Biblical plain (Neh. 6:2)
28. Arid
29. "Ye pay tithe of mint and _____ and cummin" (Matt. 23:23)
33. Follows em
34. A greeting
35. "Beaten out with a staff, and the _____ with a rod" (Isa. 28:27)
38. Sixteenth letter of the Hebrew alphabet
39. Myself
40. "Thou shouldest be for salvation unto the _____ of the earth" (Acts 13:47)
41. Sweet potatoes
43. "The smoke of the _____. . . ascended up before God" (Rev. 8:4)
45. Cereal grains
46. First day of the week, abbr.
47. Twice, prefix
49. City in Nevada
50. Native of Serbia
53. Canned meat product
54. "Such _____ as the queen of Sheba gave king Solomon" (2 Chron. 9:9)

DOWN

1. "Faith as a grain of _____ seed" (Matt. 17:20)
2. Mischievous child
3. Moslem monastery
4. "They presented unto him gifts; gold and _____" (Matt. 2:11)
5. "_____ shalt thou be with me in paradise" (Luke 23:43)
6. Record's replacement, abbr.
7. Zeus's sister
8. "Thy plants are. . .spikenard and _____" (Song of Sol. 4:13–14)
11. Bible division within a chapter
12. Printer's measure
15. "His belly is as bright _____" (Song of Sol. 5:14)
16. Grain
19. Library science, abbr.
21. "The _____ is my shepherd" (Ps. 23:1)
23. Infinite
26. Southern state, abbr.
30. Iowa University, abbr.
31. Not large, abbr.
32. To correct
34. "They filled a sponge with vinegar, and put it upon _____" (John 19:29)
36. _____ and outs

37. "They presented unto him gifts; gold, and. . .____" (Matt. 2:11)
38. Prayer endings
39. Do, re, ____
42. Opposite of nay
44. Worthless dog
48. Frozen water
50. Samarium, chem. symbol
51. Undergraduate degree, abbr.
52. Seventh note of the musical scale

PUZZLE 41

ACROSS

1. Religious leaders of Jesus' day (Matt. 23:2)
7. Jesus is called the ____ of man
10. Philadelphia's state, abbr.
11. Barnabas was this (Acts 4:36)
13. Heavy work shoe
15. Abigail, for short, alt. spelling
16. Girl, Scot.
17. Eclipse, abbr.
19. Interior, abbr.
20. Nahor's concubine (Gen. 22:24)
22. Belonging to America's spy agency, abbr.
24. National Guard, abbr.
26. Do, ____, mi
27. Doctor who delivers babies, abbr.
28. "The ____ are a people not strong" (Prov. 30:25)
29. "They. . .are choked with ____" (Luke 8:14)
30. French word used to identify a woman by her maiden name
31. Kid's candy
32. Ostrich like bird
35. Organ remover
38. "A ____ prepared for the Lord" (Luke 1:17)
42. Written composition
43. Put in writing, var. spelling
47. Jiphtah and ____ (Josh. 15:43)
49. Great arteries
50. "Which stilleth the noise of the ____" (Psalm 65:7)
51. Long, narrow fish

DOWN

1. Matthew the ____ (Matt. 10:3)
2. One who renounces his faith
3. "All our righteousnesses are as filthy ____" (Isa. 64:6)
4. "We had the ____ of death in ourselves" (2 Cor. 1:9)
5. "Rebuke not an ____" (1 Tim. 5:1)
6. Compass point
7. A brother or sister, for short
8. Off Track Betting, abbr.
9. "Love his ____ as himself" (Mark 12:33)
12. Regards as precious
14. Like a frog
18. Breakfast food
21. Account of, abbr.
23. Religious education, abbr.
25. Area of Israel that adjoins the Sinai Peninsula
32. And, Lat.
33. Pertaining to the mind
34. Extends across
36. Jesus is called the ____ of life (John 6:48)
37. French spelling of Andrew
38. Pod dwellers
39. To be, Lat.
40. Occupational Safety and Health Agency, abbr.
41. Linear Yard Area, abbr.
44. Negative
45. Resident or follower, suffix
46. Curved shape
48. Laughter sound
   by Cheryl Keiser

ACROSS

1. Person who makes perfume
8. "Ten women shall ____ your bread in one oven" (Lev. 26:26)
11. Any person
12. "The noise of the stamping of the ____ of his strong horses" (Jer. 47:3)
14. Inspector General, abbr.
15. Edible Japanese plant
16. Eggs
18. Near, abbr.
19. "No man putteth a piece of ____ cloth unto an old garment" (Matt. 9:16)
20. Temporary route
23. Teacher's helper, abbr.
24. Physician, abbr.
25. "Take thee a ____ razor, and cause it to pass upon thine head" (Ezek. 5:1)
26. Four, Rom. num.
27. South Vietnamese coin
28. Short for potassium nitrate, Br.
31. "He shall sit as a ____ and purifier of silver" (Mal. 3:3)
35. "There shall be weeping and ____ of teeth" (Matt. 8:12)
36. "This do ye; ____ your beasts, and go" (Gen. 45:17)
37. Island nation, abbr.
38. Too much of a drug, abbr.
40. Therefore
41. Putting threads together to make fabric
45. Impersonal pronoun
47. Current of warm water that affects the weather (2 words)
49. Paul's occupation
53. Peach state, abbr.
54. Dorcas's occupation (Acts 9:39)

55. "Come unto ____, all ye that labour" (Matt. 11:28)
56. "In the beginning ____ created the heaven and the earth" (Gen. 1:1)

DOWN

1. Coloring with a brush
2. "Grave upon it, like the ____s of a signet" (Exod. 28:36)
3. Track transportation, abbr.
4. Sinks below surface of water
5. "Is a candle brought to be put ____ a bushel?" (Mark 4:21)
6. Cat's cry
7. "Peter knocked. . .a damsel came to hearken, named ____" (Acts 12:13)
8. Noah's occupation (2 words)
9. Flying soldiers, abbr.
10. Dorothy's state, abbr.
13. "Shepherds. . .keeping watch ____ their flock by night" (Luke 2:8)
17. Tax enforcement organization, abbr.
21. Old English, abbr.
22. "Take I pray thee. . .And he ____ him, and he took it" (Gen. 33:11)
25. Overheat
29. Flaps
30. Extemely high frequency, abbr.
32. For example, Lat. abbr.
33. Northern continent, abbr.
34. "Though they be ____ like crimson, they shall be as wool" (Isa. 1:18)
38. Like a sheep
39. Glove

41. "We will eat our own bread, and
    ____ our own apparel" (Isa. 4:1)
42. Antlered animal
43. Musical term to indicate
    "animated," abbr.
44. "There was ____ room for them
    in the inn" (Luke 2:7)
46. Hot or cold beverage
48. A son of Zilpah (Gen. 35:26)
50. Nickel, chem. symbol
51. Total loss, abbr.
52. Southwestern state whose capital
    is Jefferson City, abbr.
53. "____ ye therefore, and teach all
    nations" (Matt. 28:19)

ACROSS

1. "The _____ of God is eternal life" (Rom. 6:23)
4. "Without him was _____ any thing made" (John 1:3)
6. "That was the _____ light" (John 1:9)
9. "The _____ shineth in darkness" (John 1:5)
11. "Which were _____, not of blood" (John 1:13)
12. "Was made flesh and _____ among us" (John 1:14)
14. Precious stone
15. Dock warrant, abbr.
17. Chemical suffix
18. Young woman
20. Also
21. His Royal Highness, abbr.
22. "Smote the _____ into his temples" (Judg. 4:21)
24. Hebrew name for God, comb. form
25. "But as many as _____ him" (John 1:12)
28. The first man
31. Electron volt, abbr.
32. Four, Rom. num.
33. Belonging to a Canaanite god
37. "A _____ commandment I give unto you" (John 13:34)
39. "The _____ comprehended it not" (John 1:5)
42. Emergency Relief Organization, abbr.
43. To balk, Scot.
44. Office of Strategic Services, abbr.
47. Year, abbr.
48. "But was sent to _____ _____ of that Light" (John 1:8) (2 words)

51. Overseas News Service, abbr.
52. European Theater of Operations, abbr.
53. "Full of grace and _____" (John 1:14)
55. "I come baptizing with _____" (John 1:31)
56. Church, abbr.
57. Negative vote

DOWN

1. "The Word was _____" (John 1:1)
2. "The Word was made _____" (John 1:14)
3. "Take thee a _____" (Ezek. 4:1)
4. New England state, abbr.
5. A division of Scripture
6. Thomas, for short
7. Railroad, abbr.
8. "To _____ the heavy burdens" (Isa. 58:6)
10. Gross ton, abbr.
11. "Them that _____ on his name" (John 1:12)
13. "The _____ was made by him" (John 1:10)
14. "But _____ and truth came" (John 1:17)
16. "In the beginning was the _____" (John 1:1)
19. Suffix
21. "Two disciples _____ him speak" (John 1:37)
23. Fifty-one, Rom. num.
26. "I am the true _____" (John 15:1)
27. "Which lighteth _____ man" (John 1:9)
29. Side by side
30. "Builder and _____ is God" (Heb. 11:10)

34. "How ye ought to ____ every man" (Col. 4:6)
35. "And ____ ____ out to husbandmen" (Mark 12:1) (2 words)
36. Church school, in other words, abbr.
38. "Thou art ____, O Lord" (Rev. 4:11)
40. Place for competition
41. "The only begotten ____" (John 1:18)
45. Son of Adam
46. Soviet Socialist Republic, abbr.
48. "Every knee should ____" (Phil. 2:10)
49. "He gave power ____ become" (John 1:12)
50. "Did shine as the ____" (Matt. 17:2)
54. Tantalum, chem. symbol
by Rebecca Souder

PUZZLE 44

ACROSS

1. Jesus is the good ____
8. Thank you, Br.
10. Jesus made water into this at Cana
11. Prophet in Jerusalem that warned Paul he would be arrested (Acts 21:10–11)
14. To set apart for a duty of the church
15. "For we wrestle not against flesh and blood. . .but. . .against the ____ of the darkness"(Eph. 6:12)
16. To have a strong smell
17. The people of Athens had an altar to an ____God(Acts 17:23)
19. This servant of God must be the husband of one wife, grave, and not double-tongued (1 Tim. 3:8–12)
20. "____, and ye shall receive" (John 16:24)
23. Tower where Jacob (Israel) camped on his way to Canaan (Gen. 35:21)
25. The opposite of live
27. Poisonous snakes (Deut. 32:33)
29. Myself
30. Where Israel was held in bondage for centuries until Moses led them to freedom
31. Remaining residue after something has been burned
33. Pertaining to farming, prefix
34. A servant of the high priest lost this momentarily to Peter's sword
36. God asks us to improve or ____ our ways (Jer. 7:3)
37. "Teaching them to ____ all things" (Matt. 28:20)
40. ____ and fro
41. Second note of the musical scale
42. People sacrificed this to atone for sin
45. Helped Moses speak before Pharaoh
48. Revise
50. One who held up Moses' hands at the battle of Amalek (Exod. 17:12)
51. "Let us draw near with a true heart in full ____ of faith" (Heb. 10:22)

DOWN

1. The Word of God is sharper than this
2. "The labourer is worthy of his ____" (Luke 10:7)
3. Terminated
4. Reached a maximum
5. "Thus saith the Lord unto the ____ that keep my sabbaths" (Isa. 56:4)
6. The absence of light
7. Ring of light
8. Spins
9. Balaam's spoke to him by God's power
12. Firearm
13. "____ of false prophets, which come to you in sheep's clothing" (Matt. 7:15)
18. Negative
21. "Seek ye first the ____ of God" (Matt. 6:33)
22. Swine
24. God's name for Himself: I ____ (Exod. 3:14)
25. The fourth of Israel's judges, a woman

26. Sight organs
27. Ancestor of family of porters who returned from exile (Neh. 7:45)
28. "Children, obey your _____ in the Lord" (Eph. 6:1)
32. "Is not my word like as a fire? saith the Lord; and like a _____ that breaketh the rock" (Jer. 23:29)
33. Sluggards should learn from this insect

35. Assyrian region from which Sargon brought men to populate devastated Samaria (2 Kings 17:24)
38. Boyfriend, Fr.
39. The conscious self
43. Woman's name
44. Linear, abbr.
46. Railed transportation, abbr.
47. Sodium, chem. symbol
49. Technetium, chem. symbol

ACROSS

1. "Let the earth bring forth. . . ____, and creeping thing, and beast of the earth" (Gen. 1:24)
8. Southern continent, abbr.
10. Precipitates
11. "The earth was without ____" (Gen. 1:2)
13. Judah's son (Gen. 38:3)
14. When you're going to leave, more or less, abbr.
15. Anger
16. "____ there be light" (Gen. 1:3)
17. Christ's followers, abbr.
19. "God ____ the heaven" (Gen. 1:1)
21. Seventh note of the musical scale
22. "Divide the waters ____ the waters" (Gen. 1:6)
23. Ruthenium, chem. symbol
24. Fiddler crab genus
26. "Let the ____ under the heaven be gathered together" (Gen. 1:9)
29. War of the ____
31. "The evening and the ____ were the third day" (Gen. 1:13)
34. Extraterrestrial, abbr.
35. "Where ____ you?" (Gen. 3:9 NIV)
37. "Breathed ____ his nostrils the breath of life" (Gen. 2:7)
38. "In the ____ God" (Gen. 1:1)
41. "The waters called he ____" (Gen. 1:10)
42. Common preposition
43. "He did ____ it under his raiment" (Judg. 3:16)
45. "There shall come a ____ out of Jacob" (Num. 24:17)
47. Touchdown, abbr.

49. Negative
50. "Thou art an ____ man" (Luke 19:21)
53. "And ____ said, Let there be light" (Gen. 1:3)
55. Day when plants were created
56. "Hath God said, ____ shall not eat of every tree?" (Gen. 3:1)
57. Iron, chem. symbol

DOWN

1. "Every living ____ that moveth" (Gen. 1:21)
2. Support organization for alcoholics, abbr.
3. Binds
4. Explosive, abbr.
5. Illegal drug referred to as acid, abbr.
6. "According to the ____-knowledge of God" (1 Pet. 1:2)
7. God's name for Himself: I ____ (Exod. 3:14)
8. "Whose ____ is in itself" (Gen. 1:11)
9. "For dust thou ____" (Gen. 3:19)
11. "God called the ____ Heaven" (Gen. 1:8)
12. One who raises
16. French article
18. Decorative loop on ribbon
19. "The ____ and the bear shall feed" (Isa. 11:7)
20. "Neither shadow of ____" (James 1:17)
25. "Ye shall be ____ gods" (Gen. 3:5)
27. Preposition
28. "Declare his works with ____" (Ps. 107:22 ASV)
30. Droops

32. Part of Scripture that contains the new covenant, abbr.
33. "And God saw that it was ____" (Gen. 1:10)
36. Smallest state, abbr.
38. "God made the ____ of the earth" (Gen. 1:25)
39. "Let the ____ bring forth grass" (Gen. 1:11)
40. "Thou shalt ____ eat of it" (Gen. 2:17)
41. Man's name, for short
44. "Under the shadow of my ____" (Gen. 19:8)

45. "God ____ every thing that he had made" (Gen. 1:31)
46. "Fools, shall not ____ therein" (Isa. 35:8)
48. "On the seventh ____ God ended his work" (Gen. 2:2)
51. East Indies, abbr.
52. Education, abbr.
54. Eastern seacoast state, abbr.
by Rebecca Souder

PUZZLE 46

ACROSS

1. "Thou art an ____ people unto the Lord" (Deut. 7:6)
3. "The Holy ____ shall teach you" (Luke 12:12)
7. "They went. . .from ____. . .into Canaan" (Gen. 11:31)
8. A short laugh
9. Moses and ____ went before Pharaoh (Exod. 5:1)
10. "____ is the way, which leadeth unto life" (Matt. 7:14)
12. Three, prefix
13. Des Moines' state, abbr.
15. One of the twelve tribes (Num. 1:38)
16. David reigned there (2 Sam. 2:1)
17. Antimony, chem. symbol
19. Twelve months
21. Europium, chem. symbol
22. Northeastern region of the U.S., abbr.
23. Earned runs, abbr.
25. Sixth note of the musical scale
27. "The eyes of Israel were dim for ____" (Gen. 48:10)
28. "If thy brother ____ against thee, rebuke him" (Luke 17:3)
32. Pa's wife
34. Poem
35. Bonds
37. "____ of every sort shalt thou bring into the ark" (Gen. 6:19)
39. "Being reviled, ____ bless" (1 Cor. 4:12)
41. "God saw that ____ was good" (Gen. 1:10)
42. An unclean thing (Lev. 11:29)
45. Coal scuttle
47. Gym, in other words, abbr.
48. Colorado's neighbor, abbr.
49. "A land whose stones are ____" (Deut. 8:9)
51. Mongrel
53. "As ____ as blood" (2 Kings 3:22)
55. "My flesh is clothed with ____" (Job 7:5)
56. Sash worn with a kimona

DOWN

1. "With his ____ spread up to heaven" (1 Kings 8:54)
2. "Confess that Jesus Christ is ____" (Phil. 2:11)
3. Guaranteed annual wage, abbr.
4. "Let there be now an ____ betwixt us" (Gen. 26:28)
5. Asian garment, alt. spelling
6. "Deliver me out of all ____" (1 Sam. 26:24)
7. The joining of two or more things
8. "Whatsoever things are ____. . . think on these things" (Phil. 4:8)
11. Sunbeam
14. Over again
18. "Abraham ____ Isaac" (Gen. 25:19)
20. "A bruised ____ shall he not break" (Matt. 12:20)
24. Regarding, abbr.
26. Airspeed indicator, abbr.
27. God's name for Himself: I ____
29. "I am the ____ and the offspring of David" (Rev. 22:16)
30. "He revealeth his ____ unto his servants" (Amos 3:7)
31. Stitches
33. "One ____ or tittle shall in no wise pass from the law" (Matt. 5:18)

36. "When we shall _____ him" (Isa. 53:2)
38. "If any _____ have children. . . , let them first learn to shew piety at home" (1 Tim. 5:4)
40. "The noise of a _____" (Nah. 3:2)
43. Great work
44. Zaccur's father (Neh. 3:2)
46. Either
50. "To be sin for us, who knew _____ sin" (2 Cor. 5:21)
51. 2000, Rom. num.
52. "Given _____ hospitality" (Rom. 12:13)
54. "Without me ye can _____ nothing" (John 15:5)

ACROSS

1. "The _____ of God is eternal life" (Rom. 6:23)
5. "Jesus Christ our _____" (Rom. 1:3)
9. Civil Servant, abbr.
11. "To God _____ wise, be glory" (Rom. 16:27)
12. "Walk in the _____, as he is" (1 John 1:7)
13. Of age, Lat. abbr.
14. "The fallow _____" (Deut. 14:5)
15. "The grace _____ our Lord Jesus Christ be with you all" (Rev. 22:21)
16. Tender loving care, abbr.
17. "Whom I _____ with my spirit in the gospel" (Rom. 1:9)
19. "The Word was made flesh, and _____ among us" (John 1:14)
21. New England state, abbr.
22. Electrical engineer, abbr.
23. Abraham's wife (Gen. 12:5)
24. Southern continent, abbr.
25. "We have seen his _____ in the east" (Matt. 2:2)
26. All news station, abbr.
27. "He ever _____ to make intercession" (Heb. 7:25)
31. Heligram, abbr.
32. Got down
33. "And _____ himself in water" (Lev. 15:5)
36. "My heart's desire and prayer to God for _____ is, that they might be saved" (Rom. 10:1)
39. "One _____ stretched forth his hand. . .unto the fire" (Ezek. 10:7)
42. French article
43. Assistant, abbr.

44. "A virgin shall conceive. . .and shall call his name _____" (Isa. 7:14)
48. Biblical land: _____ of the Chaldees
49. "I am the true _____" (John 15:1)
51. "He _____ again the third day" (1 Cor. 15:4)
52. Spring month
53. Preposition
54. "His name shall be called _____" (Isa. 9:6)

DOWN

1. "For _____ is my witness" (Rom. 1:9)
2. Chemical suffix
3. "Every spirit that confesseth that Jesus Christ is come in the _____ is of God" (1 John 4:2)
4. "The coasts of _____" (Matt. 15:21)
5. "He that hath the Son hath _____" (1 John 5:12)
6. King of Bashan (Num. 21:33)
7. The damsel that opened the door for Peter (Acts 12:13)
8. Dental technician, abbr.
9. "That ye may know what is the hope of his _____" (Eph. 1:18)
10. "After the most straitest _____ of our religion I lived a Pharisee" (Acts 26:5)
12. "He that _____ not knoweth not God" (1 John 4:8)
16. "When for the time ye ought to be _____, ye have need that one teach you again" (Heb. 5:12)
18. "We which have believed do enter into _____" (Heb. 4:3)

20. American actor and humorist, initials
21. "Except I shall. . .put my finger into the print of the _____. . . , I will not believe" (John 20:25)
23. Jr.'s dad
24. "The Lamb that was _____" (Rev. 5:12)
28. Mary was a _____ when Christ was born
29. When you'll reach your destination, more or less, abbr.
30. Bachelor of Theology, abbr.
34. "Do not think that I will _____ you to the Father" (John 5:45)

35. "Come down, and _____ his son" (John 4:47)
37. Shade tree (Hos. 4:13)
38. "Take my yoke upon you, and _____ of me" (Matt. 11:29)
40. Habitual
41. Battery, abbr.
45. Kitten's cry
46. Biblical land (Gen. 4:16)
47. Before, poetic
49. South Carolina's neighbor to the north, abbr.
50. Neuter pronoun
52. Missouri University, abbr.
by Rebecca Souder

ACROSS

1. "Except a man be born of ____ and of the Spirit, he cannot enter into the kingdom" (John 3:5)
5. Preposition
6. "Wisdom giveth ____" (Eccles. 7:12)
9. The son of Boaz (Matt. 1:5)
10. Two, prefix
11. Four, Rom. num.
12. Edge
13. Flesh-eater
16. "Let their table be a snare, and a ____" (Rom. 11:9)
18. Girl's name
19. "____. . .was wicked" (Gen. 38:7)
20. ____ Christian Anderson
21. "We remember the fish which we did eat freely in Egypt. . .and the leeks, and the ____, and the garlick" (Num. 11:5)
23. A celebration
25. Perform
26. Article
28. Osmium, chem. symbol
29. A deep breath
31. Taxis
32. "A serpent ____ him" (Amos 5:19)
33. Group of three
34. "I will not ____ out his name" (Rev. 3:5)
35. Single, prefix
36. Recover strength
37. "How long will it be ____ they attain to innocency?" (Hos. 8:5)
38. Executive order, abbr.
40. "I will ___ of mercy and judgment: unto thee, O Lord" (Ps. 101:1)

42. Library numbering system, abbr.
44. "There shall be no ____ on the vine" (Jer. 8:13)
48. Compass point
49. "As the ____ among thorns, so is my love among the daughters" (Song of Sol. 2:2)
50. "It is a ____ thing that the king requireth" (Dan. 2:11)
51. "For ____ so loved the world" (John 3:16)

DOWN

1. Value
2. Man who conspired against Moses (Num. 16:1)
3. Son of Esau (Gen. 36:11)
4. "Called the altar ____" (Josh. 22:34)
5. Pagiel's father (Num. 1:13)
6. "Why seek ye the ____ among the dead?" (Luke 24:5)
7. "Behold the ____ and the wood: but where is the lamb?" (Gen. 22:7)
8. "Whosoever believeth on him should not perish, but have ____ life" (John 3:16)
10. Bismuth, chem. symbol
14. Old Testament prophet
15. Person who lives next door—and also the person we are to love the same as we love ourselves
17. Science of the mind
22. Southern continent, abbr.
24. Cut of meat
25. Nimble
26. Story
27. This, Sp.
29. Casual walk

30. Hero of David's guard
    (1 Chron. 11:40)
31. Type of radio
32. Purchasing
39. "Break also the ____"
    (Amos 1:5)
41. New, prefix
43. 101, Rom. num.
45. Ma's mate
46. More, suffix
47. Compass point
    by Cheryl Keiser

ACROSS

1. Stepped
5. "Though ye ____ not me, believe the works" (John 10:38)
11. "His own ____ him not" (John 1:11)
13. Spoke
14. Bone, prefix
15. "A man sent from ____" (John 1:6)
17. Tissue plasminogen interceptor, abbr.
18. Seventh note of the musical scale
19. Doctor of Theology, abbr.
20. "The express ____ of his person" (Heb. 1:3)
22. Head, abbr.
23. Salvation Army, abbr.
24. Nickel, chem. symbol
25. "He gave his ____ begotten Son" (John 3:16)
27. The, Sp.
29. Preposition
31. "____ gave names to all cattle" (Gen. 2:20)
33. "The ____ is the world" (Matt. 13:38)
35. "The Word ____ with God" (John 1:1)
37. French article
38. Canadian province, abbr.
40. New Testament, abbr.
41. "Full of ____ and truth" (John 1:14)
44. "____ no man any thing" (Rom. 13:8)
47. Not down
48. "To whom be glory for ____" (2 Tim. 4:18)
49. "Go ye into all the ____" (Mark 16:15)
51. "Jesus ____ the Christ" (John 20:31)
52. That is, Lat. abbr.
53. Spirited
54. Spares
57. Doctor of Science, abbr.
58. "Sat down on the right ____ of the Majesty" (Heb. 1:3)
59. "Tempted like as we are, ____ without sin" (Heb. 4:15)

DOWN

1. Pledge
2. Dwelled
3. Fall month, abbr.
4. "Put off the old man with his ____" (Col. 3:9)
5. "In the ____ was the Word" (John 1:1)
6. Doeg was from this tribe (1 Sam. 21:7)
7. Exists
8. "I have never ____ any thing that is common or unclean" (Acts 10:14)
9. Very important person, abbr.
10. "Let us therefore follow after the things. . .wherewith one may ____ another" (Rom. 14:19)
12. Infinitesimal amount
16. District attorney, abbr.
21. "____ ye therefore, and teach all nations" (Matt. 28:19)
26. "Behold the ____ of God!" (John 1:36)
28. "The ____ was given by Moses" (John 1:17)
29. "How shall ye believe, ____ I tell you of heavenly things?" (John 3:12)
30. Widemouthed pot

31. "Truly ye bear witness that ye _____ the deeds of your father" (Luke 11:48)
32. Name for Christ: the Son of _____
34. "Neither was any _____ in his mouth" (Isa. 53:9)
36. "_____ to shew thyself approved" (2 Tim. 2:15)
39. The Anointed One
42. "After that he was _____ from the dead" (John 21:14)
43. "So is _____ one that is born of the Spirit" (John 3:8)

45. "The _____ was made flesh" (John 1:14)
46. Historic periods
50. Numbering system for library books, abbr.
55. Ex dividend, abbr.
56. Of age, Lat. abbr.
by Rebecca Souder

ACROSS

1. Pretty much
6. Off the cuff (2 words)
11. Expelled gas
12. Belonging to the earth
14. Radium, chem. symbol
15. Precious stone on the third row of the priest's breastplate (Exod. 28:19)
17. Western Canadian province, abbr.
18. All right
19. Annoyed
20. Short greeting
21. "I. . .have the ____ of hell and of death" (Rev. 1:18)
24. Creatures from outer space, abbr.
25. Slightly open
27. One who revises
29. "I was afraid, and went and hid thy ____ in the earth" (Matt. 25:25)
31. Peter once cut one off
32. Belonging to New York's largest island, abbr.
33. "The glory of the Lord ____ the house" (Ezek. 43:5)
36. First appearances
39. "Ye ____ men with burden grievous to be borne" (Luke 11:46)
40. Lemon beverage
42. "____ ____ a rod of an almond tree" (Jer. 1:11) (2 words)
43. Letter that follows el
44. Belonging to Mr. Rogers
46. A mate for Pa
47. Eastbound, abbr.
48. Cancel
49. Point, abbr.
50. Angry outburst
53. Man-made channels
56. Collapsed
57. Give off

DOWN

1. What the Mount Sinai did when the Lord descended
2. Biblical land: ____ of the Chaldees
3. Innings pitched, abbr.
4. "Lest he ____ my soul like a lion" (Ps. 7:2)
5. More nervous
6. Affirm
7. "Let us not love in word, neither in tongue; but in ____ and in truth" (1 John 3:18)
8. Living room, abbr.
9. Iridium, chem. symbol
10. "Dan. . .shall leap from ____" (Deut. 33:22)
11. Penniless
13. Part of a dress below the waist
16. Altitude, abbr.
22. "____ yourselves to the Lord" (2 Chron. 30:8)
23. Not fresh
25. A plausible excuse
26. Son of God and Son of man
28. Metal
30. Strong drink
33. Swift
34. Verse written in iambs
35. Mended socks
36. Figure out
37. Where Samuel grew up
38. "The four and twenty elders, which sat before God on their ____" (Rev. 11:16)
41. Where Daniel spent time with lions

44. Lose color
45. Shut hard
51. Royal Academy, abbr.
52. Audio-visual, abbr.
54. Negative
55. Preposition

by Sissy Magnusson

ACROSS

1. The poor godly man in Christ's parable (Luke 16:20)
6. This liquid when new is not put in old bottles (Mark 2:22)
9. Printer's measure
10. Burying this was a mistake (Matt. 25:15–28)
13. Foolish man built his house on this (Matt. 7:26)
14. Half-way
15. Before, prefix
17. The Lord promised that though our sins be scarlet, they shall be white ____ snow
18. Bear-like animal related to the raccoon
20. Each, abbr.
21. Jesus is God's only begotten (John 3:16)
23. Jesus told a story about 5 wise and 5 foolish (Matt. 25:1–2)
25. Hello
26. Underling
27. Shade tree (Hos. 4:13)
29. What the disciples fished with (Matt. 13:47)
30. Finished first
32. City in the Netherlands famous for its cheese
33. No one puts this kind of cloth into an old garment (Mark 2:21)
34. A day's wage for a hired laborer (Matt. 20:2)
36. The enemy sowed these among the wheat (Matt. 13:25)
38. Thanks, Br.
39. Discharged a firearm
41. Hush!
42. Encountered
45. Egyptian sun god
47. Full of wonder
49. We shouldn't put this under a bushel (Mark 4:21)
52. Sick
54. The wise man built on this (Luke 6:48)
55. In Christ's story, the father threw a party for this son (Luke 15:11–32)

DOWN

1. The shepherd left the 99 for this (Matt. 18:11–12) (2 words)
2. Town in Judah (Josh. 15:37)
3. No ifs, ____, or buts
4. Salt Lake's state, abbr.
5. The Jews ostracized these people (John 4:9)
6. Jesus told a parable about a king who invited people to this kind of celebration
7. Surrounded by
8. Normal temperature and pressure, abbr.
11. A dialect
12. Biblical term for yeast (Matt. 13:33)
16. Do over again, prefix
18. Yearned
19. Article that precedes a vowel
22. The wise took this for their lamps (Matt. 25:4)
23. Jesus spoke of laborers in this place (Matt. 20:1)
24. One who scatters seed (Mark 4:3)
28. "A certain ____ made a great supper" (Luke 14:16)
31. In debt

33. Nathan, for short
35. Bible part that contains the Gospels, Epistles, and Revelation, abbr.
36. Pulled
37. "True worshippers ____ worship the Father in spirit and in truth" (John 4:23)
40. Laughter syllable
43. Environment, prefix
44. Tactical Air Command, abbr.
46. European mountain
48. Delve
50. "Unforgettable" Cole, first initials
51. Son of Jose (Luke 3:28–29)
53. Californian city, abbr.

PUZZLE 52

ACROSS

1. "Behold I make all things ____" (Rev. 21:5)
2. "Praise him for his mighty ____" (Ps. 150:2)
5. Spheres or heavenly bodies
9. "Why make ye this ____ and weep?" (Mark 5:39)
10. "I will ____a place for my people" (1 Chron. 17:9)
12. Recreational vehicle, abbr.
13. "The kingdom of heaven is ____ hand" (Matt. 4:17)
15. "His teeth shall be set on ____" (Jer. 31:30)
16. Southeast, abbr.
18. Let ____ esteem other better than themselves (Phil. 2:3)
19. Registered nurse, abbr.
21. "____ so, come Lord Jesus" (Rev. 22:20)
22. "The Lord is my ____" (Heb. 13:6)
25. "____and prepare the Passover" (Luke 22:8)
27. "Adam called his wife's name ____" (Gen. 3:20)
28. "I send an ____ before thee" (Exod. 23:20)
30. "Be ____ to maintain good works" (Titus 3:8)
33. British Thermal Unit, abbr.
34. "By which it had gone down in the ____ of Ahaz" (2 Kings 20:11)
35. New York, abbr.
36. "Thou shalt bind this ____ of scarlet thread" (Josh. 2:18)

38. "For ____ are called but few are chosen" (Matt. 22:14)
40. Education, abbr.
41. "He maketh them also to ____ like a calf" (Ps. 29:6)
43. "This is my beloved ____" (Matt. 17:5)
45. "His soul shall dwell at ____" (Ps. 25:13)
47. "Though an ____ should encamp against me, my heart shall not fear" (Ps. 27:3)
49. North America, abbr.
51. Professional, abbr.
53. A post erected by certain American Indians
55. A book of Psalms
56. A yearning

DOWN

1. "This is the ____ that ye have heard" (1 Kings 1:45)
2. The year of our Lord, Lat. abbr.
3. A tutor or instructor
4. "I have not found ____ great faith" (Luke 7:9)
5. "The ____ number of them" (Num. 3:48)
6. Worthless piece of cloth
7. "And he came and touched the ____" (Luke 7:14)
8. Shipping Note, abbr.
9. "____ not yourselves" (Rom. 12:19)
11. "The plowman shall overtake the ____" (Amos 9:13)
14. Definite article
17. "For it was now ____" (Acts 4:3)
20. "They had but ____ set the watch" (Judg. 7:19)

106

23. "_____ perfect gift is from above" (James 1:17)
24. Referee, abbr.
26. "_____ things are passed away" (2 Cor. 5:17)
28. "He is _____ also to save them" (Heb. 7:25)
29. A firearm
30. A synthetic gum used in medicine
31. Alabama, abbr.
32. "Woe is me! for I am _____" (Isa. 6:5)
37. Curved shape
39. Vicious

42. "Neither was any thing _____ secret" (Mark 4:22)
44. "For there is none other _____" (Acts 4:12)
46. A king of Judah
48. Moses sprinkled the blood upon Aaron's great _____ (Exod. 29:20)
50. Associated Press, abbr.
52. A prefix meaning to do over
54. Tennessee, abbr.

by Joyce Handzo

ACROSS

1. "____ the just shall live by faith" (Heb. 10:38)
4. Breakfast food that goes with Noah's son (Gen. 5:32)
8. "____ without ceasing" (1 Thess. 5:17)
12. Dentists' group
13. Soccer great
14. Worn in a religious painting
15. "They neither sow ____ reap" (Luke 12:24)
16. No to a Scot
17. Last word in the Bible (Rev. 22:21)
18. Site of final conflict (Rev. 16:16)
22. Hath, in modern English
23. University in Carbondale, IL, abbr.
24. FL from TN, direction
26. Abraham's nephew (Gen. 14:12)
29. "She gave me of the tree, and I ____ eat" (Gen. 3:12)
31. What the lame man did (Acts 3:8)
33. Woodwind instrument
35. "____ thou on my right hand" (Matt. 22:44)
37. "Honey in the carcase of the ____" (Judg. 14:8)
38. "Get thee behind me, ____" (Matt. 16:23)
40. Time period
42. Subway system
43. ____ Salvador
44. Sun in Madrid
46. Balaam's Mr. Ed (Num. 22:28)
48. Luke's penpal (Acts 1:1)
53. "There is ____ good but one" (Matt. 19:17)

56. Canterbury's religious leader, abbr.
57. "Ye ____ the light of the world" (Matt. 5:14)
58. Pitcher
59. "Obedient by word and ____" (Rom. 15:18)
61. Missing soldier
62. Adolescent
63. Figures
64. Woman's malady

DOWN

1. Wendy's dog
2. "____ of a sweet smell" (Phil. 4:18)
3. "The flesh of the child waxed ____" (2 Kings 4:34)
4. Long play video tape setting, abbr.
5. Joseph's story told here
6. "A wise son maketh a ____ father" (Prov. 10:1)
7. What the sower sowed (Matt. 13:4)
8. Anna's father (Luke 2:36)
9. Took Isaac's place (Gen. 22:13)
10. Pub drink
11. Hither, thither, and ____
19. "____, Lord GOD" (Jer. 1:6)
20. Zilpah's lad (Gen. 30:11)
21. "Thou anointest my head with ____" (Ps. 23:5)
24. "Not having ____, or wrinkle" (Eph. 5:27)
25. Sicilian volcano
26. "He that loveth his life shall ____ it" (John 12:25)
27. Joktan's son (Gen. 10:28)
28. Child
30. "Appointed unto men once to ____" (Heb. 9:27)

32. Direct
34. Magi saw star in this sky (Matt. 2:2)
36. Stuck
39. Japanese drama
41. "He planted an ____, and the rain doth nourish it" (Isa. 44:14)
45. "____ ____ quiet and peaceable life" (1 Tim. 2:2) (2 words)
47. Yes to Julio
49. David's grandpa (Ruth 4:22)
50. "Thy word is a ____ unto my feet" (Ps. 119:105)
51. Used to cast lots (Num. 27:21)
52. Red and Dead
53. Kingdom of heaven is like one (Matt. 13:47)
54. "____ no man any thing" (Rom. 13:8)
55. Maiden name
60. Document signed, abbr.

by Mary Ann Freeman

by Elizabeth B. Smith

ACROSS

1. Definite article
3. Jewess who became queen (Esther 2:17)
7. Eastern state, abbr.
8. "All that handle the _____, . . .shall come down from their ships" (Ezek. 27:29)
11. "Upon thy belly shalt thou _____" (Gen. 3:14)
13. "Disciples believed _____ him" (John 2:11)
14. "Judah's wife, the daughter of _____" (Gen. 38:12 NIV)
16. Naomi changed her name to _____ (Ruth 1:20)
19. "He said, Behold, I am _____, Lord" (Acts 9:10)
20. Enoch's son (Gen. 4:18)
21. "I _____ no pleasant bread" (Dan. 10:3)
23. Moses' mother (Exod. 6:20)
27. Mid-west state, abbr.
29. "Ye have not chosen _____, but I have chosen you" (John 15:16)
30. "Neither do the _____ understand" (Job 32:9)
32. Wife of Nabal (1 Sam. 25:3)
35. Old card game
36. "The counsel of the Lord, that _____ stand" (Prov. 19:21)
38. This woman hid spies on her roof (Josh. 2:1)
41. He cried unto the Lord his God (2 Chron. 14:11)
42. "Father said, "Let us _____, and be merry" (Luke 15:23)
44. Samson told her everything (Judg. 16:18)
47. Judah's daughter-in-law (Gen. 38:11)
49. Hodiah was his sister (1 Chron. 4:19)
50. Short greeting

DOWN

2. Angel spoke to her (Gen. 21:17)
3. Was made from a rib (Gen. 2:22; 3:20)
4. "Wisdom is _____ high for a fool" (Prov. 24:7)
5. Mother of Samuel (1 Sam. 1:20)
6. Judah's son (Gen. 38:3)
9. "_____ rose up hastily, . . .they followed" (John 11:31)
10. Put the nail in Sisera's temple (Judg. 4:21)
12. Plural of os
14. Queen of _____ heard of Solomon's fame (1 Kings 10:1)
15. Abraham left the land of _____ (Gen. 11:31)
16. Sister of Aaron (Exod. 15:20)
17. Paid announcement
18. Ruth's mother-in-law (Ruth 1:22)
22. Topographical Engineer, abbr.
24. Single room in prison
25. David's wife (2 Sam. 3:5)
26. Eastern state, abbr.
27. Saul gave her to David (1 Sam. 18:27)
28. King of Bashan (Num. 21:33)
31. "I _____ set my bow in the cloud" (Gen. 9:13)
33. "God. . .rested. . .from _____ his work" (Gen. 2:2)
34. "He careth _____ you" (1 Pet. 5:7)
36. Wind direction
37. Jacob's first wife (Gen. 29:23)
39. Saul's concubine (2 Sam. 21:11)
40. Esau's wife (Gen. 36:12)
41. "Why make ye this _____"

(Mark 5:39)

43. "Let them be desolate. . .that say unto me, _____" (Ps. 40:15)
45. "This is the confidence that we have _____ him" (1 John 5:14)
46. Southern state, abbr.
48. Smallest state, abbr.

ACROSS

1. "Being justified freely by his grace through the _____ that is in Christ Jesus" (Rom. 3:24)
9. "I will sift the house of Israel. . . like as corn is sifted in a _____" (Amos 9:9)
10. Annoy
11. "Jesus said. . .'If thou canst _____, all things are possible to him that believeth' " (Mark 9:23)
14. "I _____ no pleasant bread" (Dan. 10:3)
15. "_____ the knot" (get married)
16. 7, Rom. num.
18. "Man shall not _____ by bread alone" (Matt. 4:4)
19. Fervor
20. Delegate, abbr.
21. A swine
22. Jacob
26. Fifth letter of Hebrew alphabet
27. Fruit of the Spirit
28. Undergraduate degree
29. Southern state, abbr.
30. James and John, to Zebedee
31. One of two faithful spies sent to search Canaan
34. A preposition, meaning to the same degree
35. Biblical weed
37. Weird
39. What Boaz plucked off to signify redeeming Ruth
41. Southern continent, abbr.
42. Possessive pronoun
43. One of four seasons
44. Roman poet
46. Support group for alcoholics, abbr.
47. Sect of Jews during time of Christ

DOWN

1. "For _____ is as the sin of witch-craft" (1 Sam. 15:23)
2. The first woman
3. "Lead us not into temptation; but _____ us from evil" (Luke 11:4)
4. Come together
5. "_____ of knowledge of good and evil" (Gen. 2:9)
6. 2, Rom. num.
7. Mount of _____
8. Compass point
9. "_____ in awe, and sin not" (Ps. 4:4)
12. Active of watching
13. "He said, 'I am the voice of one crying in the _____ ' " (John 1:23)
17. Its capital is Des Moines, abbr.
21. "And the _____ of God, which passeth all understanding, shall keep your hearts and minds through Christ Jesus" (Phil. 4:7)
23. An orderly way of getting things done
24. Stomach muscle, for short
25. "And ye shall know the truth, and the truth shall make you _____" (John 8:32)
26. Exclamation of amusement
27. One of two faithful spies sent to search Canaan
30. What disrespectful children do
32. "Therefore shall a man _____ his father and his mother, and shall cleave unto his wife" (Gen. 2:24)

33. "And the Spirit and the _____ say,
'Come' " (Rev. 22:17)
36. Unusual
38. Pronoun
40. Suffix for a growth
41. International signal of distress
45. Opposite of out
    by Kenda Turner

ACROSS

1. "Sacrifice. . .____ ____of turtle-doves" (Luke 2:24) (2 words)
5. Bashful
7. "[David] feigned himself ____" (1 Sam. 21:13)
10. "Sword of the Spirit, . . .the ____ of God" (Eph. 6:17)
11. Also known as, abbr.
12. Information
13. "Ye do ____, not knowing the scriptures" (Matt. 22:29)
14. Triple Sugar Iron agar, abbr.
15. Male singing voice
16. Jewish scriptures
18. "Neither shall the cruse of ____ fail" (1 Kings 17:14)
19. "Be it unto ____ according to thy word" (Luke 1:38)
21. "____ unto them that call evil good" (Isa. 5:20)
22. "The staff of his ____ was like a weaver's beam" (1 Sam. 17:7)
24. "A thousand shall fall ____ thy side" (Ps. 91:7)
26. To fill with joy
28. "Though he slay me, ____ will I trust in him" (Job 13:15)
30. "____and feather him!"
32. "Sharper than any two-edged ____" (Heb. 4:12)
34. A beaver____
36. "Shut the doors, and ____ them" (Neh. 7:3)
38. Accomplish
40. "____weapon that is formed against thee" (Isa. 54:17)
42. Motion picture
44. "Cain. . .dwelt in the land of ____" (Gen. 4:16)
46. "Where two ____ three are gathered" (Matt. 18:20)
48. Flying mammal
49. Southern Israeli desert
51. Regulation decreed by a church council
53. Animal pelt
54. Motorized coach
56. "Soul of Jonathan was ____ with. . . David" (1 Sam. 18:1)
57. "Cast him into the bottomless ____" (Rev. 20:3)
58. "[Samson] ____not that the Lord was departed" (Judg. 16:20)
59. "The trees of the Lord are full of ____" (Ps. 104:16)
60. "Held in with ____ and bridle" (Ps. 32:9)
61. Trivial

DOWN

1. "Stand in ____, and sin not" (Ps. 4:4)
2. Nautical left side
3. "For the ____, that flieth by day" (Ps. 91:5)
4. A part of the psyche
5. Schuss
6. "He [the horse] saith among the trumpets, ____" (Job 39:25)
7. "What is ____, that thou art mindful of him?" (Ps. 8:4)
8. Elementary particle
9. Has courage
11. Cinder
12. "That he would not ____ to come" (Acts 9:38)
14. Chinese ounces
15. "____ them about thy neck" (Prov. 6:21)
17. "The loving hind and pleasant ____" (Prov. 5:19)

18. Musical drama
20. A large tub
22. A furnace
23. "Though they be____ like crimson" (Isa. 1:18)
25. Small flap
27. "Their laying ____was known of Saul" (Acts 9:24)
29. Light brown
31. Isaac's replacement on the altar
33. Restaurant
35. Unruly throng
37. Mechanical monster
39. Piece of timber
41. "Defence shall be the munitions of ____" (Isa. 33:16)
43. Mover's truck
45. Shortfall
47. A genus of frogs
49. "A tough ____ to crack"
50. "Pike's Peak or____!"
52. "____ in the bud"
53. "Men of war ____ for the battle" (1 Chron. 12:8)
55. A pig ____
57. 3.14, the ratio of a circle's circumference to its diameter
58. "____ beseech thee" (Ps. 80:14)
by John H. Thornberg

ACROSS

1. "Then ____ was wroth with the seer" (2 Chron. 16:10)
4. "I do ____ to day and to morrow" (Luke 13:32)
9. "Behold, the ____ of the Lord cometh" (Isa. 13:9)
12. "His brethren. . .Gilalai, Maai, ____ and Judah" (Neh. 12:36)
14. "Which are blackish by reason of the ____" (Job 6:16)
15. "____ shall be as gods" (Gen. 3:5)
16. Elliptical
17. Relatives
19. "Thou shalt be for ____ to the fire" (Ezek. 21:32)
20. Female reproductive organ, comb. form
21. "I will ____ the other bullock" (1 Kings 18:23)
23. "He hath ____ the dough" (Hos. 7:4)
26. "Gather a certain ____ every day" (Exod. 16:4)
27. Makes warm
28. Northeastern area of the U.S., abbr.
29. "This is ____ of the Hebrews' children" (Exod. 2:6)
30. "The black horses. . .go forth into the ____ country" (Zech. 6:6)
31. A poem
32. King of Bashan (1 Kings 4:19)
33. "All the ____ thereof shall be burned with the fire" (Mic. 1:7)
34. Mimicked
35. "I am like a ____" (Ps. 102:6)
37. Snow vehicles
38. "And ____ gave names to all cattle" (Gen. 2:20)
39. "____ was a tiller of the ground" (Gen. 4:2)
40. "O thou fairest among ____" (Song of Sol. 1:8)

42. "Set it upon a ____" (Num. 21:8)
43. On or about, abbr.
45. "And he smote them ____ and thigh" (Judg. 15:8)
46. "To the ____ of the glory of our Lord Jesus Christ" (2 Thess. 2:14)
49. Albert, Allen, and Alex, for short
50. "The magicians and astrologers that were in all his ____" (Dan. 1:20)
51. "As it was in the days of ____" (Luke 17:26)

DOWN

1. "Not willing that ____ should perish" (2 Pet. 3:9)
2. "____ this great sight" (Exod. 3:3)
3. Preposition
4. "The people did hide themselves in ____" (1 Sam. 13:6)
5. Single
6. Religion, abbr.
7. Electrical engineer, abbr.
8. "In the hand of him that ____ thee" (Ezek. 28:9)
9. "When they had ____" (John 21:15)
10. "The ____ of violence is in their hands" (Isa. 59:6)
11. Affirmative
13. "They brought down the king from the ____ of the Lord" (2 Kings 11:19)
18. Belonging to Una
19. Festival
20. Small flying insects
21. Sag
22. "The ____ of the mountains is his pasture" (Job 39:8)
23. "The name of the third ____-Happuch" (Job 42:14)
24. "On the seventh day God ____ his work" (Gen. 2:2)

25. "Repented not of their ____"
(Rev. 16:11)
27. "Then ____ king of Gezer came
up to help" (Josh. 10:33)
30. "They chose Stephen. . .and
Philip, and Prochorus and ____"
(Acts 6:5)
31. "His ears are ____ unto their
prayers" (1 Pet. 3:12)
33. "____ me under the shadow of thy
wings" (Ps. 17:8)
34. "An ____ unto my mother's children" (Ps. 69:8)
36. "Give us of your oil: for our ____
are gone out" (Matt. 25:8)
37. "John also was baptizing in Aenon
near to ____" (John 3:23)

39. "Their visage is blacker than a
____" (Lam. 4:8)
40. World Hockey Association, abbr.
41. "All the best of the ____, and all
the best of the wine"
(Num. 18:12)
42. Teacher-parent organization, abbr.
43. "One of the villages in the plain of
____" (Neh. 6:2)
44. "When she was past ____"
(Heb. 11:11)
47. "God shall ____ with you"
(Gen. 48:21)
48. "The Lord shut him ____"
(Gen. 7:16)
by Evelyn M. Boyington

ACROSS

1. Our ____ is with the Father
   (1 John 1:3)
11. Constellation (Job 9:9)
12. The ____ chapter (1 Cor. 13)
13. Southern slang for poor
14. A populous place (Nah. 3:8)
15. Son of Peleth (Num. 16:1)
16. Printer's measure
17. To boast
20. Wonder
21. Vehicle (Amos 2:13)
23. An age
25. Otherwise
26. ____ me, expression of sorrow
27. Pure
30. Writing instrument
31. Forbidden insult (Matt. 5:22)
33. Great happiness
35. Montpelier's state, abbr.
36. Pertaining to wings
37. Astronomical unit, abbr.
38. Oldest son of Noah (Gen. 9:18)
40. Head nurse, abbr.
42. Sooner than
43. Oldest son of Adam (Gen. 4:1)
46. City on the coast of Caesarea
    (Josh. 11:2)
48. Short for Leonard
49. A riddle
51. None in Gilead? (Jer. 8:22)
53. Come in
55. Opposite of pride (1 Pet. 5:5)
56. Will come out of Jacob
    (Num. 24:17)

DOWN

1. Control of one's feelings
   (Eph. 4:2)
2. Son of Jose (Luke 3:28–29)
3. New York's largest island, abbr.
4. A fruit of the spirit "____-
   suffering" (Gal. 5:22)
5. Biblical city (1 Chron. 8:12)
6. "____ to anger" (Neh. 9:17)
7. Truthfulness
8. Intravenous, abbr.
9. The absence of strife
10. Satisfaction
13. Keep on keeping on
18. Kingly
19. Article
22. European mountain
24. Expression of satisfaction
27. Loving
28. Son of Zibeon (Gen. 36:24)
29. "Healthy" heart (Prov. 14:30)
32. Earthquake state, abbr.
34. In like manner
39. "____ of salvation" (Eph. 6:17)
41. Name meaning "wild goat"
    (Gen. 36:28)
44. Airman, abbr.
45. 2, Rom. num.
47. "To ____ is better than sacrifice"
    (1 Sam. 15:22)
50. Name meaning "my brother"
    (1 Chron. 5:15)
52. Lights, abbr.
54. Egyptian sun god
    by Sissy Magnusson

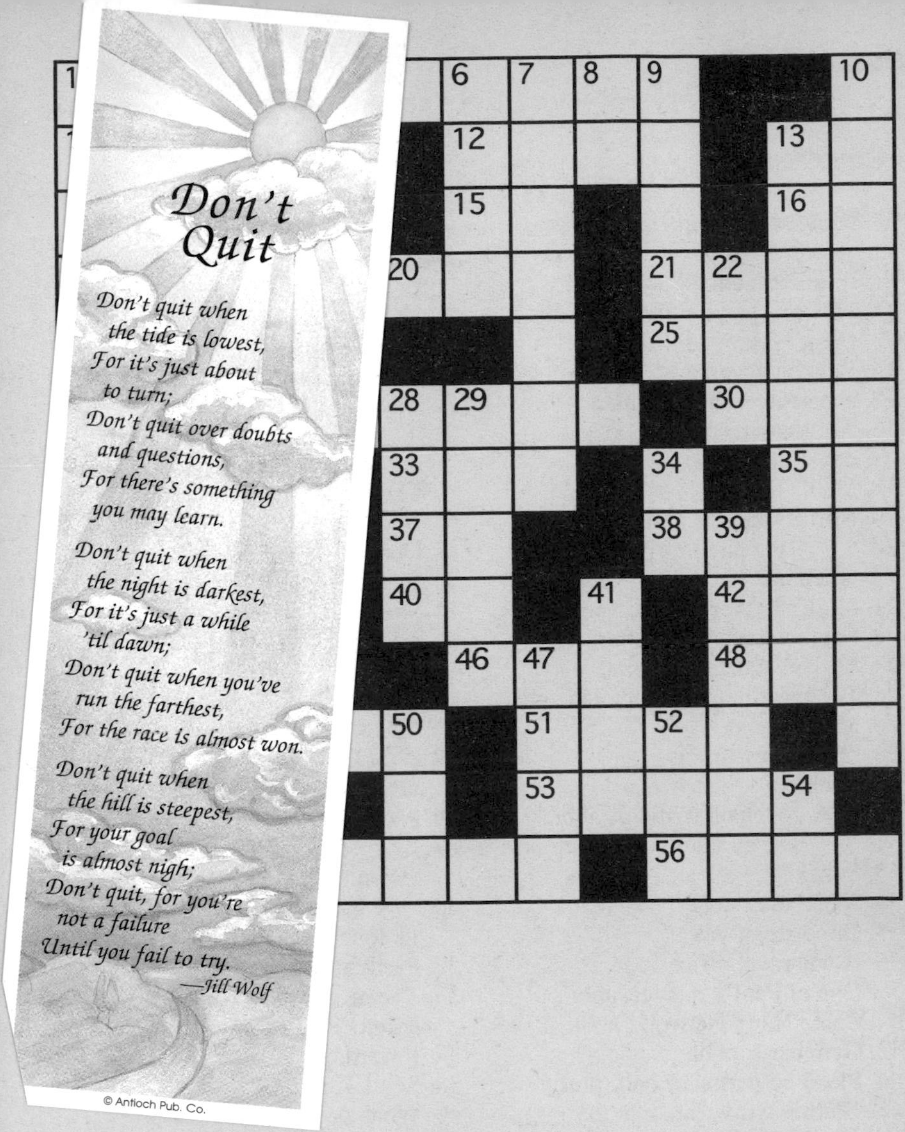

Don't Quit

Don't quit when
the tide is lowest,
For it's just about
to turn;
Don't quit over doubts
and questions,
For there's something
you may learn.

Don't quit when
the night is darkest,
For it's just a while
'til dawn;
Don't quit when you've
run the farthest,
For the race is almost won.

Don't quit when
the hill is steepest,
For your goal
is almost nigh;
Don't quit, for you're
not a failure
Until you fail to try.
    —Jill Wolf

ACROSS

1. "Confession is made unto ____" (Rom. 10:10)
8. To make a choice
11. "There ____ I in the midst of them" (Matt. 18:20)
12. Woman's name
13. A narrow fold or wrinkle
15. "To know. . .the ____ of my days" (Ps. 39:4)
18. Man's title
19. North America, abbr.
20. "____ the day in which he was taken up" (Acts 1:2)
21. "____, Father" (Mark 14:36)
22. Southwestern state, abbr.
23. Playful aquatic mammal
25. The book before Nehemiah
26. Man's name
28. "Brightness of his ____" (Heb. 1:3)
29. New covenant writings, abbr.
31. "____, I say unto you" (John 3:3)
33. Suffix
34. A precious stone
35. Opposite of yes
36. Holds royal office
39. One of Paul's epistles, abbr.
41. Cable News Network, abbr.
42. Gym class, abbr.
44. Meaning partial or half, prefix
46. "Put thou my tears into thy ____" (Ps. 56:8)
49. Prince of Islam
50. First person contraction
51. "He shall ____ like a lion" (Hos. 11:10)
53. "The ____ of the valleys" (Song of Sol. 2:1)
54. "He gave his only ____ Son" (John 3:16)
55. Helena's state, abbr.

DOWN

1. "The Lord called ____: and he answered, Here am I" (1 Sam. 3:4)
2. The end of a prayer
3. "____ the fatherless and widows" (James 1:27)
4. Grown-up
5. Black sticky substance
6. Observation post, abbr.
7. The book after Leviticus
8. Short agreement
9. A long narrow triangular flag
10. A streetcar
14. Chief ____ Horse
16. "Day of ____" (Lev. 23:28)
17. "My God; ____ will I seek thee" (Ps. 63:1)
24. A city of Judah (Josh. 15:39)
27. "____ evil with good" (Rom. 12:21)
30. "We have seen and do ____" (1 John 4:14)
32. Participle ending
33. The meek shall ____ the earth (Matt. 5:5)
37. Inward, prefix
38. South American language, abbr.
40. What David wrote
43. Plural of E
45. 1,000 x 1,000, abbr.
46. Put this on baby when feeding
47. Abram's nephew (Gen. 12:5)
48. Of every tree thou mayest ____ (Gen. 2:16)
52. Do, ____, mi
   by Beverley Barnes

ACROSS

1. God sent this man a dream of a ladder with angels ascending and descending on it (Gen. 28:12–16)
6. God called this man, from a burning bush, to free Israel from Egyptian bondage (Exod. 3:1–12)
11. Full of cheerful good humor
12. Jesus called this man to follow Him (John 1:43)
14. Osmium, chem. symbol
15. Delirium tremens, abbr.
17. Manganese, chem. symbol
18. Maine, abbr.
19. Not existing before, recently made or invented
21. Belonging to the church's first missionary (Acts 9:15–16; 13:1–2)
24. Suitable or quick at learning
25. Tailless monkeys, or large uncouth men
27. Unwell
28. Without payment, costing nothing
29. His Highness, abbr.
30. Lanthanum, chem. symbol
32. Milliliter, abbr.
33. Rural route, abbr.
34. Jesus called this man to follow Him (John 1:44–51)
35. Society of Jesus, abbr.
37. Physical Education, abbr.
38. In the matter of, about, concerning, abbr.
39. Printer's unit of measure
41. Electrically charged particles
43. Fodder
45. A narrative or story
47. Life-support system, abbr.
48. Carried
50. Central Intelligence Agency, abbr.

51. Exclamation of satisfaction
52. Laughter sound
53. Eastern Time, abbr.
55. Rue, Amer. abbr.
56. Excellent, most impressive or splendid
59. Person who worked iron
61. God called this man to become Israel's first High Priest (Lev. 8:2)
62. God called this man to marry a harlot as a picture to Israel of their relationship with God (Hos. 1:1–4)

DOWN

1. Sold into salvery by his brothers (Gen. 37:27–28)
2. Authorized Version of the Bible, abbr.
3. Criminal Investigation Department of Scotland Yard, abbr.
4. Hardy cereal plants grown in cool climates
5. Barrel, abbr.
6. Military Policeman, abbr.
7. Units of electrical resistance
8. Breaking of religious or moral law
9. Elevated railway
10. An affected smile
11. God called this man to warn Nineveh about coming judgment unless it repented (Jon. 1:1–2)
13. Jesus called this fisherman to follow Him (Matt. 4:18–20)
16. The territory of a sultan
20. Us
22. Artificial Intelligence, abbr.
23. Lines, abbr.
24. Argon, chem. symbol
26. Strikes with open hand
28. Moving swiftly, nimble

31. Consumed
32. To damage, to spoil
35. This man was called to help Paul (Acts 15:40)
36. God called this man to lead Israel into Canaan (Josh. 1:1–9)
39. God called this man to be the successor to Elijah (1 Kings 19:16–17)
40. Fleshy or full of subject matter
42. Not specified, abbr.
43. "____, every one that thirsteth" (Isa. 55:1)
44. KJV you
46. Actinium, chem. symbol
48. Tropical plant with a tuberous root used for food
49. Item used for demonstration
52. Opposite of him
54. It is, poetic contraction
57. Ma's mate
58. Battalion, abbr.
59. Hush!
60. Tellurium, chem. symbol

by Mary Louise DeMott

PUZZLE 61

ACROSS

1. Bottommost parts of faces
6. Having to do with either the North or South Poles
11. The sister of Tubal-cain (Gen. 4:22)
12. Lets up
14. Preposition
15. "The soldiers. . .____ his side" (John 19:34)
17. Military police, abbr.
18. Man's name
20. Not the clergy
21. 7, Rom. num.
22. Paul's original name
24. Root-mean-square, abbr.
25. One hundreth of a dollar
26. Motors
28. "The ____ of the wicked have robbed me" (Ps. 119:61)
29. "I will surely do thee ____" (Gen. 32:12)
30. Steal
31. Mix together
33. "The ____ of death are fallen upon me" (Ps. 55:4)
36. Rodents
37. Jesus is the ____ of man
38. Chocolate sandwich cookie
39. Article that precedes a vowel
40. "I have ____ ashes like bread" (Ps. 102:9)
42. Astronomical unit, abbr.
43. Selfish part of the psyche, according to Freud
44. "We were ____ of God to be put in trust with the gospel" (1 Thess. 2:4)
46. Physician, in other words, abbr.
47. "It is easier for a camel to go through the eye of a ____, than for a rich man to enter into the kingdom" (Mark 10:25)
49. Washes away
51. "The angel appeared to [Joseph] in a ____" (Matt. 1:20)
52. Person who gives something

DOWN

1. Biblical land
2. Expression of laughter or sarcasm
3. Mischievous child
4. "I will fasten him as a ____ in a sure place" (Isa. 22:23)
5. Cut
6. Agreements
7. "____ my voice, and I will be your God" (Jer. 7:23)
8. Boy
9. Preposition
10. Call to memory
11. "Make a joyful ____ unto God" (Ps. 66:1)
13. Expels saliva
16. Edges
19. Small chunk of gold
21. Seller
23. "Faith. . .stopped the mouths of ____" (Heb. 11:33)
25. Egyptian capital
27. Biblical land (Gen. 4:16)
28. Rod
30. Made fresh
31. Organ of thought
32. Alit
33. Dorothy's dog
34. Peruser of books
35. Turns acid

37. Melchizedek was king of this
    (Gen. 14:18)
40. Girl's name
41. Roman emperor
44. Lemon drink
45. Donald, for short
48. More, suffix
50. "____ thou that which is good"
    (2 Kings 10:5)
    by Malina D. English

ACROSS

1. "Joshua the son of ____"
   (Deut. 34:9)
4. "And I sent the ____ before you"
   (Josh. 24:12)
9. "Blessed are ____" (Matt. 5:11)
11. One of the kings of Judah
    (1 Kings 15:11)
12. "He had compassion ____ him"
    (Luke 10:33)
13. "Intending after ____ to bring him
    forth to the people" (Acts 12:4)
15. "Thy father made our ____ griev-
    ous" (1 Kings 12:4)
16. "The ____ shall be first"
    (Matt. 19:30)
17. "____ burden is light"
    (Matt. 11:30)
18. "There was one ____, a prophet-
    ess" (Luke 2:36)
21. "And a certain woman named
    ____" (Acts 16:14)
24. "When I am weak, then am I
    ____" (2 Cor. 12:10)
25. "____ strong" (1 Sam. 4:9)
26. "I am that bread of ____"
    (John 6:48)
28. "As the apple ____"
    (Song of Sol. 2:3)
29. "What must I do to be ____?"
    (Acts 16:30)
31. "Better is it that thou shouldest not
    ____" (Eccles. 5:5)
34. "O generation of ____"
    (Matt. 3:7)
37. "And the glory of the Lord abode
    upon mount ____" (Exod. 24:16)
39. Seeds that can be made into soup
42. A natural substance containing a
    valuable metal
43. New Testament, abbr.

44. Latin that is, abbr.
45. "____ man can serve two masters"
    (Matt. 6:24)
46. "And whatsoever goeth upon his
    ____" (Lev. 11:27)
50. "He hath ____ great things"
    (Joel 2:20)
52. "There shall be weeping and ____
    of teeth" (Luke 13:28)
55. "Though they be ____ like crim-
    son, they shall be as wool"
    (Isa. 1:18)
56. "Rebekah. . .the daughter of
    Bethuel the ____"
    (Gen. 25:20)
57. "We remember the. . .____"
    (Num. 11:5)

DOWN

1. "I tell you, ____ " (Luke 13:3)
2. United Service Organizations,
   abbr.
3. "I was afraid, because I was ____"
   (Gen. 3:10)
4. "____, everyone that thirsteth"
   (Isa. 55:1)
5. "Believe ____, and she shall be
   made whole" (Luke 8:50)
6. "Birds of the air have ____"
   (Luke 9:58)
7. "Arise, Peter; slay and ____"
   (Acts 11:7)
8. Poet Elliot's initials
9. "Sing unto the Lord, O ____
   saints" (Ps. 30:4)
10. One of the sons of Judah
    (Gen. 46:12)
14. A male voice part
17. "And [Jesus] called, saying, ____,
    arise" (Luke 8:54)
18. "Thou ____ my King" (Ps. 44:4)
19. Compass direction, abbr.
20. "Rock of ____, cleft for me"

21. Pounds, abbr.
22. "_____, though I walk" (Ps. 23:4)
23. French word for island
27. "I will fear no _____" (Ps. 23:4)
30. "I am the true _____" (John 15:1)
32. "Who is worthy to _____ the book?" (Rev. 5:2)
33. "So they two _____ until they came to Bethlehem" (Ruth 1:19)
35. Right, abbr.
36. Yes, in Italian or Spanish
37. "Speaking to yourselves in psalms and. . .spiritual _____" (Eph. 5:19)
38. Sarcasm

40. "Fine _____ is the righteousness of saints" (Rev. 19:8)
41. "Some _____ fell by the way side" (Matt. 13:4)
46. 23rd letter of the Greek alphabet
47. Expression of triumph
48. "That I may _____ Christ" (Phil. 3:8)
49. Chemical symbol for tin
51. Spanish word for gold
53. "To the dwelling of _____" (Num. 21:15)
54. "_____ ye therefore" (Matt. 28:19)
by Linda Nunn

Puzzle 63

ACROSS

1. "[I] will _____ praise to the name of the Lord most high" (Ps. 7:17)
5. "Famine and pestilence shall _____ him" (Ezek. 7:15)
7. "He hath chosen Solomon my son to _____ upon the throne" (1 Chron. 28:5)
8. "When it shall turn to the LORD, the _____ shall be taken away" (2 Cor. 3:16)
10. Letter before dee
11. "_____ is confounded and dismayed" (Jer. 48:1)
13. Self-addressed envelope, abbr.
14. Religious group
15. "There _____ him ten men that were lepers" (Luke 17:12)
17. "And hired counsellors against them to frustrate their _____" (Ezra 4:5)
19. "And if he trespass against thee _____ times in a day. . .forgive him" (Luke 17:4)
21. Plural ending
22. Belonging to Judah's first son (Gen. 38:2–3)
23. Prohibit
24. Alcoholics Anonymous, abbr.
25. Robinson Crusoe author
27. "They found him. . .sitting in the midst of the _____" (Luke 2:46)
29. "_____ thy morsel in the vinegar" (Ruth 2:14)
30. "I will _____ in thy truth" (Ps. 86:11)
31. Amount, abbr.
32. Girl's name
34. Late general/president
35. Father of Ahira (Num. 1:15)
36. Saints, abbr.
37. Fur-bearing aquatic animals
39. Syringe, for short

DOWN

1. "I will _____ no wicked thing before mine eyes" (Ps. 101:3)
2. Method of administering medication, abbr.
3. "Not a _____, lest. . .he fall" (1 Tim. 3:6)
4. "That he was gone to be _____ with a man that is a sinner" (Luke 19:7)
5. Expire
6. Equip
7. "And Samuel answered Saul. . . 'I am the _____' " (1 Sam. 9:19)
9. "Gird yourselves, and _____, ye priests" (Joel 1:13)
10. "I have _____ you to be carried away captives" (Jer. 29:7)
11. "And there followed him a _____ of meat from the king" (2 Sam. 11:8)
12. Girl's name, for short
13. "Have they not _____?" (Judg. 5:30)
14. "For they were _____ afraid" (Mark 9:6)
16. "They did _____ _____ and ceased not" (Ps. 35:15) (2 words)
18. "Let my _____ go, that they may serve me" (Exod. 9:1)
19. "And the cup was found in Bejamin's _____" (Gen. 44:12)
20. Political cartoonist

128

23. Gaucho's weapon
26. "No grapes on the vine, nor figs on the _____ tree" (Jer. 8:13)
27. "All things which were _____ and goodly are departed" (Rev. 18:14)
28. "He was strong as the _____" (Amos 2:9)
30. "For the fierce _____ of the Lord is upon you" (2 Chron. 28:11)
33. "Let us meet. . .in the plain of _____" (Neh. 6:2)
34. Contraction
36. Theatre sign when there are no more seats, abbr.

38. European Plan, abbr.
by Janet Adkins

ACROSS

1. "Do him no ____" (Jer. 39:12)
5. Abbott, Fr.
9. "Also I shook my ____"
   (Neh. 5:13)
12. Oil of ____, skin softener
13. "The ____ of the Lord is
   clean, enduring for ever"
   (Ps. 19:9)
14. "Do they not ____ that devise
   evil?" (Prov. 14:22)
15. Puts on
16. "And it is a ____ thing that the
   king requireth" (Dan. 2:11)
17. "Now as he walked by the ____ of
   Galilee" (Mark 1:16)
18. Father of Enos (Gen. 5:6)
19. "Blessed ____ the pure in heart"
   (Matt. 5:8)
20. "And ____ ye not, but pursue
   after your enemies"
   (Josh. 10:19)
21. One of the sons of Gad
   (Gen. 46:16)
23. Librarian's whisper
25. "Ye have ____ treasure together
   for the last days" (James 5:3)
28. "For ____ is the kingdom of
   heaven" (Matt. 5:10)
32. "And it shall be unto them. . .that
   have sworn ____" (Ezek. 21:23)
33. Weird
34. Welcomes
36. "____, and be baptized every one
   of you" (Acts 2:38)
37. "He. . .chooseth a tree that will not
   ____" (Isa. 40:20)
38. "That which groweth of ____ own
   accord" (Lev. 25:5)
39. "I will bless the ____ at all times"
   (Ps. 34:1)

42. "Let us ____ with patience the
   race that is set before us"
   (Heb. 12:1)
44. "And I will give unto thee the
   ____ of the kingdom of heaven"
   (Matt. 16:19)
48. ____ Maria
49. Mongrels
50. "And the rest will ____ in order
   when I come" (1 Cor. 11:34)
   (2 words)
51. 22nd letter of alphabet
52. Swedish name
53. Nickname for Nathaniel
54. "Make thee an ____ of gopher
   wood" (Gen. 6:14)
55. "That the ____ men be sober,
   grave, temperate, sound in faith"
   (Titus 2:2)
56. "I will give thee. . .a ____ of
   apparel" (Judg. 17:10)

DOWN

1. Bricklayers' troughs
2. "Burn plant"
3. To speak vehemently
4. "The Lord is ____ ____"
   (Ps. 23:1) (2 words)
5. "They fell on their face, and were
   sore ____" (Matt. 17:6)
6. "____ ye one another's burdens"
   (Gal. 6:2)
7. "Because thou ____ the ark
   of the Lord GOD" (1 Kings 2:26)
8. "And ____ the lamp of God went
   out in the temple of the Lord"
   (1 Sam. 3:3)
9. "Neither shall ye touch it, ____ ye
   die" (Gen. 3:3)
10. Length times width
11. "____ without ceasing"
   (1 Thess. 5:17)

20. "They wandered about in _____ and goatskins" (Heb. 11:37)
22. "Return unto thy _____ my soul" (Ps. 116:7) (2 words)
24. "A great _____, knit at the four corners" (Acts 10:11)
25. Domesticated swine
26. "That which ye have spoken in the _____" (Luke 12:3)
27. "I _____ no pleasant bread" (Dan. 10:3)
29. Anger
30. _____-tin-tin, hero dog
31. "And God _____ them in the firmament of the heaven" (Gen. 1:17)

35. Put beads on a string
36. "It shall be both scoured, and _____ in water" (Lev. 6:28)
39. Molten rock
40. "Stretch forth thine hand with thy rod _____ the streams" (Exod. 8:5)
41. To stink
43. "The Pharisees began to _____ him vehemently" (Luke 11:53)
45. Jacob's brother (Gen. 25:26)
46. Abominable snowman
47. Editor's instruction
49. Government agency
by Elaine Okupski

ACROSS

1. "Away with such a fellow from the earth, for it is not ____ that he should live" (Acts 22:22)
4. "The joy of thy ____" (Matt. 25:21)
7. "Do thyself no ____" (Acts 16:28)
9. "A feast of wines on the ____" (Isa. 25:6)
11. "Believe also in ____" (John 14:1)
12. "And sow wickedness, ____ the same" (Job 4:8)
13. "Called to be ____ apostle" (1 Cor. 1:1)
14. A son of Benjamin (Gen. 46:21)
17. "Seeing he giveth to all ____" (Acts 17:25)
18. "Chains had been plucked asunder by him, and the fetters broken in pieces: neither could any man ____ him" (Mark 5:4)
19. "His life a ____ for many" (Matt. 20:28)
22. "Hath the ____ of the Lord been revealed?" (John 12:38)
25. "Because Judas had the ____, that Jesus had said unto him" (John 13:29)
26. "____, and do thou likewise" (Luke 10:37)
27. "Wash his feet with ____" (Luke 7:38)
28. "And stamp with thy foot, and say, ____ for all the evil abominations of the house of Israel!" (Ezek. 6:11)
29. "That where I am, there ye may ____" (John 14:3)

30. "Let him ____ the death" (Matt. 15:4)
32. "Whose shoes I am not worthy to ____" (Matt. 3:11)
34. "Be ye not as the horse, ____ as the mule" (Ps. 32:9)
35. "Do ye not therefore ____, because ye know not the scriptures?" (Mark 12:24)
36. "I ____ in Sion a chief corner stone" (1 Pet. 2:6)
38. Blew trumpet before ark of God (1 Chron. 15:24)
40. Preposition
41. Forefather of Jesus, El-mo-dam was the son of him (Luke 3:28)
42. "Simon ____ -Jona" (Matt. 16:17)
43. 11th letter of Hebrew alphabet

DOWN

1. "His eyes were as a ____ of fire" (Rev. 19:12)
2. Same as, or that is, Lat. abbr.
3. "Thou shalt not ____ the Lord thy God" (Matt. 4:7)
5. "Whose ____ have I taken?" (1 Sam. 12:3)
6. "Mighty in ____ and word" (Luke 24:19)
7. "That they should seek the Lord, if ____ they might feel after him" (Acts 17:27)
8. "Is not ___ to give" (Mark 10:40)
10. "Who shall ____ us from the love of Christ?" (Rom. 8:35)
13. "But having seen them ____ off" (Heb. 11:13)
15. "Whose is this ____ and superscription?" (Matt. 22:20)

The crossword grid contains handwritten letters spelling "SEPARATE" vertically in column, with an "M" at 11.

16. "Honour all ____ " (1 Pet. 2:17)
20. "The pen of the ___ is in vain" (Jer. 8:8)
21. First Gospel, abbr.
22. "Believe ye that I am ____ to do this?" (Matt. 9:28)
23. "Thou shalt forget thy ____" (Job 11:16)
24. "And being in an ____ he prayed more earnestly" (Luke 22:44)
28. "The prince of the power of the ____" (Eph. 2:2)
29. "To ____ I am ashamed" (Luke 16:3)

30. Gold coin used in Palestine (Ezra 2:69 RSV & ASV)
31. "The troops of ____ looked, the companies of Sheba waited for them" (Job 6:19)
33. Period of time
34. "Neither by any other ____" (James 5:12)
36. "Lot is cast into the ____" (Prov. 16:33)
37. Greek, abbr.
38. Hebrew 5th month
39. "Pass over through ____, the coast of Moab" (Deut. 2:18)

by Michael J. Landi

ACROSS

1. "Whose _____ is in his hand" (Matt. 3:12)
4. To sink downward
7. "Turn not _____ from following the Lord" (1 Sam. 12:20)
9. Half quarts
12. Where David's story begins (2 words)
14. Nothing
15. Doze
17. Raw material
18. "Queen of _____" (1 Kings 10:1)
20. "_____ the kine to the cart" (1 Sam. 6:7)
21. "Cast him into the _____ of lions" (Dan. 6:16)
22. Deoxyribonucleic acid, abbr.
23. "Under a pomegranate _____" (1 Sam. 14:2)
24. "Sing unto the Lord _____ _____ song" (Isa. 42:10) (2 words)
25. Prohibit
28. _____ and flow
31. A friend, Fr.
32. Former
33. Sheltered side
34. Marker
35. "As the _____ ran, he shot an arrow" (1 Sam. 20:36)
36. David was one, in other words
43. Fixed gaze
44. "Jonah was exceeding glad of the _____" (Jon. 4:6)
45. Light brown
46. "_____ no man any thing" (Rom. 13:8)

DOWN

1. "Instruments made of _____" (2 Sam. 6:5)
2. Advertisements, abbr.
3. "Cast the _____ on the right side" (John 21:6)
4. A mineral spring
5. Point at target
6. Wildebeest
7. "_____ _____ shall devour before him" (Ps. 50:3) (2 words)
8. A Christmas carol (2 words)
10. One who lives in a tent
11. "Worthy is the Lamb that was _____" (Rev. 5:12)
13. "A rod out of the _____ of Jesse" (Isa. 11:1)
14. Affirmative expression
16. A legume
18. "A deep _____ fell on Abram" (Gen. 15:12)
19. "_____ the son of Ner" (2 Sam. 2:8)
25. A baseball _____
26. Gather great numbers
27. "Jonah was in the belly of the _____" (Jon. 1:17)
29. "His spittle [fell] down upon his _____" (1 Sam. 21:13)
30. "David arose from off his _____" (2 Sam. 11:2)
37. "[David] did _____ the shew-bread" (Matt. 12:4)
38. An epoch
39. "The _____ of a ready writer" (Ps. 45:1)
40. The conscious self
41. "Frankincense upon each _____" (Lev. 24:7)
42. "A word spoken in _____ season" (Prov. 15:23)
by John Thornberg

ACROSS

1. Father of 23 and 48 Across (Gen. 4:21)
4. Father of those who dwell in tents (Gen. 4:20)
8. A tract of open grassland
10. Pursuing wild animals for food
13. A length measured in yards
16. To rub or scrape out
17. Serial, abbr.
18. Suitable
20. Iridium, chem. symbol
21. Dry cut stalks of grain
23. Musical instrument with strings stretched on a roughly triangular frame
24. Barium, chem. symbol
26. Fermented grape juice
28. No
30. Using land to grow crops
33. Color of the sky
35. First note of the musical scale
36. Argon, chem. symbol
37. "____ the mighty hunter" (Gen. 10:8–9)
40. A bag, or envelope, inflated with air
41. Rural Electrification Administration, abbr.
42. Einsteinium, chem. symbol
43. Mystery writer Christie's first name
46. Latin, Locus Sigilli, means place of the seal, abbr.
47. School, abbr.
48. Musical instrument made of pipes, that air is forced through

DOWN

1. A summer month
2. A person who carries something
3. Unit of money in Turkey
4. A summer month
5. Thorny or prickly plant with woody stem
6. Forward section of lowest balcony
7. Tending a flock of sheep
9. Opposite of west
11. Walk or run with quick, light steps
12. Not specified, abbr.
14. To pull back his hunting equipment for 37 Across
15. Gallium, chem. symbol
19. Tantalum, chem. symbol
21. Number 39 Down turns this when he works
22. Opposite of husband
24. Bachelor of Arts, abbr.
25. Opposite of 28 Across
27. Sodium, chem. symbol
28. National Guard, abbr.
29. Fluid, abbr.
31. Mother
32. Noncommissioned Officer, abbr.
34. Mottled yellow and green citrus fruits
36. Father of 7 Down (Gen. 4:2)
37. Built the ark, the father of zoology (Gen. 6:13–14)
38. To pull something with difficulty
39. Father of 30 Across
44. Preposition
45. Home run, abbr.
   by Mary Louise DeMott

PUZZLE 68

ACROSS

1. "Rule them with a ____ of iron" (Rev. 2:27)
3. "At the ____ of Jesus every knee should bow" (Phil. 2:10)
6. A bitter compound used in drugs and dyes
10. Utah, abbr.
11. "The ____ fell upon Jonah" (Jon. 1:7)
12. To regard with affection
14. Rhode Island, abbr.
15. "Go thee one way ___ other" (Ezek. 21:16)
17. "____ thy mouth wide" (Ps. 81:10)
18. For example, Lat. abbr.
20. "The days that Adam lived were ____ hundred and thirty" (Gen. 5:5)
21. Street, abbr.
23. "Jesus died and ____ again" (1 Thess. 4:14)
24. One who selects the contents of a publication
27. Associate in Applied Science, abbr.
29. Officer of the British Empire, abbr.
30. "Women ____ themselves in modest apparel" (1 Tim. 2:9)
32. "We are not ____ to answer thee" (Dan. 3:16)
35. Ribonucleic acid, abbr.
36. "They ____ unto it a lace of blue" (Exod. 39:31)
37. Northeast, abbr.
38. "The angels of God ____ him" (Gen. 32:1)
39. "____ that man" (2 Thess. 3:14)
41. Social Security, abbr.
42. Metal containers
44. "And the ____ stood still" (Josh. 10:13)
46. "The coat was without ____" (John 19:23)
48. Anno Domini, abbr.
50. "For God ____ loved the world" (John 3:16)
52. "Ye do ____, not knowing the scriptures" (Matt. 22:29)
54. "All the fiery ____ of the wicked" (Eph. 6:16)
56. "His ____ went to Jerusalem every year" (Luke 2:41)
57. "The ____ of all flesh is come before me" (Gen. 6:13)

DOWN

1. "Thou shalt not speak evil of the ____ of thy people" (Acts 23:5)
2. Old Testament, abbr.
3. "There is none righteous, ____, not one" (Rom. 3:10)
4. Makes amends for sin
5. Each, abbr.
6. Ampere, abbr.
7. "A faithful witness will not ____" (Prov. 14:5)
8. Vessels used to make tea or coffee
9. Maine, abbr.
11. Measurement in only one direction
13. "Gamaliel, a ____ of the law" (Acts 5:34)
16. "In the first chariot were ____ horses" (Zech. 6:2)
19. "Surely ____ and mercy shall follow me" (Ps. 23:6)
22. "Write them upon the ____ of thine heart" (Prov. 7:3)
25. Very fat
26. Referee, abbr.

28. "Go to the ____, thou sluggard" (Prov. 6:6)
30. "He took them up in his ____" (Mark 10:16)
31. A cereal plant
32. "Take up the ____ out of the burning" (Num. 16:37)
33. "Why make ye this ____, and weep?" (Mark 5:39)
34. "The lord commended the ____ steward" (Luke 16:8)
40. "Their ____ hath been to feed cattle" (Gen. 46:32)
42. California, abbr.

43. "These things saith the ____" (Rev. 3:14)
45. "Canst thou put a hook into his ____?" (Job 41:2)
47. "Give ____, O Lord, unto my prayer" (Ps. 86:6)
49. "____ shall judge his people" (Gen. 49:16)
51. General Practitioner, abbr.
53. Right, abbr.
55. Road, abbr.
by Joyce Handzo

by Linda Nunn

ACROSS

1. "Like the roaring of the ____" (Isa. 5:30)
4. "For ____ thou art" (Gen. 3:19)
8. "The ____ shall live by faith" (Rom. 1:17)
12. "There was no room for them in the ____" (Luke 2:7)
13. "They called his name ____" (Gen. 25:25)
14. "And the rain was ____ the earth forty days and forty nights" (Gen. 7:12)
15. A desert region of south Israel
17. Virtual Reality, abbr.
18. New Testament, abbr.
19. "And the king loved ____ above all the women" (Esther 2:17)
20. "I have given ____ unto the children of Lot for a possession" (Deut. 2:9)
22. "We have sent therefore Judas and ____ " (Acts 15:27)
24. "And will ____ their land" (2 Chron. 7:14)
27. Sun Devil school (abbr.)
28. "But if ye ____ and devour one another" (Gal. 5:15)
31. As easy as ____
32. God's name for Himself: I ____ (John 8:58)
33. "The wicked is ____ in the work of his own hands" (Ps. 9:16)
35. A historical period
37. "The ____ women, likewise, that they be in behavior as becometh holiness" (Titus 2:2)
38. Chemical symbol for tin
39. "And she named the child Ichabod, saying, The ____ is departed from Israel" (1 Sam. 4:21)
42. "O come, ____ us sing unto the Lord" (Ps. 95:1)
43. "And they slew the kings of Midian, beside the rest of them that were slain;. . .____ . . ." (Num. 31:8)
45. Reverend, abbr.

46. Article
48. "Come unto me, all ____ that labor " (Matt. 11:28)
49. Cast a ballot
52. World War II day of triumph celebrated May 8, 1945
53. "Therefore say thou unto them, Thus saith the Lord of hosts; Turn ye unto ____ " (Zech. 1:3)
54. "Thou shalt therefore ____ this ordinance in his season from year to year" (Exod. 13:10)
56. "There was a ____ round about the throne " (Rev. 4:3)
59. "Now if ye be ready that at what time ye hear the sound of the. . . ____ " (Dan. 3:15)
60. Most, suffix

DOWN

1. "Whatsoever is not of faith is ____ " (Rom. 14:23)
2. Compass direction, abbr.
3. "Some have entertained ____ unawares" (Heb. 13:2)
4. "Forgive us our ____ " (Matt. 6:12)
5. "The Lord seeth ____ not" (Ezek. 8:12)
6. "The same shall ____ it" (Mark 8:35)
7. Having turrets
8. "And ____ did evil in the sight of the Lord" (1 Kings 14:22)
9. "He was parted from them, and carried ____ into heaven" (Luke 24:51)
10. "Joshua the ____ of Nun was full of the spirit of wisdom" (Deut. 34:9)
11. An explosive
16. "His hand took hold on ____ heel" (Gen. 25:26)
21. "____ ye for the kingdom of heaven is at hand" (Matt. 3:2)
23. "Jesus saith unto them ____ ____ he" (John 18:5) (2 words)
25. "Behold the fowls of the ____ " (Matt. 6:26)
26. "Will thou break a ____ driven to and fro?" (Job 13:25)
28. "For some of them thought, because Judas had the ____ " (John 13:29)

29. Anger, wrath
30. "And the children of Reuben and the children of Gad called the altar _____" (Josh. 22:34)
32. "Be ye _____, and sin not" (Eph. 4:26)
34. "But let your communication be, Yea, yea; _____" (Matt. 5:37)
36. "Behold, we count them happy which endure. Ye have heard of the patience of _____" (James 5:11)
38. "And there came one of the _____ angels" (Rev. 17:1)
40. "We remember. . .the _____, and the onions, and the garlick" (Num. 11:5)
41. French composer
42. "And he shall purify the sons of _____" (Mal. 3:3)
44. And, Lat.
46. "The words of _____, who was among the herdmen of Tekoa" (Amos 1:1)
47. Mr. Gingrich
50. To choose
51. "It is a people that do _____ in their heart" (Ps. 95:10)
55. Each, abbr.
57. _____ me, expression of sorrow
58. "Then will the Lord _____ jealous for his land, and pity his people" (Joel 2:18)

ACROSS

1. "With trumpets and sound of _____ make a joyful noise before the Lord, the King" (Ps. 98:6)
7. "The people piped with _____, and rejoiced" (1 Kings 1:40)
11. Able to give way
13. "And the fish of the _____" (Ps. 8:8)
14. Motor torpedo boat, abbr.
15. "David took an _____, and played with his hand: so Saul was refreshed" (1 Sam. 16:23)
16. "Praise him with stringed instruments and _____" (Ps. 150:4)
18. 51, Rom. num.
19. Fourth tone of the music scale
21. Lincoln's state, abbr.
22. Tellurium, chem. symbol
23. "That at what time ye hear the sound of the cornet, _____, harp" (Dan. 3:5)
26. "Ye _____ the light of the world" (Matt. 5:14)
29. First day of the week, abbr.
31. Black sticky substance
32. "That at the sound of the cornet, flute, harp, _____, psaltery" (Dan. 3:5)
35. "That chant to the sound of the _____" (Amos 6:5)
36. Gold, chem. symbol
37. Suffix: more
38. Kind of molding
39. "And the seven angels which had the seven _____ prepared themselves to sound" (Rev. 8:6)
42. Maritime province, abbr.
43. Inches per second, abbr.
44. Contraction of it was, poetic

45. "I _____ the way, the truth, the life" (John 14:6)
47. French article
48. "Come unto _____, all ye that labour and are heavy laden" (Matt. 11:28)
49. Miriam took one of these instruments (Exod. 15:20)
50. "For we have seen his _____ in the east, and are come to worship him" (Matt. 2:2)

DOWN

1. "Praise him upon the loud _____: praise him upon the high sounding _____" (Ps. 150:5)
2. Office of International Trade, abbr.
3. A blunt rejection
4. U.S. National League (baseball), abbr.
5. Suffix: forms the past tense of many words
6. "And the harp, and the viol, the _____, . . .are in their feasts" (Isa. 5:12)
7. Gym class, abbr.
8. "Thanksgivings. . .with singing, with cymbals, _____ and with harps" (Neh. 12:27)
9. Weird
10. "The trees of the Lord are full of _____" (Ps. 104:16)
12. "Give thee seed of this woman for the _____ which is lent to the Lord" (1 Sam. 2:20)
17. Opposite of untidy
20. Man's name
24. Messy
25. A large Australian bird similar to an ostrich

142

27. "No lion. . .nor any _____ beast shall go up thereon" (Isa. 35:9)
28. "That at that time ye hear the sound of the cornet, flute, . . . psaltery, _____, and all kinds of music, ye fall down" (Dan. 3:5)
30. "Nor to _____ authority over the man" (1 Tim. 2:12)
33. Witch's concoction
34. Throws
36. Not straight
40. "Come now, and let _____ reason together, saith the Lord" (Isa. 1:18)

41. High stature
45. American Medical Association, abbr.
46. Same source, Lat. abbr.
by Janet Kennedy

PUZZLE 71

by Michael Landi

ACROSS

1. Enemy (Luke 12:58)
7. "He is a _____ creature"
   (2 Cor. 5:17)
10. "He turned the _____ into dry
    land" (Ps. 66:6)
11. "Upon _____ stone shall be seven
    eyes" (Zech. 3:9)
12. Meaning abundant flow of water;
    John was baptizing near there
    (John 3:23)
14. "_____ us not into temptation"
    (Matt. 6:13)
15. "Woe unto you, Pharisees! For ye
    tithe mint and _____"
    (Luke 11:42)
16. "It shall _____ given him"
    (James 1:5)
17. God cannot live in its presence
    (Isa. 59:2)
18. "And _____ the sacrifices of the
    dead" (Ps. 106:28)
19. "The race that is _____ before us"
    (Heb. 12:1)
20. "The kingdom of heaven is like
    unto a _____, that was cast into
    the sea" (Matt. 13:47)
21. "_____ his feet in the blood of the
    wicked" (Ps. 58:10)
23. "Light of the body is the _____"
    (Luke 11:34)
27. Collection of 27 books, abbr.
28. "Felling a _____, the axe head
    fell into the water"
    (2 Kings 6:5)
29. The only son of Abraham by
    Sarah (Gen. 17:17–19)
32. The coarse and broken part of
    flax ready for spinning
    (Judg. 16:9)

33. "I the Lord search the heart, I
    _____ the reins" (Jer. 17:10)
34. "Of the _____ of Benjamin"
    (Phil. 3:5)
37. Place in the land of the Chaldees
    (Neh. 9:7)
38. "Shall be as an oak whose _____
    fadeth" (Isa. 1:30)
40. "The _____ of the disciples was
    multiplied" (Acts 6:1)
42. "Your eyes shall see, and _____
    shall say" (Mal. 1:5)
43. "And _____ about the paps with a
    golden girdle" (Rev. 1:13)
44. "Breastplates of fire, and of
    _____" (Rev. 9:17)

DOWN

1. "The _____ saw the angel of the
   Lord" (Num. 22:23)
2. Famine (Acts 11:28)
3. "Ye are of more _____ than many
   sparrows" (Matt. 10:31)
4. "They offered a _____ of the
   flock" (Ezra 10:19)
5. "Said unto her, What _____ thee,
   Hagar?" (Gen. 21:17)
6. "Went to Jerusalem every _____ at
   the feast of the passover"
   (Luke 2:41)
7. "The multitude of _____"
   (Jer. 46:25)
8. Hostility, hatred (Luke 23:12)
9. "Therefore _____ conclude that a
   man is justified by faith"
   (Rom. 3:28)
13. That is, Lat. abbr.
16. "Bring forth the _____ robe"
    (Luke 15:22)
17. "If any man among you _____ to
    be religious" (James 1:26)
19. Make holy (Eph. 5:26)

144

22. Temporary dwelling
    (2 Kings 7:8)
24. Another name for "bishop"
    (1 Tim. 5:1)
25. "Fall into a ____ on the sabbath
    day" (Matt. 12:11)
26. "The earth ____, and trembled"
    (Ps. 97:4)
30. "Lusts, which war against the
    ____" (1 Pet. 2:11)
31. Religious ode (Matt. 26:30)
35. Literally means "master;" title
    given by Jews to teachers of their
    law (John 1:38)

36. "I hate robbery for ____ offering"
    (Isa. 61:8)
39. "And smote off his ____"
    (Matt. 26:51)
41. Example, Lat. abbr.

145

PUZZLE 72

ACROSS

1. "The _____ is unto you, and to your children" (Acts 2:39)
8. "_____ loves me, this I know"
12. "_____ and perfume rejoice the heart" (Prov. 27:9)
14. Mississippi's neighbor, abbr.
15. "_____ unto you, scribes and Pharisees, hypocrites!" (Matt. 23:25)
16. "When they had. . .gone six _____, he sacrificed oxen" (2 Sam. 6:13)
18. Personal smell, in other words, for short
19. Extra-terrestrials, abbr.
20. Central state, abbr.
21. Craggy hill
22. "_____ and outs"
24. "Forsake me not _____" (Ps. 119:8)
25. The book between Joel and Obadiah
26. Garment belted at the waist
28. "_____ Shaddai"
29. Single
31. Bachelor of Education degrees, abbr.
32. "The Spirit and the _____ say, Come" (Rev. 22:17)
34. Beverly, for short
35. Road, abbr.
36. "_____ your enemies" (Matt. 5:44)
37. Compass point
38. Charges
40. Birds build these
44. Need this to solve a mystery
46. Compass point
48. Vowels: _____, _____, _____, o, u and sometimes y

50. Bends
52. Pluck guitar strings
54. Doctor of Divinity, abbr.
55. "Ye are not your _____" (1 Cor. 6:19)
56. "One of the least of _____" (Matt. 25:40)

DOWN

1. "Not in word, but in _____" (1 Cor. 4:20)
2. Violent uprising
3. A faithful and beloved brother (Col. 4:9)
4. _____ Sinai, abbr.
5. "With God nothing shall be _____" (Luke 1:37)
6. "Even the wind and the _____ obey him" (Mark 4:41)
7. Enclosure, abbr.
9. Spanish article
10. Southern continent, abbr.
11. "I love to tell the _____ of Jesus and His love"
13. "Aquila. . .with his wife Priscilla. . .were _____-makers" (Acts 18:2–3)
17. "Make you perfect, stablish, strengthen, _____ you" (1 Pet. 5:10)
18. "In whom we have _____ and access with confidence" (Eph. 3:12)
21. Transmit/receive, abbr.
23. Not, prefix
24. Biblical land: _____ of the Chaldees
25. Having, suffix
27. Jesus died on the _____
28. Garden of _____
29. Pregnancy doctor, abbr.

146

30. The first woman
31. The Israelites needed straw to make this (Exod. 5:7)
33. 4, Rom. num.
38. Money supply
39. Mouse's noise
41. "As far as the _____ is from the west" (Ps. 103:12)
42. A son of Adam (Luke 3:38)
43. The wheel of a car
45. The top of a jar
47. Earn
49. American English, abbr.
51. Therefore

53. "Unto every one of _____ is given grace" (Eph. 4:7)

by Beverly Barnes

ACROSS

1. "That the Lord spake unto _____ the son of Nun" (Josh. 1:1)
6. "_____ and her towns, and the inhabitants" (Josh. 17:11)
11. "And Hur begat _____" (1 Chron. 2:20)
12. "Behold, this _____ shall be a witness" (Josh. 24:27)
14. "Jephunneh, and Pispah, and _____" (1 Chron. 7:38)
15. "_____ thyself now with majesty" (Job 40:10)
17. "_____ and all that are with her in the house" (Josh. 6:17)
18. "And it _____ worms" (Exod. 16:20)
19. "Whether they will _____ the way of the Lord" (Judg. 2:22)
21. "Gideon said, _____, O Lord GOD!" (Judg. 6:22)
23. "The children of Gad called the altar _____" (Josh. 22:34)
25. "Oliveyards which ye _____ not" (Josh. 24:13)
27. Preposition
28. "Shalt not give unto his _____, nor his daughter shalt thou _____" (Deut. 7:3) (2 words)
30. "As the _____, and all that came to hand" (Judg. 20:48)
32. Preposition
33. "Behold, the silver is with _____" (Judg. 17:2)
34. Bachelor of Arts degree, abbr.
35. Common nickname for a soldier
36. "Paul and Silas by night unto _____" (Acts 17:10)
38. "When I therefore was thus _____, did _____ use lightness?" (2 Cor. 1:17) (2 words)
41. Nickname for Edward
42. "Else if ye do in _____ wise go back" (Josh. 23:12)
44. "And upon the great _____ of his right foot" (Lev. 8:23)
45. "Judah took a wife for _____ his firstborn" (Gen. 38:6)

46. "It shall be that, _____ I _____, so shall ye do" (Judg. 7:17) (2 words)
47. "Tappuah, and _____" (Josh. 15:34)
49. _____, cosine, tangent
51. "And they burnt the city with _____" (Josh. 6:24)
53. "And _____ the kine to the cart" (1 Sam. 6:7)
54. "Go in this thy _____" (Judg. 6:14)
56. "Go and _____ in wait in the vineyards" (Judg. 21:20)
57. "He sat him down in a _____ of the city" (Judg. 19:15)
58. "Shelemiah the son of _____" (Jer. 36:26)

DOWN

1. "Nevertheless the Lord raised up _____" (Judg. 2:16)
2. Source of metals in the earth
3. "Behold, thy father is _____" (Gen. 48:1)
4. "All that thou commandest _____ we will do" (Josh. 1:16)
5. "Beat _____ the door, and _____ to the master" (Judg. 19:22) (2 words)
6. "_____ that they _____ with the blood" (1 Sam. 14:33) (2 words)
7. "They _____ come to search out all the country" (Josh. 2:3)
8. "Proclaim in the _____ of the people" (Judg. 7:3)
9. "We _____ thy servants" (Josh. 9:8)
10. "Thou _____ him to have dominion" (Ps. 8:6)
13. "_____ my Lord, if the Lord be with us" (Judg. 6:13)
16. "The Lord hath _____ me alive" (Josh. 14:10)
18. "Joshua did unto them as the Lord _____ him" (Josh. 11:9)
20. "There is _____ _____ all her multitude" (Ezek. 32:24) (2 words)
22. "From the wilderness and this _____ even unto the great river" (Josh. 1:4)
24. "She _____ upon the Assyrians her neighbours" (Ezek. 23:12)

26. Compass point, abbr.
27. "And they turned ____ thither" (Judg. 19:15)
29. "I will not fail thee, ____ forsake thee" (Josh. 1:5)
31. "I am old and stricken in ____" (Josh. 23:2)
34. "At the last it ____ like ____ serpent" (Prov. 23:32) (2 words)
36. "He is like the ____ that perish" (Ps. 49:12)
37. "Trode them down with ____" (Judg. 20:43)
39. "Thou shalt not curse the ____" (Lev. 19:14)
40. "And Rekem, and ____, and Taralah" (Josh. 18:27)

43. "The Lord your God giveth ___ to possess ___" (Josh. 1:11) (2 words)
46. "Brother of Eshcol, and brother of ____" (Gen. 14:13)
48. "Whosoever shall compel thee to go a ____, go with him twain" (Matt. 5:41)
50. "For ____ will give ____ into thine hand" (Josh. 8:18) (2 words)
52. "But the wheat and the ____ were not smitten" (Exod. 9:32)
54. "Hearken unto ____, ye men of Shechem" (Judg. 9:7)
55. Tuberculosis, abbr.
by Diana N. Rowland

149

PUZZLE 74

ACROSS

1. Sister of David
   (1 Chron. 2:15–16)
7. "Unto ten virgins which took their
   ____" (Matt. 25:1)
10. City of Asher (Josh. 19:30)
12. "The ____ of the Lord"
   (Prov. 9:10)
14. "So let it be" (Matt. 6:13)
16. "____ no man any thing"
   (Matt. 13:8)
18. Acted as both judge and high
   priest in Israel (1 Sam. 1:9)
19. "____, yet regarded as imposters"
   (2 Cor. 6:8 NIV)
20. A priest who returned from
   Babylon to Jerusalem with
   Zerubbabel (Neh. 12:1)
22. David's book, abbr.
23. Physician, abbr.
26. "____ their swords into plow-
   shares" (Isa. 2:4)
28. "For ____ to the faith among
   all nations, for his name"
   (Rom. 1:5)
30. Loyal member of David's court
   (1 Kings 1:8)
31. "He threw him into the ____"
   (Rev. 20:3 NIV)
33. Last book of the Bible, abbr.
34. "Upon the tip of the right ____ of
   Aaron" (Exod. 29:20)
37. "Yet have I set my ____ upon my
   holy hill" (Ps. 2:6)
39. "Turned about with a very small
   ____, whithersoever the governor
   listeth" (James 3:4)
40. Light of the body
   (Matt. 6:22)
41. Associate in Arts, abbr.

42. "Thou shalt not muzzle the ____"
   (Deut. 25:4)
43. "____ block" (Rom. 14:13)

DOWN

2. "If they have called the master of
   the house ____" (Matt. 10:25)
3. When King Ahaziah fled from
   Judah he went here
   (2 Kings 9:27)
4. "I ____ Alpha and Omega"
   (Rev. 1:8)
5. "Thou, O king, sawest, and
   behold a great ____" (Dan. 2:31)
6. "Then shall the ____ man leap as
   an hart" (Isa. 35:6)
8. "The sun and the ____ and the
   eleven stars" (Gen. 37:9)
9. "I was blind, now I ____"
   (John 9:25)
11. Son of Zephaniah (Zech. 6:14)
12. "Every prostitute receives a
   ____" (Ezek. 16:33 NIV)
13. "Not as one that beateth the
   ____" (1 Cor. 9:26)
15. "More in ____ than the sand"
   (Ps. 139:18)
17. "Peter went out, and ____ "
   (Luke 22:62)
21. "Shall not ____ unto the word"
   (Deut. 4:2)
24. "A second, like to a bear, and it
   raised up itself on one side, and it
   had three ____ in the mouth of
   it" (Dan. 7:5)
25. "They will lick dust like a ____"
   (Mic. 7:17 NIV)
27. Firstborn of Hiel (1 Kings 16:34)
29. Son of Alphaeus (Mark 2:14)
31. "Satan himself is transformed
   into an ____" (2 Cor. 11:14)

32. "Thy father made our _____ griev-
    ous" (1 Kings 12:4)
35. Son of Omri and seventh king of
    the northern kingdom of Israel
    (1 Kings 16:29)
36. "For my flesh is _____ food"
    (John 6:55 NIV)
38. "In vain the _____ is spread"
    (Prov. 1:17)
42. Amorite king of Bashan
    (Deut. 31:4)
    by Michael J. Landi

PUZZLE 75

ACROSS

1. What the Israelites did in Egypt
8. Preposition
9. "For the kingdom of heaven is ____ hand" (Matt. 3:2)
10. Rural Electrification Administration, abbr.
12. Simile preposition
13. "And thou shalt make a hanging . . .wrought with ____" (Exod. 26:36)
17. "And his raiment became. . . exceeding white . . .so as no ____. . . can white them (Mark 9:3)
18. Inspector General, abbr.
20. "Saying [to Philip], ____, we would see Jesus" (John 12:21)
22. Each, abbr.
23. These people built a house for David (2 Sam. 5:11)
28. Railroad, abbr.
29. "They. . .bought with [the money] the ____ field, to bury strangers in" (Matt. 27:7)
30. South Dakota, abbr.
31. Institute, abbr.
34. "Esau, who is ____" (Gen. 36:1)
36. People with the same profession as Simon (Acts 9:43)
39. "He that heareth the word, and ____ with joy receiveth it" (Matt. 13:20)
40. "Though they be ____ like crimson" (Isa. 1:18)
41. Alcoholics Anonymous, abbr.
42. Common Era, abbr.
43. Stitching a picture on cloth
48. "It is a ____ thing that the king requireth" (Dan. 2:11)
50. "He stood by the ____ of Gennesaret" (Luke 5:1)
51. Streets, abbr.
52. Persons who fill seams or joints so they will not leak

DOWN

1. People who work with brass
2. Impersonal pronoun
3. People who make candies, cake, etc. for sale
4. A vegetable which looks similar to spinach
5. Repetitive
6. An earner
7. "And Pharaoh was wroth against . . .the chief of the butlers, and against the chief of the ____" (Gen. 40:2)
11. More, suffix
14. Good; well; true, prefix
15. Elevated railroad
16. 550, Rom. num.
19. People who grow flowers and vegetables
21. Internal Revenue Service, abbr.
24. Revolutions per second, abbr.
25. "We are the clay, and thou our ____; and we all are the work of thy hand" (Isa. 64:8)
26. And, Lat.
27. A person between 13 and 19
32. Measurement at sea, abbr.
33. "____ ____ can you see?" (2 words)
35. "Why ____ the heathen rage?" (Ps. 2:1)
37. "Why make ye this ___, and weep?" (Mark 5:39)
38. More scarce
39. Alternating current, abbr.
40. Rubidium, chem. symbol
44. "Jesus. . .findeth Philip, and saith unto him, Follow ____" (John 1:43)
45. Not well

152

46. A relay type of transportation of men or horses in India
47. _____ out: barely making a living
49. Preposition showing location or time

by Janet Kennedy

ACROSS

1. Jacob's other name
5. Mr., Sp. abbr.
7. Selenium, chem. symbol
9. Middle Latin, abbr.
10. "The gift. . .perverteth the words of the ____" (Exod. 23:8)
13. "Tola the son of ____" (Judg. 10:1)
16. Concise
17. Each, abbr.
18. "For the statues of ____" (Mic. 6:16)
19. Neon, chem. symbol
20. Wisconsin, abbr.
21. Antimony, chem. symbol
22. "Why dost thou. . .cause me to behold ____?" (Hab. 1:3)
26. "Great well that is in ____" (1 Sam. 19:22)
28. "Melech, and ____, and Ahaz" (1 Chron. 8:35)
30. "Rekem, and ____, and Taralah" (Josh. 18:27)
32. Boy
34. "We were willing to have imparted unto you. . .also ____ own souls" (1 Thess. 2:8)
36. Conjunction
37. "One that is proud and ____" (Isa. 2:12)
41. "Will he ____ thy riches?" (Job 36:19)
44. Adam's wife
45. Where Joseph, Mary, and Jesus went to escape Herod
47. Not him
48. "Barley was in the ____" (Exod. 9:31)
51. Smallest state, abbr.
52. Impossible to deny
57. "____ thy cause with thy neighbour" (Prov. 25:9)
58. "Your own husbands. . .may without the word be ____ by the conversation of the wives" (1 Pet. 3:1)

DOWN

1. "But without faith it is ____" (Heb. 11:6)
2. "God hath given them the spirit of ____" (Rom. 11:8)
3. Judah's firstborn (Gen. 38:6)
4. "____, and Shimei" (Num. 3:18)
5. "Then the ____ said within himself, What shall I do?" (Luke 16:3)
6. "I. . .will ____ them as silver " (Zech. 13:9)
7. "If any man will ____ thee at the law" (Matt. 5:40)
8. "Out of the mount of ____?" (Obad. 8)
11. "____ them that love us" (Titus 3:15)
12. A greeting
14. Argon, chem. symbol
15. "Hosanna in the ____" (Mark 11:10)
23. "Ye tithe mint and ____" (Luke 11:42)
24. Organization to assist those who have served in the armed forces, abbr.
25. "Pass ye unto ____, and see" (Amos 6:2)
27. Condition that affects motor coordination, abbr.
29. Part of the Freudian psyche
31. "For, ____, the winter is past" (Song of Sol. 2:11)

33. "Doe, ____ ____, a female deer, Re . . ." (2 words)
35. Say again
36. Preposition
38. Above
39. "I ____ the Lord" (Jon. 1:9)
40. You, King James Eng.
42. Address abbreviation
43. Magnetic resonance imaging, abbr.
46. Food, slang
49. Moses parted the ____ Sea
50. Peninsula state, abbr.
52. "____ thou count me therefore" (Philem. 17)
53. Iron, chem. symbol
54. Tantalum, chem. symbol
55. "Lest. . .I myself should ____ a castaway . . ." (1 Cor. 9:27)
56. Enlisted woman, abbr.

by Teri Grottke

by Mary Louise DeMott

ACROSS

1. "Seeking goodly ____" (Matt. 13:45)
6. This Bible treasure is the last stone inserted in the High Priest's breastplate (Exod. 28:17–20)
12. Be
14. People or things close at hand
15. Department of Defense, abbr.
16. Seventeenth letter of the Greek alphabet
18. American Kennel Club, abbr.
19. Commercials, in other words, for short
20. These Bible treasures are plants with leaves or seeds used for food
22. A statement the speaker knows to be untrue
23. Thirteenth letter of the Greek alphabet
24. Rather gray
26. Doctor's degree
27. Emperor of Russia
29. Woodwind instrument of treble pitch
31. Woman church leader
32. A coagulated mass
34. Every one
37. Abbreviation of 34 Across
38. This Bible treasure is a rich green color, the first stone in the second row of the High Priest's breastplate (Exod. 28:17–20)
43. Old English, abbr.
44. Ribonucleic acid, abbr.
46. Iridescent gems
47. Opposite of nay
48. Yards, abbr.
49. "And ____ did that which was right" (1 Kings 15:11)
50. Creator and ruler of the universe
51. A rope with a running noose
54. This Bible treasure is beautifully veined, semi-transparent, a variety of quartz (Exod. 28:17–20)
56. A guarantee
57. Trapped

DOWN

1. Boring teacher
2. Second book of the OT
3. Helps
4. Recording Secretary, abbr.
5. Lieutenant, abbr.
7. Preposition
8. Hush
9. Loud ringing of a bell
10. A member of a people living near the arctic coast of North America and eastern Siberia
11. Shrink back
13. Apple-green chalcedony
16. Rural Electrification Administration, abbr.
17. A bright broad sash worn with a kimono
20. House of Representatives, abbr.
21. Religious education, in other words, abbr.
24. A diving bird
25. Watered or sprayed
28. Fuss, trouble, excitement
30. Boy Scouts of America, abbr.
32. These Bible treasures, found in the High Priest's breastplate, are identical to the emerald except in color, a light or bluish green (Exod. 28:17–20)

33. A four wheeled carriage with a folding top
35. North American prairie wolf
36. Paid careful attention to
39. Central state whose capital is Jefferson City, abbr.
40. Environmental Protection Agency, abbr.
41. Montgomery's state, abbr.
42. Left side, abbr.
45. Autonomous Soviet Socialist Republic, abbr.
47. A gelatinous substance, from seaweed, used as a laxative

52. Selenium, chem. symbol
53. Writings that belong to both Jews and Christians, abbr.
54. Article used before a vowel
55. Peach state, abbr.

ACROSS

1. "The children of the ____ were gathered together" (Judg. 6:33)
5. "Why ____ ye not the breaches of the house?" (2 Kings 12:7)
7. "I cannot redeem it for myself, lest I ____ mine own inheritance" (Ruth 4:6)
8. A son of Helem (1 Chron. 7:35)
10. "How ____ I endure to see the destruction of my kindred?" (Esther 8:6)
11. Moves covertly
13. Etruscan god
14. "And they straightway left their ____, and followed him" (Matt. 4:20)
15. A Babylonian chief god
17. "____, with Sapphira his wife, sold a possession" (Acts 5:1)
19. "And Josiah gave to the people, of the flock, ____ and kids" (2 Chron. 35:7)
21. Doctor's degree
22. "Go to the ____, thou sluggard" (Prov. 6:6)
23. Capuchin monkey
24. Artificial language
25. "Even upon his forefront, did he put the golden ____" (Lev. 8:9)
27. Political representative
29. "Of ____, the family of the Erites" (Num. 26:16)
30. "Have they not ____?" (Judg. 5:30)
31. "Of every tree of the garden thou mayest freely ____" (Gen. 2:16)
32. A vessel in which substances are pounded

34. "He shall not search whether it be good or ____" (Lev. 27:33)
35. "And the priest may bring her ____ and set her before the Lord" (Num. 5:16)
36. Swiss river
37. "Bear your iniquities, even forty years, and ye shall know my ____ of promise" (Num. 14:34)
39. Revise, prepare for publication

DOWN

1. Poetic "ever"
2. News agency, abbr.
3. "Gather my ____ together unto me" (Ps. 50:5)
4. "What have I done. . .that thou hast smitten me these three ____?" (Num. 22:28)
5. "And he ____ before, and climbed up into a sycamore tree to see him" (Luke 19:4)
6. Genetic material
7. "Call me not Naomi, call me ____" (Ruth 1:20)
9. Modern Achai in Greece
10. "Her ____ goeth not out by night" (Prov. 31:18)
11. "Nor sitteth in the ____ of the scornful" (Ps. 1:1)
12. "Arphaxad, which was the son of ____, which was the son of Noe" (Luke 3:36)
13. "Thy word is a ____ unto my feet" (Ps. 119:105)
14. "Were there not ten cleansed? but where are the ____?" (Luke 17:17)
16. "Till ye have scattered them ____" (Ezek. 34:21)

18. "And ___ was destroyed of nation, and city of city" (2 Chron. 15:6)
19. "Behold, the people of the ____ now are many" (Exod. 5:5)
20. "Certain lewd fellows of the baser ____" (Acts 17:5)
23. "And Samuel answered Saul, and said, I am the ____" (1 Sam. 9:19)
26. "With a strong hand, and with a stretched out ____" (Ps. 136:12)
27. "He ____ not their soul from death" (Ps. 78:50)

28. "The wild beast shall ____ them" (Hos. 13:8)
30. "They look and ____ upon me" (Ps. 22:17)
33. Confederate soldier Johnny ____
34. ____, humbug!
36. Play division
38. "And Joshua sent men from Jericho to ____" (Josh. 7:2)
by Janet W. Adkins

159

ACROSS

1. "Many shall ____ to and fro" (Dan. 12:4)
3. "An half ____ of land" (1 Sam. 14:14)
6. "And ____ his son reigned" (2 Kings 21:18)
10. "As ____ is written" (Mark 1:2)
11. Certified Public Accountant, abbr.
12. A type of bird that wasn't to be eaten (Lev. 11:13)
14. Master of Arts, abbr.
15. Louisiana, abbr.
17. "The ____ of heaven" (Jer. 33:22)
18. "The children of Gad called the altar ____" (Josh. 22:34)
20. "A Prophet was beforetime called a ____" (1 Sam. 9:9)
21. "____ that believeth on him is not condemned" (John 3:18)
23. "And Jacob ____ his clothes" (Gen. 37:34)
24. "For the grace of God that ____ salvation" (Titus 2:11 NKJV)
27. The sixth note of the musical scale
29. One of the sons of Gad (Gen. 46:16)
30. "A ____ work of a sapphire stone" (Exod. 24:10)
32. "He passed through the midst of ____" (Luke 17:11)
35. "Ye ____ of this world" (John 8:23)
36. "I will nourish you, and your little ____" (Gen. 50:21)
37. North Dakota, abbr.
38. "That which groweth of ____ own accord" (Lev. 25:5)

39. "The mountains skipped like ____" (Ps. 114:4)
41. Northeast, abbr.
42. "Whatsoever a man soweth, that shall he also ____" (Gal. 6:7)
44. "I ____ daily with you" (Matt. 26:55)
46. "I am he that liveth, and was ____" (Rev. 1:18)
48. New Testament language, abbr.
50. "____ ye now believe?" (John 16:31)
52. "The ____ shall take him by the heel" (Job 18:9)
54. "Jael the wife of ____" (Judg. 5:24)
56. "Be ____ with such things as ye have" (Heb. 13:5)
57. "____ the kine to the cart" (1 Sam. 6:7)

DOWN

1. "A pure ____ of water of life" (Rev. 22:1)
2. Utah, abbr.
3. Associated Press, abbr.
4. "____ stilled the people before Moses" (Num. 13:30)
5. Ex Officio, abbr.
6. Army Post Office, abbr.
7. A title before the surname of a married woman
8. "God had sworn with an ____" (Acts 2:30)
9. New York, abbr.
11. "David dwelt in the ____" (1 Chron. 11:7)
13. "Elisha passed to ____" (2 Kings 4:8)
16. Arranged, abbr.
19. "Abram ____ as the Lord had spoken" (Gen. 12:4)

22. "____ and Medad do prophesy in the camp" (Num. 11:27)
25. "All flesh is as ____" (1 Pet. 1:24)
26. "And I said unto him, ____, thou knowest" (Rev. 7:14)
28. "Why make ye this ____, and weep?" (Mark 5:39)
30. "Neither shall there be any more ____" (Rev. 21:4)
31. Vessel, abbr.
32. "The ____ beguiled me" (Gen. 3:13)
33. "____ did that which was right in the eyes of the LORD" (1 Kings 15:11)

34. "He will ____ them with his troops" (Hab. 3:16)
40. "I am come that they ____ have life" (John 10:10)
42. Rear Admiral, abbr.
43. "Escaped the ____ of the sword" (Heb. 11:34)
45. "The unclean spirit had ____ him" (Mark 1:26)
47. A period of time
49. One of the men who was not with Adonijah (1 Kings 1:8)
51. Alternating Current, abbr.
53. "____ the beginning" (Gen. 1:1)
55. "Let there ____ light" (Gen. 1:3)
by Joyce Handzo

PUZZLE 80

ACROSS

1. "Though they be red like _____, they shall be as wool" (Isa. 1:18)
6. "Thou shalt also make a laver of _____" (Exod. 30:18)
10. Omissions excepted, abbr.
11. A long period of time
12. "And thou shalt make a veil of _____, and purple" (Exod. 26:31)
13. Lead, chem. symbol
14. Upper case, abbr.
15. Association of American Railroads, abbr.
16. Californian city, abbr.
17. "Lydia, a seller of _____" (Acts 16:14)
19. Academy, abbr.
20. _____ out: barely making a living
22. Kiloliter, abbr.
23. Elevated railroad
24. "And in the place of the boil there be a. . .spot. . .somewhat _____" (Lev. 13:19)
28. Consumed
29. Actress McGraw
30. "They had on their heads crowns of _____" (Rev. 4:4)
32. Base hit (baseball), abbr.
33. "A dove. . .her feathers with _____ gold" (Ps. 68:13)
34. 6, Rom. num.
35. "He. . .saw a publican, named _____. . .and said unto him, Follow me" (Luke 5:27)
38. A liquid adhesive
40. "Of the tribe of _____ were sealed twelve thousand" (Rev. 7:6)
42. "The same came therefore to Philip, . . .saying, _____, we would see Jesus" (John 12:21)
44. "Lie down in _____ pastures" (Ps. 23:2)
47. Bear, Sp.
48. Estimated time of arrival, abbr.
49. "Neither knoweth _____ man the Father, save the Son" (Matt. 11:27)
50. Uncooked
51. "But let your yea be yea; and your _____ . . ." (James 5:12)
52. But
53. "Let not the _____ go down upon your wrath" (Eph. 4:26)

DOWN

1. "Two vessels of fine _____, precious as gold" (Ezra 8:27)
2. "He _____ the sea, and maketh it dry" (Nah. 1:4)
3. "Come unto _____, all ye that labour" (Matt. 11:28)
4. "Be in health, even as thy _____ prospereth" (3 John 2)
5. "For Christ also hath _____ suffered for sins" (1 Pet. 3:18)
6. "Canst not make one hair white or _____" (Matt. 5:36)
7. Country area
8. At the age of, abbr.
9. "They clothed Daniel with _____, and put a chain of gold about his neck" (Dan. 5:29)
12. Sound of sheep
18. "Though they be _____ like crimson, they shall be as wool" (Isa. 1:18)
21. An interjection of surprise
23. And, Lat.
25. "One _____ is with the Lord as a thousand years" (2 Pet. 3:8)
26. Able, suffix

27. "Peter said, _____ and gold have I none; but such as I have give I thee" (Acts 3:6)
28. Those who give counsel
30. "I saw seven _____ candlesticks" (Rev. 1:12)
31. "_____ no man any thing, but to love one another" (Rom. 13:8)
32. "He made for the altar a _____ grate" (Exod. 38:4)
36. Southern state, abbr.
37. "I will pass through. . .removing . . .all the _____ cattle among the sheep" (Gen. 30:32)
38. "Yea, _____ hairs are here and there upon him, yet he knoweth not" (Hos. 7:9)
39. Repulsive to the eye
41. Jacob's brother
43. Independent T.V. Authority, abbr.
45. Take food
46. Empire state, abbr.
by Janet Kennedy

PUZZLE 81

ACROSS

1. "Take up thy ____, and walk" (John 5:8)
3. "They were ____ asunder" (Heb. 11:37)
6. "Casting all your ____ upon him" (1 Pet. 5:7)
9. "A continual dropping in a very ____ day and a contentious woman are alike" (Prov. 27:15)
11. Preposition
12. Underwriters Laboratories, abbr.
13. "Joshua sent men from Jericho to ____" (Josh. 7:2)
15. A wager
16. "God made them male and ____" (Mark 10:6)
18. South Dakota, abbr.
19. "My foot standeth in an ____ place" (Ps. 26:12)
21. The desert area in southern Israel
22. "Thou shalt make a ____ of pure gold" (Exod. 28:36)
24. Associated Press, abbr.
26. Ripped
27. "Touch the ____ of his garment" (Matt. 14:36)
28. "The ____ of the land is gone" (Isa. 24:11)
30. Tin, chem. symbol
31. "They found a plain in the land of ____" (Gen. 11:2)
34. "The Lord said unto Moses in ____" (Exod. 4:19)
36. A different spelling of Jehovah
38. Old covenant writings, abbr.
39. To ooze gently
41. A stringed musical instrument
43. "Will they not say that ye are ____?" (1 Cor. 14:23)

45. A religious service held in late afternoon
47. "One ____ contained forty baths" (1 Kings 7:38)
49. "Go thee one way ____ other" (Ezek. 21:16)
50. Electrical engineer, abbr.
51. The top of a hill or wave
52. "Prepare ye the ____ of the Lord" (Matt. 3:3)
53. "With God ____ things are possible" (Mark 10:27)
54. "Till a ____ strike through his liver" (Prov. 7:23)

DOWN

1. "Do not they ____ that worthy name?" (James 2:7)
2. Physician's title, abbr.
3. "Corn is sifted in a ____" (Amos 9:9)
4. Prefix meaning before
5. Cheyenne's state, abbr.
6. "Joy ____ in the morning" (Ps. 30:5)
7. "We wrestle not against flesh and blood, but. . .the ____ of the darkness" (Eph. 6:12)
8. "And about the ____ hour he went out" (Matt. 20:6)
10. To help, especially in bad conduct
11. "Ye shall have tribulation ____ days" (Rev. 2:10)
14. "An ____ soul shall suffer hunger" (Prov. 19:15)
17. "They would have repented long ____" (Matt. 11:21)
20. "He went into a city called ____" (Luke 7:11)
23. "I ____ Alpha and Omega" (Rev. 22:13)

164

25. "We made our ____ unto our God" (Neh. 4:9)
28. "Bring me a ____" (2 Kings 3:15)
29. "They set a ____" (Jer. 5:26)
31. Exercises to strengthen stomach muscles
32. "He saith among the trumpets, ____" (Job 39:25)
33. Compass point, abbr.
35. "Give not that which is holy unto the ____" (Matt. 7:6)
37. "Abraham said unto his ____ servant" (Gen. 24:2)
40. A stand for supporting a painting

42. That is, Lat. abbr.
43. Naomi's new name for herself (Ruth 1:20)
44. To declare in a positive manner
45. "Let me go and pay my ____" (2 Sam. 15:7)
46. A period of time
47. Liquid crystal, diode, abbr.
48. Opposite of left, abbr.
    By Joyce Handzo

ACROSS

1. "And Adam called his wife's name
   ____" (Gen. 3:20)
4. "____, the family of the Punites"
   (Num. 26:23)
7. "And ____. . .did evil. . .above all
   that were before him"
   (1 Kings 16:30)
11. "What seemeth you ____ I will do"
    (2 Sam. 18:4)
13. "There was no room for them in the
    ___" (Luke 2:7)
14. "The price of his ____ shall be
    according unto the number of years"
    (Lev. 25:50)
15. ____ Stanley Gardner
16. Alfonzo's queen
17. Irish Gaelic
18. "He wrote also letters to ____ on the
    Lord God of Israel"
    (2 Chron. 32:17)
19. "I have perfumed my bed with myrrh,
    aloes, and ____" (Prov. 7:17)
21. Sarah might have called her husband
    ____ for short
23. That is, Lat. abbr.
24. "____ off all his hair" (Lev. 14:8)
27. "Martha, thou art ____. . .about many
    things" (Luke 10:41)
32. "Bring the tribe of ____ near, and
    present them before Aaron the priest"
    (Num. 3:6)
33. "But it ____ thou, a man mine equal"
    (Ps. 55:13)
34. "____ that man, and have no
    company with him" (2 Thess. 3:14)
35. "Wrought with labour and ____ night
    and day" (2 Thess. 3:8)
37. "Cursed is every one that hangeth
    on ____ ____ " (Gal. 3:13)
    (2 words)
38. Doctor's assistant, abbr.
39. "A bird of the ____ shall carry the
    voice" (Eccles. 10:20)
40. "The ____ shall melt with fervent
    heat" (2 Pet. 3:12)

45. "Abner went also to speak in the
    ____ of David" (2 Sam. 3:19)
49. "There come in also a poor man in
    ____ raiment" (James 2:2)
50. Belonging to the first son of Judah
    (Gen. 38:3)
51. "When he speaketh ____ ____
    he speaketh of his own" (John 8:44)
    (2 words)
52. "The same is Micaiah the son of
    ____" (2 Chron. 18:7)
53. "Bind them. . .upon thine heart, and
    ____ them about thy neck"
    (Prov. 6:21)
54. Ocean movement
55. "Neither rend your clothes; ____ ye
    die" (Lev. 10:6)
56. Her Majesty's ship, abbr.
57. Air, prefix

DOWN

1. "And ships shall come. . .and shall
   afflict ____" (Num. 24:24)
2. Woman's name
3. Father of Naum (Luke 3:25)
4. "For a ____ of bread that man will
   transgress" (Prov. 28:21)
5. "Also Bakbukiah and ____, their
   brethren, were over against them"
   (Neh. 12:9)
6. "____, with Sapphira his wife, sold a
   possession" (Acts 5:1)
7. "There was ____ ____ of glass like
   unto crystal" (Rev. 4:6) (2 words)
8. "Do thyself no ____: for we are all
   here" (Acts 16:28)
9. "There come in ____ a poor man"
   (James 2:2)
10. "They took knowledge of them, that
    they had ____ with Jesus"
    (Acts 4:13)
12. Seaport in W. Israel, formerly Jaffa
20. "Abner the son of ____"
    (1 Kings 2:32)
22. "____ merciful, O Lord, unto thy
    people Israel" (Deut. 21:8)
24. Weatherman's abbreviation

25. "Rachel weeping for ____ children" (Matt. 2:18)
26. "And the king of Assyria brought men from Babylon, . . .Cuthah, . . . and from ____" (2 Kings 17:24)
27. "Silent" ____ Coolidge
28. To petition, supplicate
29. "____ I am meek and lowly in heart" (Matt. 11:29)
30. Shoshonean
31. Confederate general
33. "He that ____ souls is wise" (Prov. 11:30)
36. "The mighty ____ gathered against me" (Ps. 59:3)
37. "The men went up and viewed ____" (Josh. 7:2)

39. "And the ____ of Kish. . .were lost" (1 Sam. 9:3)
40. "So thou shalt put away ____ from among you" (Deut. 22:24)
41. "He burned the bones of the king of Edom into ____" (Amos 2:1)
42. House additions
43. "And make me savoury ____, such as I love" (Gen. 27:4)
44. Cut
46. Other, Lat.
47. "And he made him to ____ in the second chariot" (Gen. 41:43)
48. "For he that is now called a Prophet was beforetime called a ____" (1 Sam. 9:9)
by Janet Adkins

ACROSS

1. Belonging to the father of Leah & Rachel (Gen. 29)
7. Kansas City, abbr.
9. Son of Abda (1 Kings 4:6)
11. Eosinophil, abbr.
13. South, abbr.
14. Indium, chem. symbol
15. Son of Noah
17. Royal Military College, abbr.
18. Comes after spring
21. "The wall of ____" (Amos 1:14)
23. Beryllium, chem. symbol
24. City near Bethel
25. Bind
26. "Destroy ____ kings and people" (Ezra 6:12)
27. Preposition
29. Belonging to Jacob's first wife (Gen. 29)
33. "____ that ye refuse not him that speaketh" (Heb. 12:25)
34. Village in Simeon (1 Chron. 4:32)
36. Very warm
37. Belonging to Eve's husband
39. "____ are spies" (Gen. 42:9)
40. Iridium, chem. symbol
41. Before, poetic
43. An altar (Josh. 22)
45. Arsenic, chem. symbol
46. "It shall no more be called. . .the valley of the son of____" (Jer. 7:32)
49. "For ____ is ordained. . ." (Isa. 30:33)
52. Recede
53. A thousand thousands, abbr.
55. Ordinance Officer, abbr.
56. Mister, abbr.
57. Length overall, abbr.
58. Mother-of-pearl
60. Exposure index, abbr.
61. Picosecond, abbr.
62. Convulsion
63. Nanogram, abbr.

DOWN

1. "For, ____, the winter is past" (Song of Sol. 2:11)
2. "Eshtemoh, and ____" (Josh. 15:50)
3. Moza's son (1 Chron. 8:37)
4. Capital of Moab (Num. 21:28)
5. No, slang
6. Intelligent
7. Edge of the road, Br. spelling
8. Deep unconsciousness
9. Donkey
10. Duplicated
12. School, abbr.
16. Letters, etc.
19. Menan's son (Luke 3:31)
20. Brawl
22. Buzzing stinger
26. Solomon's great-grandson (Matt. 1:7)
28. No, old English
30. Ahitub's son (1 Sam. 14:3)
31. Equestrians
32. Address abbreviation
34. "____ begat Aram" (Matt. 1:3)
35. Encounter
38. "And, lo, three ____ stood by him" (Gen. 18:2)
42. A race of giants
44. Entrances
46. "Another to ____ him up" (Eccles. 4:10)
47. Members of a Nigerian tribe
48. Basketball organization, abbr.
50. A composition in verse
51. Advanced mathematics, abbr.

54. Where a child likes to sit
59. San Diego's state, abbr.
   by Teri Grottke

ACROSS

1. "Ye who _____ were far off are made nigh" (Eph. 2:13)
9. Car manufacturing union, abbr.
12. Removal of a mistake
13. Book that follows Daniel
15. Electrical engineer, abbr.
16. Memphis' state, abbr.
17. Not here
19. "_____, and ye shall find," (Matt. 7:7)
21. Contraction for I have
23. "I _____ the Lord, and he heard me" (Ps. 34:4)
27. West Indies, abbr.
28. "The eye cannot say unto the hand, I have no _____ of thee" (1 Cor. 12:21)
29. Article
30. A long, low soft couch or sofa
31. Geomagnetic electrokinetograph, abbr.
32. Book, abbr.
34. Inspector General, abbr.
35. Letter of the alphabet before "en"
37. "Jesus saith unto her, . . .whom _____ thou?" (John 20:15)
39. "Like the _____ birth of a woman" (Ps. 58:8)
40. Foot, suffix
41. Mercury, chem. symbol
42. "And Joshua sent men from Jericho to _____" (Josh. 7:2)
43. "But _____ for the promise of the Father" (Acts 1:4)
44. "My heart is like wax; _____ is melted" (Ps. 22:14)
46. "Make me as one of thy _____ servants" (Luke 15:19)
47. Royal Horse Guard, abbr.

49. "[Abram] sat in the _____ door in the heat of the day" (Gen. 18:1)
51. Center fielder (baseball), abbr.
52. "Therefore _____ said unto Samuel, Go, lie down. . .if he call thee. . .say, speak, Lord" (1 Sam. 3:9)
54. "For my yoke is _____, and my burden is light" (Matt. 11:30)
55. "And the people _____ for Zacharias, . . .he tarried so long" (Luke 1:21)

DOWN

1. "As a roaring lion. . ._____ whom he may devour" (1 Pet. 5:8)
2. A rock or soil containing some metal
3. Mother
4. This, Sp.
5. Musical ditties
6. Iridium, chem. symbol
7. Encountered
8. "The woman was a Greek, . . .and _____ besought [Jesus] that he would cast forth the devil" (Mark 7:26)
9. Took advantage of
10. First 2 vowels
11. "So that ye come behind in no gift; _____ for the coming of our Lord" (1 Cor. 1:7)
14. Either
18. To squeeze with the arms
19. "There is none that _____ after God" (Rom. 3:11)
20. A valuable tree of Hawaii
22. Symbol of victory
24. "Lord I believe; help thou mine _____" (Mark 9:24)
25. Hand, abbr.

26. "No man hath seen God at any _____" (John 1:18)
27. "Our soul _____ for the Lord; he is our help" (Ps. 33:20)
33. "He opened not the doors. . . therefore they took a _____, and opened them" (Judg. 3:25)
36. "A sound from heaven as of a rushing _____ wind" (Acts 2:2)
37. "Find me, when ye shall _____ for me with all your heart" (Jer. 29:13)
38. "I will pour out of my _____ upon all flesh" (Acts 2:17)
39. Bring together into one
45. A hot or cold beverage
48. "In the beginning _____ created the heavens and the earth" (Gen. 1:1)
50. Maritime province, abbr.
52. Apiece, in other words, abbr.
53. 51, Rom. num.
   by Janet Kennedy

171

by Janet W. Adkins

ACROSS

1. "For there is nothing. . .____, that shall not be known" (Matt. 10:26)
4. "Wizards that ____, and that mutter" (Isa. 8:19)
8. Same, prefix
12. "Why make ye this ____, and weep?" (Mark 5:39)
13. Belonging to Adam's wife
14. Book that follows Joel
15. Third son of Levi (Gen. 46:11)
17. Plan
19. Handle of a weapon
21. "For, lo, I will ____ up a shepherd in the land" (Zech. 11:16)
22. An aromatic herb
25. "Learn to maintain good works for necessary ____" (Titus 3:14)
27. "For this ____ is Mount Sinai in Arabia" (Gal. 4:25)
28. Pocket bread
29. "The ____ of violence is in their hands" (Isa. 59:6)
32. "____ that thou forget not the Lord thy God" (Deut. 8:11)
34. Father of Mahath (1 Chron. 6:35)
36. "____, Lord: yet the dogs. . .eat of the children's crumbs" (Mark 7:28)
37. "Then Pharaoh's ____ was come forth out of Egypt" (Jer. 37:5)
39. "Let us not ____ it, but cast lots for it" (John 19:24)
40. "Which in other ____ was not made known unto the sons of men" (Eph. 3:5)
41. "Not with broided hair, or gold, or pearls, or costly ____" (1 Tim. 2:9)
42. "As I wrote ____ in few words" (Eph. 3:3)

45. Angel's aura
47. "____ the spoil of your enemies with your brethren" (Josh. 22:8)
49. "Their ____ are desolate" (Zeph. 3:6)
53. Thoroughfares, abbr.
54. Existed
56. Furnish with special gear
57. Only
58. Naked
59. "My ____ also will I spread upon him" (Ezek. 12:13)

DOWN

1. "And Noah begat Shem, ____, and Japheth" (Gen. 5:32)
2. Chemical suffix
3. "The inhabitants of ____ and her towns" (Josh. 17:11)
4. "Who shall separate us from the love of Christ? shall. . .famine, or nakedness, or ____, or sword?" (Rom. 8:35)
5. "Deliver me, O Lord, from the ____ man" (Ps. 140:1)
6. Electrical engineer, abbr.
7. Letter addendums, abbr.
8. Words that can be laughter or scorn (Job 39:25)
9. Buddhist sacred mountain
10. Mothers
11. "In ____, I will call them my people, which were not my people" (Rom. 9:25)
16. "____ the son of Enan" (Num. 1:15)
18. The yellowish fatty part of milk
20. Parson bird
22. Infant
23. "After him was Shammah the son of ____" (2 Sam. 23:11)
24. "Sawed with ____" (1 Kings 7:9)

26. "____, and I will tell thee what the Lord hath said to me this night" (1 Sam. 15:16)
28. Father, Fr.
29. Tribe of Anna the prophetess (Luke 2:36)
30. "There was a marriage in ____ of Galilee" (John 2:1)
31. Neat
33. "The heathen ____" (Ps. 46:6)
35. "Nor shoot an ____ there" (2 Kings 19:32)
38. Melanocyte-stimulating hormone, abbr.
40. "____, O God, judge the earth" (Ps. 82:8)
41. "Who can forgive sins, but God ____?" (Luke 5:21)
42. "For ____ was first formed, then Eve" (1 Tim. 2:13)
43. "Wilt thou destroy all the city for lack of ____?" (Gen. 18:28)
44. "The Lord will pass ____ the door" (Exod. 12:23)
46. "The children of ____, the children of Talmon" (Ezra 2:42)
48. Recede
50. Sea eagle
51. "But the wheat and the ____ were not smitten" (Exod. 9:32)
52. A noncommissioned officer, abbr.
55. Apiece, in other words, abbr.

173

ACROSS

1. "As the _____ _____ for silver, and the furnace for gold" (Prov. 27:21)
7. Proof of who you are, abbr.
9. Woman's name
10. "Open up and say _____"
12. Nickel, chem. symbol
13. With reference to, abbr.
14. "The pots also, and the shovels, and the _____" (2 Chron. 4:16)
17. Consume
18. Mountain, abbr.
19. Way to cook meat
20. "A man that beareth false witness. . .is a _____, and a sword" (Prov. 25:18)
22. Task force, abbr.
23. "And pierce his ear with an _____" (Exod. 21:6 NIV)
25. "They sacrifice. . .under oaks, and poplars and _____" (Hos. 4:13)
28. Compass point, abbr.
31. Father
32. "From _____ the face of the earth" (Gen. 7:4)
34. "She layeth her hands to the _____, and her hands hold the distaff" (Prov. 31:19)
37. Tellurium, chem. symbol
39. "It were better for him that a _____ were hanged about his neck" (Luke 17:2)
41. A short time of sleep
42. Preposition
43. Californian city, abbr.
44. "For the _____ which is lent to the Lord" (1 Sam. 2:20)
46. Building cooler, abbr.

48. "Hide them in the clay in the _____" (Jer. 43:9)
52. "Gideon threshed wheat by the _____" (Judg. 6:11)
53. New, prefix

DOWN

1. "The basins, and the _____, and the bowls, and the caldrons" (Jer. 52:19)
2. A thought
3. Northern continent, abbr.
4. Nothing
5. "Shouldest bray a fool in a mortar among wheat with a _____" (Prov. 27:22)
6. Asian goat
7. Draws with a black liquid
8. "Her hands to the spindle, and her hands hold the _____" (Prov. 31:19)
11. Makes an owl's cry
15. A large Australian bird resembling an ostrich
16. Simpleton
21. "Fear not, . . .arise, go up to _____" (Josh. 8:1)
24. "Jesus _____" (John 11:35)
26. Long playing phonograph record, abbr.
27. "Yet they had a file for the _____, and for the coulters" (1 Sam. 13:21)
29. To remove men from a ship
30. Building wing
33. "Come near, . . .that I may _____ thee, my son, whether thou be . . .Esau" (Gen. 27:21)
35. "Let him _____ his foot in oil" (Deut. 33:24)

36. "Samuel. . .arose and went to _____, and said, Here am I" (1 Sam. 3:8)
38. A very long period of time
40. "The sluggard will not _____ by reason of the cold" (Prov. 20:4)
41. "He went into a city called _____" (Luke 7:11)
45. Make a mistake
46. American Cancer Society, abbr.
47. Noise
48. The temperature at which a liquid boils, abbr.
49. That is, Lat. abbr.
50. Article, Fr.

51. "_____ man can serve two masters" (Matt. 6:24)
by Janet Kennedy

ACROSS

1. This spiritual fruit means to bear provocation patiently
10. Diving bird with loud wild cry
11. White, foot-length robes worn by some Christian priests
12. Loose-fitting brightly colored shirt
13. Family doctor, for instance, abbr.
15. Rooms, abbr.
17. Philadelphia's state, abbr.
18. Do, ____, mi
19. This spiritual fruit means a deep emotion of pleasure
20. That is, Lat. abbr.
22. Young adults, abbr.
25. Either
26. Myself
27. Church, abbr.
29. An exclamation of surprise, delight, or pain
30. To perform or carry out
31. Juno's state, abbr.
32. Verity
33. Nautical mile, abbr.
34. Memphis' state, abbr.
35. Dorothy's state, abbr.
36. Beast of burden
38. Each, abbr.
39. Suffix that means "dear little one"
40. Girl Scouts of America, abbr.
42. Tin, chem. symbol
43. Osmium, chem. symbol
44. Miami's state, abbr.
45. Prosecuting officer, in other words, abbr.
47. Silicon, chem. symbol
48. Anne of Green Gables province, abbr.
49. Excessively submissive

51. A mark left where a wound has healed
52. Makes a living laboriously
54. "The kingdom of God is. . .____, and peace, and joy" (Rom. 14:17)

DOWN

1. A flow of tears
2. National League, abbr.
3. Creator and ruler of universe
4. Used for washing and cleaning things
5. To take back or retract
6. Carnivals
7. A Swedish woman's name
8. Runs batted in, in baseball, abbr.
9. Longest book of prophecy, abbr.
13. This spiritual fruit means the quality of being good
14. People with uncontrollable impulse to set things on fire
16. This spiritual fruit means quietness and obedience
21. Actinium, chem. symbol
23. Has common boundaries
24. An exclamation of doubt, inquiry, or surprise
28. Heights, abbr.
29. An exclamation of surprise or exultation
35. Blue grass state, abbr.
37. Christian, abbr.
40. Angry stare
41. Good-bye, Fr.
44. Flavorless
46. Inquires
49. School, abbr.
50. Egg layer
51. Surgeon general, abbr.
53. Compass point, abbr.
    by Mary Louise DeMott

ACROSS

1. "The foundations of the wall of
   the city. . .the tenth, a ____, the
   eleventh, a jacinth"
   (Rev. 21:19–20)
11. An enzyme which causes
    decay
12. "And David's two wives. . .
    and Abigail the wife of ____
    the Carmelite"
    (1 Sam. 30:5)
14. Air Force Base, abbr.
16. Pale and wan
17. Stone or soil containing metal
18. A flower necklace
19. For each
20. Beverage
21. The third letter of the alphabet
22. City of Angels, abbr.
23. The seventh tone on the musical
    scale
24. Edward and Edwin
25. Iridium, chem. symbol
27. Local magistrate able to perform
    marriages, abbr.
29. "____ man hath seen God at any
    time" (John 1:18)
31. Prefix: twice, double
32. Prefix: again, once more
33. "The first foundation was ____"
    (Rev. 21:19)
35. Unity, agreement
38. National Guard, abbr.
39. Third day of the week, abbr.
40. "Out of the ____ palaces"
    (Ps. 45:8)
43. Reverence
44. "But they that wait upon the Lord
    shall ____ their strength"
    (Isa. 40:31)

46. "And the third row a ligure, an
    ____, and an amethyst"
    (Exod. 28:19)
47. Gold, chem. symbol
48. "And the fourth row a ____, and
    an onyx" (Exod. 28:20)
52. KJV verb suffix
53. Wager
54. "And the second row shall be an
    emerald, a sapphire, and a ____"
    (Exod. 28:18)
55. A washing of the body

DOWN

1. "And the foundations of the wall
   of the city were. . .the third a
   ____; the fourth, an emerald"
   (Rev. 21:19)
2. "For the price of wisdom is above
   ____" (Job 28:18)
3. 12 months, abbr.
4. "The God of Israel: and. . .under
   his feet. . .a paved work of a
   ____ stone" (Exod. 24:10)
5. "As he saith also in ____, I will
   call them my people"
   (Rom. 9:25)
6. "And the twelve gates were
   twelve pearls; every. . .gate was
   of one ____" (Rev. 21:21)
7. "Wisdom cannot be valued with
   the ____" (Job 28:16)
8. Southern continent, abbr.
9. A submarine
10. "And he that sat was to look
    upon like a jasper and a ____
    stone" (Rev. 4:3)
13. Man's name
15. "And there was an herd of many
    swine ____ on the mountain"
    (Luke 8:32)

26. "Come unto me, . . .and I will give you ____" (Matt. 11:28)
27. "And the foundations of the wall of the city were. . .the eleventh, a ____; the twelfth, an amethyst" (Rev. 21:19–20)
28. Letter addendum, abbr.
30. Either
34. "Doth the plowman ____ all day to sow?" (Isa. 28:24)
36. "No man also seweth a piece of ____ cloth on an old garment" (Mark 2:21)
37. Swelled or heaved with great force

41. The symbol of victory
42. "My manner of life from my ____" (Acts 26:4)
43. Magic word: ____ - cadabra
45. "Take, ____; this is my body" (Matt. 26:26)
47. Of age, Lat. abbr.
48. Bachelor of Divinity, abbr.
49. A, ____, ____, O, U
50. Young Men's Christian Association, abbr.
51. "____, I am with you alway" (Matt. 28:20)
53. Barium, chem. symbol
by Janet Kennedy

ACROSS

1. Cat comment
5. "Thou ____ cast out in the open field" (Ezek. 16:5)
9. Glass container
12. Johanan's grandfather (Neh. 6:18)
13. "____ begat Asa" (Matt. 1:7)
14. Flightless bird
15. "That thou mayest be clothed; and that the shame of thy ____ do not appear" (Rev. 3:18)
17. Rodent
18. A Latvian
19. "And the ____ shall make you free" (John 8:32)
21. "And the ____ of the locusts were like unto horses" (Rev. 9:7)
24. "For he hath founded it upon the ____, and established it upon the floods" (Ps. 24:2)
25. Buddy
26. Zany
28. "Moses' father in law went up out of the city. . .into the wilderness of Judah, . . .in the south of ____" (Judg. 1:16)
30. "To him which ____ his people through the wilderness" (Ps. 136:16)
31. "And they came to ____, where were twelve wells of water" (Exod. 15:27)
33. "And whosoever shalt exalt himself shall be ____" (Matt. 23:12)
35. Compass direction, abbr.
36. "____, and Dumah, and Eshean" (Josh. 15:52)
37. "For an ____, the hope of salvation" (1 Thess. 5:8)
40. "Certain lewd fellows of the ____ sort" (Acts 17:5)
42. Half, prefix
43. Map abbreviation

44. "And he. . .began to publish in ____ how great things Jesus had done for him" (Mark 5:20)
49. National Stock Exchange, abbr.
50. "Of the tribe of Issachar, ____ the son of Joseph" (Num. 13:7)
51. "Salathiel, which was the son of ____" (Luke 3:27)
52. "Neither did Manasseh drive out the inhabitants of Bethshean. . .nor Taanach. . ., nor the inhabitants of ____" (Judg. 1:27)
53. "Now the ____ of Jacob were twelve" (Gen. 35:22)
54. "Then Herod. . .enquired of them diligently what time the ____ appeared" (Matt. 2:7)

DOWN

1. "The Son of ____ must be lifted up" (John 12:34)
2. Equal Rights Amendment, abbr.
3. "Behold, I saw Absalom hanged in an ____" (2 Sam. 18:10)
4. "Judah is a lion's ____" (Gen. 49:9)
5. "Your messenger, and he that ministered to my ____" (Phil. 2:25)
6. Aid
7. Sibling
8. "If so be ye have ____ that the Lord is gracious" (1 Pet. 2:3)
9. "Abiathar carried the ark of God again to ____" (2 Sam. 15:29)
10. "I ____ ____ the point to die" (Gen. 25:32) (2 words)
11. "The name of the one was Orpah, and the name of the other ____" (Ruth 1:4)
16. River in Scotland
20. "The ____ is not to the swift" (Eccles. 9:11)
21. Health bath
22. "Brought them unto Halah, and Habor, and ____" (1 Chron. 5:26)

23. "There came unto him a woman having an ____ box of very precious ointment" (Matt. 26:7)
24. "Her countenance was no more ____" (1 Sam. 1:18)
26. Little name for a big sea
27. "But ye shall ____ away for your iniquities" (Ezek. 24:23)
29. "For we ____ not make ourselves of the number" (2 Cor. 10:12)
30. This country was once famous for its cedars, abbr.
32. "There ____ him two possessed with devils" (Matt. 8:28)
34. One of the seven churches of Asia
37. Cures
38. Electromagnetic pulse, abbr.

39. "Whose faces were like the faces of ____" (1 Chron. 12:8)
40. "For I was ashamed to require of the king a ____ of soldiers" (Ezra 8:22)
41. "Lord, wilt thou slay ____ a righteous nation?" (Gen. 20:4)
42. Read over hastily
45. Self
46. "____ there be no strife. . .between me and thee" (Gen. 13:8)
47. "And ____ also the Jairite was a chief ruler about David" (2 Sam. 20:26)
48. "____, thou hast nothing to draw with" (John 4:11)
by Janet W. Adkins

ACROSS

1. Has ability
4. "Thou that liftest me up from the ____ of death" (Ps. 9:13)
9. Astatine, chem. symbol
11. A son of Bela (1 Chron. 7:7)
12. "Henoch, and ____, and Eldaah" (1 Chron. 1:33)
13. Fuss
14. A little woman
15. Chief among the captains of David's mighty men (2 Sam. 23:8)
16. "Iniquity of ____ house" (1 Sam. 3:14)
17. A Colossian woman Paul greets (Philem. 2)
19. The Israelites craved this fruit in the wilderness (Num. 11:5)
21. "He shall be like the ____ in the desert" (Jer. 17:6)
22. Sprint
23. Gaius was from here (Acts 20:4)
24. "Their coast was from ____" (Josh. 19:33)
27. "Out of whose womb came the ____?" (Job 38:29)
28. Obadiah, abbr.
30. Account of, abbr.
31. The woman on the scarlet beast had this written on her forehead (Rev. 17:4–5)
34. Race of giants (Deut. 2)
37. Not him
38. "He that is washed needeth not save to wash his feet, but is clean every ____" (John 13:10)
39. Capital of Moab (Num. 21:28)
40. He was the officer over Solomon's household (1 Kings 4:6)
43. Grow
47. Exhaust
48. Also
49. "____ will I sit" (Joel 3:12)
51. Poetic contraction that means early night
52. To stitch
53. Employed
54. Boy

DOWN

1. "Michmash, and ____" (Neh. 11:31)
2. "The gift of ____" (1 Cor. 13:2)
3. Titanium, chem. symbol
4. Someone from Gad
5. Hezron's wife (1 Chron. 2:24)
6. Stannum, other name
7. "Wise men out of ____" (Obad. 8)
8. Southern continent, abbr.
9. Returned exiles (Ezra 2:15)
10. Throw
13. By oneself
15. Jezebel's husband (1 Kings 16:30–31)
16. 6th month of the Hebrew year (Neh. 6:15)
18. Machir's son (1 Chron. 7:16)
20. Before, poetic
23. Unclear
24. A laugh
25. Girl's name
26. Hosea, abbr.
28. Either
29. Near
32. Drop of sadness
33. "He that refuseth reproof ____" (Prov. 10:17)

34. A son of Benjamin (Gen. 46:21)
35. Haze
36. Jesaiah's son (Neh. 11:7)
38. Adverb of location
40. "Of the tribe of _____ were
    sealed" (Rev. 7:6)
41. Length x width
42. Rip
43. Possessive pronoun
44. Greek form of Noah
45. Female bovine
46. Son of Abdiel (1 Chron. 5)
50. An altar (Josh. 22:34)
    by Teri Grottke

ACROSS

1. "Meat offering baken in the ____" (Lev. 2:7)
7. Part of a curved line
9. The sound of a cow
10. "As a man wipeth ____, wiping it, and turning it upside down" (2 Kings 21:13)
12. "My heart standeth in ____ of thy word" (Ps. 119:161)
14. Sweaty smell, in other words
16. Gold, chem. symbol
17. Peach state, abbr.
18. A cow's baby
20. Rounded dishes
21. Old Testament, abbr.
22. "The tongue of the wise ____ knowledge aright" (Prov. 15:2)
24. Electrical engineer, abbr.
25. Compass point, abbr.
26. Tap gently
27. U.S. island commonwealth, abbr.
28. A man's name
31. Dish
34. Velocity, in other words, abbr.
35. Plan again
37. "Certain also of your own ____ have said, For we are also his offspring" (Acts 17:28)
39. By way of
40. "Come unto ____, all ye that labour" (Matt. 11:28)
41. Occupational therapy, abbr.
42. "And he struck it into the pan, or ____, or caldron, or pot" (1 Sam. 2:14)
44. A shady place formed by trees or plants
46. A Catholic sister

48. Of the Navy
50. "___ maketh me to lie down in green pastures" (Ps. 23:2)
51. Mouths or openings, Lat.
52. "For my ____ are many, and my heart is faint" (Lam. 1:22)
53. "Yet they had a file for the. . . ____, and the axes" (1 Sam. 13:21)

DOWN

1. "A ____ of wine" (2 Sam. 6:19)
2. Contraction of I am
3. "____ man hath seen God at any time" (John 1:18)
4. A kind of drinking glass
5. Advertisement, abbr.
6. Nickel, chem. symbol
7. An exclamation of satisfaction
8. "Take thou now the spear. . .and the ____ of water" (1 Sam. 26:11)
11. Cause to be seen
13. "The woman then left her ____, and went her way" (John 4:28)
15. "This do ye, as ____ as ye drink it, in remembrance of me" (1 Cor. 11:25)
16. On guard
18. "Ye hold the tradition of men, as the washing of pots and ____" (Mark 7:8)
19. Belonging to Abia's son (Matt. 1:7)
23. A laugh
27. "Meat offering baken in a ____" (Lev. 2:5)
29. Poem
30. "So the eyes of man are ____ satisfied" (Prov. 27:20)

31. "Make clean the outside of the cup and the ____" (Luke 11:39)
32. California city, abbr.
33. "Believeth in him should not perish, but have ____ life" (John 3:15)
34. "The bowls, and the ____, . . . wherewith they ministered, took they away" (Jer. 52:18)
36. "To him was given the key of the bottomless ____" (Rev. 9:1)
38. "And ____ lived seventy years, and begat Abram, Nahor, and Haran" (Gen. 11:26)
42. Knock out (boxing), abbr.

43. "And Seth lived. . .and begat ____" (Gen. 5:6)
44. Average, abbr.
45. Barrels, abbr.
47. "I am the Lord that brought thee [Abram] out of ____ of the Chaldees" (Gen. 15:7)
49. "And Joshua sent men from Jericho to ____" (Josh. 7:2)
50. "____, everyone that thirsteth" (Isa. 55:1)
by Janet Kennedy

185

by Janet W. Adkins

ACROSS

1. Engrossed
5. "In God will I praise ____ word" (Ps. 56:10)
8. "The Lord came unto the prophet Gad, David's ____" (2 Sam. 24:11)
12. "Wilt thou ____ destroy the righteous with the wicked?" (Gen. 18:23)
13. "Of ____, the family of the Erites" (Num. 26:16)
14. "He would not spend the time in ____" (Acts 20:16)
15. Seriously wound
16. "But it ____ thou" (Ps. 55:13)
17. "Rejoicing, so that the city ____ again" (1 Kings 1:45)
18. Chemical suffix
20. "Let my last ____ be like his!" (Num. 23:10)
22. "There is nothing ____ for me" (1 Sam. 27:1)
25. "It is ____ a spiritual body" (1 Cor. 15:44)
29. "They are vanity, and the work of ____" (Jer. 10:15)
30. "A soft ____ turneth away wrath" (Prov. 15:1)
31. American Institute of Electronics, abbr.
32. Mine product
33. "His hands were ____ until the going down of the sun" (Exod. 17:12)
37. Girl's name
40. Exam taker
41. "It ____ fire and brimstone from heaven" (Luke 17:29)
42. Hot and cold beverage

43. "His master shall bore his ear through with an ____" (Exod. 21:6 NKJV)
44. "I will speak but this ____" (Judg. 6:39)
47. Agent, in other words, abbr.
49. Greek god of love
53. "Where the body of Jesus had ____" (John 20:12)
54. Confederate general
55. "And they ____ upon horses" (Jer. 6:23)
56. "Exceeding in ____ attire upon their heads" (Ezek. 23:15)
57. "____, of the Gentiles also" (Rom. 3:29)
58. Spit out

DOWN

1. "The ____ of consecration" (Exod. 29:27)
2. In the manner of, Fr.
3. Greek letter
4. Love apple
5. "Let them be ____ of wood" (Josh. 9:21)
6. "And ____ also the Jairite was a chief ruler about David" (2 Sam. 20:26)
7. The captain of Jabin's army (Judg. 4:7)
8. "Unto Thyatira, and unto ____" (Rev. 1:11)
9. That, Sp.
10. One, Ger.
11. Old piece of cloth
19. The father of Abner (1 Sam. 26:5)
21. Girl's name
22. "Ye shall slay the ____" (Lev. 20:15)
23. A descendant of 13-Across

24. "I see men as ____, walking" (Mark 8:24)
26. "For they had ____ with all their heart" (2 Chron. 15:15)
27. Inspiring fear
28. "____ not, nor be dismayed" (1 Chron. 22:13)
34. "____unto my cry" (Ps. 17:1)
35. River in Scotland
36. "And this man went up out of his city ____" (1 Sam. 1:3)
37. "For our vines have tender ____" (Song of Sol. 2:15)
38. "There is one ____ for them" (Lev. 7:7)
39. Tankers for refueling ships
44. "And a nourisher of thine ____ age" (Ruth 4:15)
45. "____, my son, let us not all now go" (2 Sam. 13:25)
46. Business house, Fr. abbr.
48. Shoe width
50. "And ___ up their women with child" (2 Kings 8:12)
51. Poem
52. "Woe to the women that ____ pillows to all armholes" (Ezek. 13:18)

ACROSS

1. The prophet who went up to heaven in a whirlwind (2 Kings 2:11)
6. A son of Jeroboam (1 Kings 14:1)
11. Moses' brother
12. Humble
13. "Even unto Ithiel and ____" (Prov. 30:1)
14. Capital of Moab (Isa. 15:1)
15. "That ___ should be a kind of firstfruits" (James 1:18)
16. Preposition
17. His Highness, abbr.
18. A snooze
21. Iron, chem. symbol
22. Giants (Deut. 9:2)
25. A minor objection
27. Europium, chem. symbol
28. "____ tempteth he any man" (James 1:13)
31. "____, supposing him to be the gardener" (John 20:15)
33. The fourth son of Midian (Gen. 25:4 NKJV)
34. "They came to ____" (2 Sam. 24:6)
35. There were 70 ____ (Exod. 1:5)
37. Smallest state, abbr.
38. Reflection of sounds
41. Not consulted
42. Ahasuerus' chamberlain (Esther 1:10)
44. Last book of the Old Testament
45. "I will praise thee with uprightness of ____" (Ps. 119:7)
49. "To the dwelling of ____" (Num. 21:15)
50. French article
51. Los Angeles, abbr.
52. General Motors, abbr.

DOWN

1. "Two years before the ____" (Amos 1:1)
2. A note to follow So
3. Eldest son of Caleb (1 Chron. 4:15)
4. Moses' mother (Exod. 6:20)
5. A son of Seir the Horite (Gen. 36:20)
6. A river of Damascus (2 Kings 5:12)
7. The general under Deborah (Judg. 4:8)
8. "Surely the Lord ____ in this place" (Gen. 28:16)
9. "There is neither ____ nor Greek" (Gal. 3:28)
10. "____, every one that thirsteth" (Isa. 55:1)
19. Pastry crust and filling
20. "David. . .dwelt in strong holds at ____" (1 Sam. 23:29)
21. "His hands shall also ____ it" (Zech. 4:9)
22. "____ the works were finished" (Heb. 4:3)
23. Nehemiah, abbr.
24. To become absorbed in thought
26. Prejudice
29. One of David's wives (1 Chron. 3:3)
30. 17th camp of Israel from Egypt (Num. 33:5–21)
32. Less soft
36. "____ I make thine enemies thy footstool" (Ps. 110:1)
39. Scorch
40. A son of Joktan (Gen. 10:28)
43. "Out of whose womb came the ____?" (Job 38:29)
44. Pa's wife

46. For example, Lat. abbr.
47. "I _____ Alpha and Omega"
   (Rev. 21:6)
48. Preposition
   by Teri Grottke

by Janet Kennedy

ACROSS

1. "In the _____ God created the heaven and earth" (Gen. 1:1)
8. "And on the seventh _____ God ended his work" (Gen. 2:2)
11. "Generations of Esau, who is _____" (Gen. 36:1)
12. "The word of the _____ came unto Abram in a vision" (Gen. 15:1)
13. Prefix: again, anew, once more
14. Germanium, chem. symbol
15. "And Cain talked with _____ his brother" (Gen. 4:8)
18. Kiloliter, abbr.
19. Inches, abbr.
20. Jelly
21. Eager
23. "And I will put _____ between thee and the woman" (Gen. 3:15)
25. "Why make ye this _____, and weep? The damsel is not dead" (Mark 5:39)
27. "Cain went. . .and dwelt in the land of _____" (Gen. 4:16)
29. Address abbreviation
30. Declare
31. Surrounded by
32. Once more
34. Contraction for I am
35. "I was afraid, because I was _____; and I hid myself" (Gen. 3:10)
37. A part of a curved line
38. Not bright
40. Car manufacturer, abbr.
41. 6, Rom. num.
42. Common era, abbr.
44. Compass point, abbr.
45. "And she [Eve] bare a son. . . called. . ._____. . .another seed instead of Abel" (Gen. 4:25)

47. Not a liquid or a gas
49. Sound of a sheep
51. Hebrews, abbr.
53. The sun, Sp.
54. A young seed
56. Edge of a roof
58. Northeastern U.S., abbr.
59. "Shew you a _____ upper room furnished and prepared" (Mark 14:15)
60. Snakelike fish

DOWN

1. "In the _____ was the Word, . . . and the Word was God" (John 1:1)
2. "And the Lord God planted a garden eastward in _____; and there he put the man whom he had formed" (Gen. 2:8)
3. "_____ ye therefore, and teach all nations" (Matt. 28:19)
4. "And God said, Let us make man in our _____, after our likeness" (Gen. 1:26)
5. Not well
6. "_____ man hath seen God at any time" (John 1:18)
7. A sauce for potatoes
9. "And God said unto Noah, . . . Make thee an _____ of gopher wood" (Gen. 6:13–14)
10. "Her feathers with _____ gold" (Ps. 68:13)
16. Nickname for Benjamin
17. A tree
21. "Can a maid forget her ornaments, or a bride her _____?" (Jer. 2:32)
22. "Obed: he is the father of Jesse, the father of _____" (Ruth 4:17)

24. "And Abraham called. . .his son
    . . .whom Sarah bare to him,
    ____" (Gen. 21:3)
26. Kingdom
28. One of Shobal's children
    (Gen. 36:23)
32. Confused, nervous
33. Virginia's neighbor, abbr.
36. "And Adam called his wife's
    name ____" (Gen. 3:20)
39. A group of songs combined to
    make one song
43. "____, everyone that thirsteth"
    (Isa. 55:1)
45. "Then ____, (who also is called
    Paul,)" (Acts 13:9)

46. "____ leadeth me beside the still
    waters" (Ps. 23:2)
47. "One lawgiver, who is able to
    ____ and to destroy"
    (James 4:12)
48. Library Science, abbr.
49. "And God said, . . .I do set my
    ____ in the cloud, . . .a token of a
    covenant" (Gen. 9:12–13)
50. Avenue, abbr.
52. A honey maker
55. Fa, so, ____, ti
57. Electrical Engineer, abbr.

ACROSS

1. Croaker
5. "The priest shall pronounce him clean: it is but a ____" (Lev. 13:6)
9. Female sibling, for short
12. South American country
13. Layer
14. Gold, Sp.
15. "And they bowed their heads, and made ____" (Gen. 43:28)
17. Familiar name for Saul's son (1 Sam. 14:42)
18. "Master, the Jews of ____ sought to stone thee" (John 11:8)
19. "Then Saul fell straightway all ____ on the earth" (1 Sam. 28:20)
20. "Though thou shouldest bray a fool in a mortar among wheat with a ____" (Prov. 27:22)
23. Plural suffix
24. "And be ye kind ____ to another" (Eph. 4:32)
25. "Stolen ____ are sweet" (Prov. 9:17)
28. "Woe unto them that draw iniquity. . .and sin as it were with a cart ____" (Isa. 5:18)
30. "The liberal soul shall be made ____" (Prov. 11:25)
31. Conceited person
33. "Cut the bars of iron in ____" (Ps. 107:16)
35. Before, poetic
36. Talking horse
37. "And the harp, and the viol, and the ____. . ." (Isa. 5:12)
40. "They fell on their ____: and they said, The Lord he is the God" (1 Kings 18:39)
42. Volcano output
43. Burned residue

44. "If. . .I may provoke to ____ them which are my flesh" (Rom. 11:14)
49. Black sticky substance
50. "And his allowance was a. . .daily ____ for every day" (2 Kings 25:30)
51. Sharpen
52. Compass point, abbr.
53. "Thou sawest the feet and ____" (Dan. 2:41)
54. Precipitation

DOWN

1. Fleet post office, abbr.
2. Confederate soldier
3. Mine product
4. "But thou shalt put away the ____ of innocent blood from Israel" (Deut. 19:13)
5. "For I have learned, in whatsoever ____ I am, therewith to be content" (Phil. 4:11)
6. Motion picture
7. Atomic Energy Commission, abbr.
8. "That the ____ may be waved for a wave offering" (Lev. 7:30)
9. "For I am a stranger with thee, and a ____ as all my fathers were" (Ps. 39:12)
10. "Thou shalt not lift up any ____ tool upon them" (Deut. 27:5)
11. "And he hath put a new ____ in my mouth" (Ps. 40:3)
16. My Gal ____
20. For, Sp.
21. "And Seth. . .begat ____" (Gen. 5:6)
22. "Their throat is an open ____" (Ps. 5:9)
23. "And they shall ____ the flesh in that night, roast with fire" (Exod. 12:8)

25. "Joshua made _____ a long time with all those kings" (Josh. 11:18)
26. Einstienium, chem. symbol
27. Painful
29. Printer's measure
30. "When saw we thee an hungered and _____ thee?" (Matt. 25:37)
32. Wager
34. "The _____ shall rejoice and blossom as the rose" (Isa. 35:1)
37. "And their words seemed to them as idle _____" (Luke 24:11)
38. "The king of Assyria brought men from Babylon. . .Cuthah, and from _____" (2 Kings 17:24)
39. Twenty thousand measures of barley, and twenty thousand _____ of wine" (2 Chron. 2:10)
40. Destiny
41. Belonging to Abia's son (Matt. 1:7)
42. Ancient musical instrument
45. Late Chinese Communist Chairman
46. Charged particle
47. "The children of Lod, Hadid, and _____" (Ezra 2:33)
48. Not old

by Janet W. Adkins

ACROSS

1. Disney deer
6. Giver
11. Belonging to Robert E.
12. Girl's name
14. "I am like an _____ of the desert" (Ps. 102:6)
16. Wipe clean
18. Adam's companion
20. Peach state, abbr.
21. The main central parts of churches
22. Impersonal pronoun
23. *Exodus* author, Leon _____
26. Price mark-down
28. Esau's pottage was made from this legume (Gen. 25:34)
30. Cain did this to the ground (Gen. 4:2)
32. Digital audiotape, abbr.
33. Tree trunk
34. Horned African mammals
37. "Yea, the sparrow hath found an house. . .even thine _____, O Lord of hosts" (Ps. 84:3)
40. "Thou anointest my _____ with oil" (Ps. 23:5)
41. "It shall bruise thy head, and thou shalt bruise his _____" (Gen. 3:15)
42. You, KJV English
43. Stay away from
46. Nickel, chem. symbol
47. Physicians, abbr.
49. Naaman was one of these because of his disease (2 Kings 5:1)
50. "My tongue is the _____ of a ready writer" (Ps. 45:1)
51. Social equal
53. "The wringing of the _____ bringeth forth blood" (Prov. 30:33)
55. "A time to mourn, and a time to _____" (Eccles. 3:4)
56. Game

DOWN

2. "Israel loved Joseph more than _____" (Gen. 37:3)
3. Myself
4. Existed
5. God's chosen nation
6. To abandon
7. Metals
8. A silver-white metal, abbr.
9. "Ye are all _____ in Christ" (Gal. 3:28)
10. A bump in a ski slope
13. Doled
15. "A certain man, which had devils long time, and _____ no clothes" (Luke 8:27)
17. Address abbreviation
19. Foul
24. Asian nation
25. "_____ fast therefore in liberty" (Gal. 5:1)
26. Slow-moving mammal
27. Seaweed
29. International Trade Organization, abbr.
31. Sick
34. Poem
35. Pay attention to
36. Harsh
37. Strangers
38. French name
39. What David used to kill Goliath
43. Man's name
44. Kind of modern art

45. Fall
48. Health facility
50. Apiece
52. Printer's measure
54. Therefore
    by Janet Kennedy

ACROSS

1. Tiny insect
4. Facts
9. Undergraduate degree, abbr.
11. "By his name ____" (Ps. 68:4)
12. "____, and make thy bed" (Acts 9:34)
13. Small arms ammunition, abbr.
14. "____ Lord God! behold" (Jer. 1:6)
15. Liquid extracted from a fruit
16. "In the province of ____" (Dan. 8:2)
17. A family of returning Nethinims (Neh. 7:48)
19. Scold
21. 1004, Rom. num.
22. Walked at the head of the line
23. Bedad's son (Gen. 36:35)
24. Give instruction
27. Single
28. Decay
30. Exclamation
31. Brawling
34. Capture
37. Not, prefix
38. Traps (Ps. 140:5)
39. Preposition
40. "Ye shall be. . .____ upon her knees" (Isa. 66:12)
43. Announced
47. Heber's father (Luke 3:35)
48. "And ____ also the Jairite" (2 Sam. 20:26)
49. "They must ____ be borne" (Jer. 10:5)
51. Neither
52. Male adults
53. Jehaleleel's son (1 Chron. 4:16)
54. Expire

DOWN

1. Zibeon's son (Gen. 36:24)
2. "Azariah, Raamiah, ____ " (Neh. 7:7)
3. Thorium, chem. symbol
4. Smear
5. Opera solos
6. Muscle twitch
7. One who takes advantage
8. Myself
9. Chief idol of the Canaanites
10. Identical
13. Slip
15. Indonesian island
16. Always
18. This man had 70 sons (Judg. 8:30)
20. Father of Hophni (1 Sam. 1:3)
23. Aaron's grave (Num. 20:27–28)
24. Daylight time, abbr.
25. Son of Caleb (1 Chron. 4:8)
26. Definite article
28. Hospital caregiver, abbr.
29. King of Bashan (Num. 21:33)
32. Implement
33. Baby
34. Iniquity
35. Terminates
36. Land surrounded by water
38. One of the twelve spies (Num. 13:11)
40. "And the fallow ____" (Deut. 14:5)
41. One of Christ's words on the cross (Mark 15:34)
42. Challenge
43. Unclear
44. Before
45. Able
46. Real estate investment, abbr.
50. Southern continent, abbr.

by Teri Grottke

ACROSS

1. "And the ferret, and the ____, and the lizard" (Lev. 11:30)
6. "A living ____ is better than a dead lion" (Eccles. 9:4)
9. "The ____ of money that Haman had promised" (Esther 4:7)
10. "As a ____ robbed of her whelps in the field" (2 Sam. 17:8)
11. Put into a capsule form
15. Man's name
16 "Judas. . .drew near unto Jesus to ____ him" (Luke 22:47)
17. "And the river shall bring forth ____ abundantly" (Exod. 8:3)
18. Elevated railroad
20. "They all are brass, and ____, and iron" (Ezek. 22:18)
21. Married woman's title
23. "And God created great ____," (Gen. 1:21)
28. Exclamation of doubt or surprise
29. Card that tells who you are, abbr.
30. "Five loaves and the two ____" (Mark 6:41)
33. Field officer, abbr.
34. Compound, abbr.
35. An explosive material
36. "The swine. . .ran violently down a ____ place into the sea" (Mark 5:13)
38. "I am like a ____ of the wilderness" (Ps. 102:6)
41. "David took an ____ and played with his hand" (1 Sam. 16:23)
42. Gloomy; ill-humored
43. Egg, prefix
45. "The Lord had laid on him the iniquity of ____ all" (Isa. 53:6)
46. Massachusetts neighbor, abbr.

48. "There came a ____ out of the heat, and fastened on his hand" (Acts 28:3)
51. Dover's state, abbr.
52. A thought
54. "I have given ____ unto the children of Lot" (Deut. 2:9)
55. "And the ____ shalt thou trample under feet" (Ps. 91:13)
56. "And the ____, and the pelican" (Lev. 11:18)

DOWN

1. "The night hawk, and the ____, and the hawk" (Lev. 11:16)
2. "The cruel venom of ____" (Deut. 32:33)
3. A salt-water mollusk
4. A large Australian bird
5. "Or wings and feathers unto the ____?" (Job 39:13)
6. Belief God has no influence on man
7. "And all that handle the ____, the mariners" (Ezek. 27:29)
8. "And the ____ shall be a burden" (Eccles. 12:5)
12. "Joshua sent men from Jericho to ____" (Josh. 7:2)
13. At the back of the boat
14. A long period of time
19. A liberal or radical
22. To direct the attention
24. Large African mammals, for short
25. "And stingeth like an ____" (Prov. 23:32)
26. "Have ye received the Holy Ghost ____ ye believed?" (Acts 19:2)
27. Esther, abbr.

31. Station, abbr.
32. Einsteinium, chem. symbol
37. Each, abbr.
39. One who loves
40. "For there is ____ respect of persons with God" (Rom. 2:11)
42. "They have caused him to ride upon the king's ____" (1 Kings 1:44)
44. Eggs
47. "Why make ye this ____, and weep?" (Mark 5:39)
49. Dog's foot
50. Historical period

51. Doctor of divinity, abbr.
52. Inspector general, abbr.
53. To cause to be, prefix

by Janet W. Adkins

ACROSS

1. "And her ____ was to light on a part of the field belonging unto Boaz" (Ruth 2:3)
4. "And ____ gave names to all cattle" (Gen. 2:20)
8. Not fast
12. See 17-Across "____ ye come out. . ."
13. "Master, the Jews of ____ sought to stone thee" (John 11:8)
14. Ankle bones
15. "How are the ____ fallen" (2 Sam. 1:27)
17. "Are ye come out. . .with swords and with ____ to take me?" (Mark 14:48)
19. "Take thine ____, eat, drink, and be merry" (Luke 12:19)
21. Expunge
22. "Woe is me, . . .that I dwell in the tents of ____!" (Ps. 120:5)
25. "Made the fourteenth day of the month ____ a day of gladness" (Esther 9:19)
27. Ogle
28. "The children of Shallum, . . .of ____, of Talmon" (Ezra 2:42)
29. Spanish Mrs., abbr.
32. "The governor under ____ the king kept the city of the Damascenes with a garrison" (2 Cor. 11:32)
34. "And ____ was as light of foot as a wild roe" (2 Sam. 2:18)
36. Falstaff's follower
37. "Honour the face of the old man, and ____ thy God" (Lev. 19:32)
39. "Then Job arose, and ____ his mantle" (Job 1:20)
40. "It had been good for that man if he had not been ____" (Matt. 26:24)
41. Trig functions
42. "____ into his gates with thanksgiving" (Ps. 100:4)

45. Chop finely
47. Scold
49. "The carved images, and the ____ images" (2 Chron. 34:3)
53. You are, Sp.
54. Mend a sock
56. Anger
57. "There was a continual ____ given him of the king of Babylon" (Jer. 52:34)
58. Ballet position
59. Each

DOWN

1. "And Noah begat Shem, ____, and Japheth" (Gen. 5:32)
2. Onassis
3. Cribbage pin
4. "Zacharias which perished between the ____ and the temple" (Luke 11:51)
5. "In those ____ also saw I Jews that had married wives of Ashdod" (Neh. 13:23)
6. Preposition
7. French pronoun
8. Brenda or Belle
9. Volcano output
10. Spanish cheers
11. "Hear instruction and be ____" (Prov. 8:33)
16. "I will praise the Lord with my whole ____" (Ps. 111:1)
18. "Mine eye poureth out ____ unto God" (Job 16:20)
20. "Therefore shall they ____ of the fruit of their own way" (Prov. 1:31)
22. Part of KKK
23. Weird, alt. spelling
24. Believe
26. "Hath translated us into the kingdom of his ____ Son" (Col. 1:13)
28. Tribe of Anna the prophetess (Luke 2:36)

29. "Then Samuel took a stone, and set it between Mizpeh and _____" (1 Sam. 7:12)
30. French name
31. Heights, in other words, abbr.
33. "Lay siege against it, and built _____ _____ against it" (Ezek. 4:2) (2 words)
35. "Woe to ___. . .the city where David dwelt!" (Isa. 29:1)
38. Conjunction
40. "But let man and _____ be covered with sackcloth" (Jon. 3:8)
41. Scottish quick bread
42. "And Gaal the son of _____ came with his brethren" (Judg. 9:26)

43. In Luke's geneology of Christ, the father of Salathiel (Luke 3:27)
44. "Shall these. . .natural branches, be grated into their own olive _____?" (Rom. 11:24)
46. Father of Zaccur (Neh. 3:2)
48. Electronic data processing, abbr.
50. "That he may dip the _____ of his finger in water" (Luke 16:24)
51. "Sir, come down _____ my child die" (John 4:49)
52. "The captain of his host was Abner, the son of _____, Saul's uncle" (1 Sam. 14:50)
55. Alvin, Albert, or Allen

ACROSS

1. "Keep me as the _____ of the eye" (Ps. 17:8)
5. A person who runs errands
11. "For the _____ which is lent to the Lord" (1 Sam. 2:20)
12. A citrus fruit the color of its name
13. Second day of the week, abbr.
14. "And the _____ father shall say unto the elders" (Deut. 22:16)
16. "Wert graffed contrary to nature into a good _____ tree" (Rom 11:24)
17. Fa, so, _____, ti
18. A shot for an air rifle
19. "When thou was under the _____ tree, I saw thee" (John 1:48)
21. "Orpah kissed her mother in law, but _____ clave unto her" (Ruth 1:14)
23. District Attorney, abbr.
25. "Our Lord, and his Christ; and he shall _____ for ever and ever" (Rev. 11:15)
27. Common Era, abbr.
28. "I _____ that bread of life" (John 6:48)
29. "The sons of Ram . . . were, Maaz, and Jamin, and _____" (1 Chron. 2:27)
31. "And Jacob took him rods of the . . . hazel and _____ tree" (Gen. 30:37)
35. "Where neither moth _____ rust doth corrupt" (Matt. 6:20)
36. Advertisement (abbr.)
37. Drug danger (abbr.)
38. "There is none that doeth good, no, not _____" (Ps. 14:3)
39. To be idle
40. Spills water upon
42. California city, for short
43. Heat, abbr.
44. Garden of _____ (singular, SS 6:11)

46. "When thou shalt hear a sound going in the tops of the _____ trees . . . thou shalt go out to battle" (1 Chron. 14:15)
51. Book that follows Jeremiah, abbr.
52. A vein of metal ore
53. A sour fruit used to make a cool drink

DOWN

1. "I see a rod of an _____ tree" (Jer. 1:11)
2. "Go, wash in the _____ of Siloam" (John 9:7)
3. A great fear causing loss of control
4. Lane, abbr.
5. Pom- _____
6. American Rocket Society, abbr.
7. A Scottish Highlander
8. "For I will cast out the nations before thee, and _____ thy borders" (Exod. 34:24)
9. Brigadier generals, abbr.
10. Old English, abbr.
14. Rebels
15. "Thou that _____ idols, dost thou commit sacrilege?" (Rom. 2:22)
18. Bachelor of Theology, abbr.
20. Rio _____
22. "I found an altar with this inscription, TO THE _____ GOD" (Acts 17:13)
24. Air Coordinating Committee, abbr.
26. A large Australian bird
27. To give up
30. A very long time
32. "And Jacob took him rods . . . of the _____ and chestnut tree" (Gen. 30:37)
33. "But the answer of a good conscience _____ God" (1 Peter 3:21)

34. An examination of knowledge
39. A green citrus fruit
41. "_____ word is a lamp unto my
   feet" (Ps. 119:105)
42. A northern constellation
45. Unidentified flying object, abbr.
47. "There was a man in the land of
   _____, whose name was Job"
   (Job 1:1)
48. Bachelor of law, abbr.
49. Again, anew, once more, suffix
50. "But that the world through him
   might _____ saved" (John 3:17)

PUZZLE 101

ACROSS

1. "But whoso hath this____ good" (1 John 3:17)
6. Ratio of the weight of a given volume of a substance to that of an equal volume of another substance (abbr.)
8. Operatic solo
9. Mother of Hezekiah
12. Kind; sort (pl.)
15. Gorged
17. Tall spar
18. Time frame? (abbr.)
19. O.T. bk.
20. Crush
22. Angered
27. Frequent follower of what or as
28. Good buy (colloq.)
29. Great Commission verb
30. Relative of corp.
31. Teacher
32. Near
33. Capital of Moab
34. Father of Heber (Luke 3:35)
35. Cried
37. Pile
39. "And he [Josiah] defiled ____ " (2 Kings 23:10)
42. Absalom rode one
45. ____ down
46. "False teachers...who...bring in ____ heresies" (2 Peter 2:1)
49. Noxious weed
52. Outside; outer (prefix)
53. Those not included in the clergy
55. Conjunction
56. Benign skin tumor
57. Greek letter
58. Engineering field (abbr.)

DOWN

1. "Before Abraham____, I am" (John 8:58)
2. Mouth (pl.)
3. Traditions
4. Father-in-law of Michal (1 Samuel 25:44)
5. What Lot did in the gate of Sodom
6. "____ called Zelotes" (Luke 6:15)
7. Mirror
10. Chem. symbol
11. Part of the psyche
13. Midwest state (abbr.)
14. State or Main (abbr.)
16. Preposition
19. Father of Mary's husband (Luke 3)
20. Minor prophet
21. Prior to this (arch.)
22. Type style (abbr.)
23. Father of Solomon's adversary (1 Kings 11:26)
24. Thing to hail
25. Land of Moses' birth
26. Kind of doctor (abbr.)
28. Spanish matron (abbr.)
32. One of the sons of Zophah (1 Chronicles 7:37)
34. "And all the women...brought that which they had ____ " (Exodus 35:25)
35. Reporter's question
36. Chem. symbol
38. "I will not give thee of the land of the children of ____ " (Deuteronomy 2:19)
40. Is in debt (arch.)
41. Favorite school subject, for some (abbr.)

43. ____ land
44. Son of Shobal (Genesis 36:23)
46. What washed Nebuchadnezzar in
    the wilderness for seven years
47. Hatchet
48. ____ service
50. Fish eggs
51. Before (poet.)
54. How one pronounces *ja*
    by Teri Grottke

PUZZLE 102

ACROSS

1. Son of Benjamin
   (Genesis 46:21)
4. Ruth's sister-in-law
9. Pronoun
11. Son of Zephaniah
    (Zechariah 6:14)
12. Wake
13. ____ what?
14. Son of Aram (Genesis 10:23)
15. Where the shewbread was
16. Skin
17. "____ thy cause with thy neigh-
    bour himself" (Proverbs 25:9)
19. Made useless
21. Family of exiles (Ezra 2:44)
22. The Great ____
23. More astute
24. Assistant to Ezra (Nehemiah 8:7)
27. Consume
28. Certain muscles, according to
    your personal trainer
30. Conjunction
31. Parched
34. City in Asher (1 Chronicles 6:75)
37. Grain mentioned in Isaiah 28:25
38. Exhaust
39. Are
40. "Come before his presence with
    ____ " (Psalm 100:2)
43. Give heed to
47. Esau's father-in-law
    (Genesis 26:34)
48. Miner's trove
49. Father of Jeroboam
    (1 Kings 11:26)
51. Solomon's great-grandson
    (1 Kings 15)
52. U.S. founder of Girl Scouts
53. Grate the teeth
54. Carve

DOWN

1. Second judge of Israel
2. He was given fifteen more years
   to live
3. Preposition
4. Daniel Webster, for one
5. What kings and sleepyheads
   wear
6. King of Assyria
   (1 Chronicles 5:26)
7. "Of the tribe of ____ were sealed
   twelve thousand"
   (Revelation 7:6)
8. Pronoun
9. Created
10. Regarded
13. Commandment mountain
15. Bible weed
16. ____ the Bethelite
    (1 Kings 16:34)
18. Exert or busy
20. Employ
23. Blanket or suit
24. Where Auntie Em lived (abbr.)
25. Also
26. Eight adults lived aboard this
28. Preposition
29. Near
32. Eve was made from one of
    Adam's
33. To Thomas, this was believing
34. Ancient Hebrew liquid measure
35. "The Pharisees began to ____
    him vehemently" (Luke 11:53)
36. "Will the men of ____ deliver me
    and my men into the hand of
    Saul?" (1 Samuel 23:12)
38. One of the sons of Japheth
    (1 Chronicles 1:5)
40. One of the sons of Cush
    (1 Chronicles 1:9)

41. Probiscus
42. Chew
43. N.T. book (abbr.)
44. Mountain (comb. form)
45. "Behold, I make all things ____"
    (Revelation 21:5)
46. Lair
50. Chemical symbol (abbr.)
by Teri Grottke

ACROSS

1. 66 or 80, for example (abbr.)
4. Father of Ethan (1 Chronicles 6:44)
9. Laughing sound
11. Jether's son (1 Chronicles 7:38)
12. One of two
13. Preserve
14. Compass dir.
15. "Bread corn is bruised;...nor break it with the _____ of his cart" (Isaiah 28:28)
16. Ancient entrance
17. One of the families of the tribe of Benjamin (Numbers 26:39)
19. "They made their lives bitter... and in all _____ of service" (Exodus 1:14)
21. Certain vessels
22. _____ fried
23. Laziness
24. Achieve
27. Poetic contraction
28. April correspondent
30. Together with (prefix)
31. Wife of Joseph (Genesis 41)
34. Possessor
37. Commit larceny
38. Son of Roboam (Matthew 1:7)
39. Note on diatonic scale
40. Reluctant visitor to Saul in Damascus
43. "Surely Moab shall be as Sodom...even the _____ of nettles" (Zephaniah 2:9)
47. Biblical verb, KJV
48. Drum or drop
49. Son of Gad (Genesis 46:16)
51. Bind
52. She may be out to pasture
53. Identifies
54. Occurrence (arch.)

DOWN

1. Measles symptom
2. "For my soul is full of _____" (Psalm 88:3)
3. Apiece (abbr.)
4. Son of Levi (Genesis 46:11)
5. List components
6. Pronoun
7. Ship steering
8. European isle (abbr.)
9. Loathe
10. Unit of measure for manna
13. Father of Melchi (Luke 3:24)
15. "_____ meanest thou, O sleeper?" (Jonah 1:6)
16. Tiny winged insect
18. More destitute
20. Likely
23. Red or Dead
24. Simile component
25. "Out of whose womb came the _____? and the hoary frost of heaven" (Job 38:29)
26. Conjunction
28. Pronoun
29. With "factor," a group of antigens
32. Memo
33. Son of Gideoni (Numbers 1:11)
34. Minor prophet (abbr., var.)
35. "Who hath gathered the _____ in his fists?" (Proverbs 30:4)
36. Refuge for David, when first fleeing Saul (1 Samuel 19)
38. Hook
40. City of the tribe of Issachar (1 Chronicles 6:73)
41. Continent
42. Instruction manual word
43. Competition

44. Weather beaten
45. Before (poet.)
46. Gershwin
50. Linking verb
    by Teri Grottke

ACROSS

1. "The earth shall ____ before them" (Joel 2:10)
6. Edify
11. Repast
12. Father of "mighty men" (1 Chronicles 11:34)
14. Pronoun
15. Fearful things
17. Look, see! (arch.)
18. Printer's measure
19. Bosc, Anjou, et al.
20. Name of two O.T. books (abbr.)
21. Date approx. 100 yrs. before Babylonian captivity, to Caesar
23. Age of Joshua when he died: one hundred ____
24. "Before Abraham ____, I am" (John 8:58)
25. Son of Judah (Genesis 38)
28. "Believe not every ____" (1 John 4:1)
31. "To meet the Lord in the ____" (1 Thessalonians 4:17)
32. Take advantage of
33. Gem in the fourth row of the ephod
36. Son of Pashur (Ezra 10:22)
39. Consumed
40. Owns
42. Article
43. Country part of the British Commonwealth, until 1961 (abbr.)
44. Sponsors
46. Linking verb
47. Conjunction
48. Fullness of this dwells bodily in Jesus
50. Number one?

51. "Doth not even ____ itself teach you" (1 Corinthians 11:14)
53. Son of Chislon (Numbers 34:21)
55. "A ram caught in a thicket by his ____ " (Genesis 22:13)
56. Jobab king of ____ (Joshua 11:1)

DOWN

1. Extinguish
2. "What's ____ ?"
3. Suitable
4. Part of a castle
5. Maketh a mistake?
6. "Sow not among ____ " (Jeremiah 4:3)
7. "Bringest certain strange things to our ____" (Acts 17:20)
8. Balaam's beast
9. Abbreviation preceding AKC winner
10. Son of Meraioth (Nehemiah 12:15)
11. What a dog often does
13. "Nor eat ____ grapes, or dried" (Numbers 6:3)
16. Feminine name
22. Put an end to
24. "They that are unlearned and unstable ____ " (2 Peter 3:16)
26. Insolent talk
27. Linking verb
29. King of Assyria (2 Kings 15)
30. O.T. book
33. Thessalonian Christian (Acts 17)
34. Wife of Jerahmeel (1 Chronicles 2:26)
35. Island Paul visited on his way to Tyre (Acts 21)
36. "Will he ____ thy riches?" (Job 36:19)

37. One of the children of Anak
    (Numbers 13:22)
38. His son was one of Solomon's
    twelve officers (1 Kings 4:10)
41. Residue
44. Symbol of power
45. Father of Heber (Luke 3:35)
48. King Ahaziah was wounded near
    here (2 Kings 9:27)
49. Accomplished
52. Preposition
54. Word in a command
    by Teri Grottke

ACROSS

1. Returning exiles, the children of
   ____ (Ezra 2:44)
6. Standoffish
11. ____ of refuge
12. Mother of Samuel
14. "____ if!"
15. Encountered
17. Biblical pronoun
18. Latin abbr.
19. Made with yeast
23. Take a wrong turn
24. City where Isaac died
    (var., Genesis 35:27)
25. Physicians' group (abbr.)
26. Looked at
27. Greet
28. Gossips
30. Brother of Harnepher
    (1 Chronicles 7:36)
32. On the outside (prefix)
33. Son of Midian (Genesis 25:4)
35. O.T. minor prophet (abbr.)
38. Father of Azareel
    (Nehemiah 11:13)
40. More painful
42. Hearts, for one
43. Offering
46. Preposition
47. Hospital inits.
48. King Og's kingdom
    (Numbers 21)
49. Pronoun
50. Aka Belteshazzar
53. He prophesied bondage for Paul
55. Bear or bee
56. Included in the inheritance of the
    tribe of Asher (Joshua 19:27)

DOWN

1. He was "smote" by Jael
2. Clara Bow, the ____ Girl
3. City near Bethel
4. Part of the hemoglobin molecule
5. Wife of Joseph (Genesis 41)
6. "Say ____"
7. ____ it on
8. Single
9. ____ a roll
10. Prettier
11. City in Assyria (Genesis 10:11)
13. Cattle crowds
16. Arabian city (Isaiah 21)
20. Brother of Joab
    (1 Chronicles 2:16)
21. Assign worth to (arch.)
22. Palm or line
23. "He that hath a bountiful ____
    shall be blessed" (Proverbs 22:9)
26. Son of Zerahiah (Ezra 8:4)
29. Relative of a borough (abbr.)
31. Son of Jether (1 Chronicles 7:38)
33. Alleviated
34. Servant of Gideon (Judges 7:10)
36. Middle Eastern language (abbr.)
37. City in the inheritance of the
    children of Simeon (Joshua 19:4)
39. Southern European country
40. His son Jonathan served in
    David's army
    (1 Chronicles 11:34)
41. Asiatic deer (pl.)
44. Linking verb
45. Comparative conjunction
48. Get-together, for a purpose
51. Favorite first word?
52. Preposition
54. Command word
    by Teri Grottke

1 2 3 4 5 6 7 8 9 10
11 12 13
14 15 16 17 18
19 20 21 22 23
24 25 26
27 28 29
30 31 32
33 34 35 36 37
38 39 40 41
42 43 44 45 46
47 48 49
50 51 52 53 54
55 56

ACROSS

1. Cake mix maker (last name)
6. Amasses
11. Store under pressure
12. Has (arch.)
14. Conjunction
15. Touched
17. City near Bethel
18. Military abbr.
19. Marian, et al.
20. Chemical element (abbr.)
21. N.T. book (abbr.)
23. Gilded or Jazz
24. Son of Jether (1 Chronicles 7:38)
25. Wipe away (arch.)
28. Ammonite who invaded Jabesh-gilead (1 Samuel 11)
31. More than one orthopedist (abbr.)
32. Normal, but maybe not for Nicklaus
33. "For the ____ shall be prosperous" (Zechariah 8:12)
35. "Smote all their enemies with the ____ of the sword" (Esther 9:5)
38. Familiar cavern sight
40. Exclamation
42. Son of Elishama (1 Chronicles 7:27)
43. I ____ (Jehovah)
44. Struck (arch.)
46. Laughing sound
47. Eastern seaboard state (abbr.)
48. Worn by the disciples, among others
50. Simile word
51. Hackneyed
53. Son of Reuel (Genesis 36:13)
55. ____ days
56. "A sceptre...shall...destroy all the children of ____" (Numbers 24:17)

DOWN

1. Dread
2. Pronoun
3. ____ degree
4. Son of Shem (Genesis 10:22)
5. Family of returning exiles (Ezra 2:35)
6. Grasp (arch.)
7. Some of Bo-Peep's brood?
8. Conjunction
9. Required subject in school (abbr.)
10. Escalator option
11. Room or walk
13. Judah stayed with him in Adullam (Genesis 38)
16. Archaeological site
22. In the course of
24. Brother of Moses
26. Before (poet.)
27. Double this for a deadly fly
29. Likely
30. Laughing sound
34. Condemned
35. Belonging to the evil one
36. Son of Levi (Genesis 46)
37. Son of Seth (1 Chronicles 1:1)
38. Prohibit
39. Wrong
41. Son of Zophah (1 Chronicles 7)
44. Father of Heber (Luke 3:35)
45. King of Israel, son of Baasha (1 Kings 16:8)
48. "Gal" of songdom
49. Pronoun
52. 'Bye, to Brits
54. Preposition
       by Teri Grottke

PUZZLE 107

ACROSS

1. Regal
6. "Beeroth of the children of _____" (Deuteronomy 10:6)
11. Pronoun
12. "A workman that _____ not to be ashamed" (2 Timothy 2:15)
14. Dir.
15. Hot _____
17. Old Testament book
19. Medical abbr. for delirious state
20. Tyre and _____
21. Son of Aram (Genesis 10)
23. Yes!
24. Arsenic (abbr.)
26. "As thou goest unto _____ a mount of the east" (Genesis 10:30)
30. Another name for Hagar
34. Son of Midian (Genesis 25:4)
35. _____ wave
36. Jesse's third son (1 Chronicles 2)
38. Name that means "son of my sorrow"
39. Note on diatonic scale
40. "Where his tent had been...between Bethel and _____" (Genesis 13:3)
42. Linking verb
43. O.T. bk.
46. Wheat by-product
50. Ignore
51. Expiates
53. _____ art
54. In nearest proximity
56. Pronoun
58. What to do with rosebuds?
59. Reposed

DOWN

1. Chess piece (abbr.)
2. Possessive pronoun
3. Insect
4. Some tennis serves
5. Biblical pronoun
6. Warrior in David's army (1 Chronicles 12:6)
7. Site of threshing floor where Joseph mourned Jacob (Genesis 50)
8. Son of Abinadab (2 Samuel 6:3)
9. Furniture tree
10. Dir.
13. Basketball pass (colloq.)
16. Masculine nickname
18. Article
21. Biblical verb
22. Son of Eliphaz (1 Chronicles 1:36)
23. Capital of Moab (Numbers 21:15)
24. Naaman preferred this river in Damascus to the Jordan (2 Kings 5)
25. Near where John the Baptist baptized (John 3:23)
27. Greek letter
28. Part of a garment
29. Band or chair
31. Consumed
32. Cotton _____
33. Fuss
37. Sighing sound
38. Grievous
41. King of Judah, et al.
43. Preposition
44. So extreme
45. Competent
47. Tea, for one
48. Picnic pests

49. The royal ____
50. Retreat, for some
52. Pronoun used for a country
53. King of Bashan (Numbers 21)
55. Conjunction
57. "Mr. ____" of TV fame
by Teri Grottke

ACROSS

1. Dignity
6. Solomon's throne had six of these
11. What Benjamin was first named
12. Trusts (arch.)
14. Son of Aram (Genesis 10)
15. Brother of Rephah (1 Chronicles 7:25)
17. City near Bethel
18. O.T. bk. (one of two)
19. Stickers
20. Union Pacific, e.g.
21. Airport code on the Big Island
23. "Of Keros, the children of____" (Nehemiah 7:47)
24. Son of Jether (1 Chronicles 7:38)
25. Baby
28. One of Levites named in the book of the kings (1 Chronicles 9:15)
31. Mountain (comb. form)
32. "They have gone in the way of Cain, and ____ greedily" (Jude 1:11)
33. Became stable
36. Jesus healed his mother-in-law
39. Biblical verb (KJV)
40. Fish eggs
42. O.T. bk.
43. Laughing sound
44. Where Abraham pursued those who had captured Lot (Genesis 14:15)
46. ____ a tee
47. Preposition
48. He accompanied Paul into Asia (Acts 20:4)
50. Pronoun
51. Interior or inner part
53. Among the new generation of Israel (pl., Numbers 26:16)
55. Prepared
56. Amorite king (Joshua 10:3)

DOWN

1. Father of Tabrimon (1 Kings 15:18)
2. Subatomic particle (suffix)
3. Conjunction
4. Column name in multidigit addition
5. Got up (arch.)
6. Son of Judah (Genesis 38:5)
7. A-one
8. N.T. bk.
9. Subject taught by a coach? (abbr.)
10. Comics heroine Brenda, and others
11. Son of Jogli (Numbers 34:22)
13. Adullamite who was Judah's friend (Genesis 38)
16. City near Bethel (var.)
22. "Many knew him, and ran ____ thither" (Mark 6:33)
24. John the Baptist baptized here (John 3)
26. Masculine nickname
27. "But as the days of ____ were" (Matthew 24:37)
29. "Of ____,the family of the Erites" (Numbers 26:16)
30. Strike with force
33. She hid the Hebrew spies
34. Keynote speaker
35. Jesus healed a man with this disease on the Sabbath
36. "There, in a portion of the law-giver, was he ____" (Deuteronomy 33:21)
37. Lying below the earth's surface

38. The ____ of the Fisherman
    (West novel)
41. O.T. minor prophet (abbr., var.)
44. Out or over
45. There's companion
48. Baltic, for example
49. Tease
52. "As ____ forgive our debtors"
    (Matthew 6:12)
54. Note on the diatonic scale
    by Teri Grottke

ACROSS

1. The great I ____
3. Stay and chat
8. Article
10. Son of Dishan (Genesis 36:28)
12. Son of Shemaiah (1 Chronicles 26:7)
13. Santa's sound
14. "Today shalt thou be with me in ____" (Luke 23:43)
16. "____ paint"
17. "I see"
18. Minor prophet (abbr.)
19. Electrical abbr.
21. Linking verb
22. "____ hath good report of all men" (3 John 12)
25. Single bill
27. Hence
28. Hospital inits.
29. Continent (abbr.)
31. Brother of Shoham (1 Chronicles 24:27)
33. Middle Eastern crop
35. Capital of Moab
36. Exists
38. Chemical symbol for tin (abbr.)
39. Acorn tree
40. Ooze
42. Handles clumsily
44. Grain named in Isaiah 28
46. City near Bethel
47. Commercial spelling of a word that means facile
48. Preposition
50. Retirement acct.
51. Returning Jew from exile (Nehemiah 7:7)
55. The Holy Spirit wouldn't let Paul and Silas go here
58. Manna measure
59. Understanding
60. Masculine nickname

DOWN

1. Son of Ulla (1 Chronicles 7:39)
2. Disfigure
3. Expresses
4. Possessive pronoun
5. Cut off
6. Preposition
7. Electronics giant (abbr.)
8. "Ir, and Hushim, the sons of ____" (1 Chronicles 7:12)
9. Memo
10. Away from (prefix)
11. "That at the ____ of Jesus" (Philippians 2:10)
15. Unclear
16. Used to be
20. Sky, to Simone
22. Family room
23. Dressed ____ the nines
24. Eastern U.S. university (abbr.)
25. Minor prophet (var., abbr.)
26. Abner's father (1 Samuel 14)
29. What a veteran is
30. Question
32. Slick or skin
33. Atop
34. Promise
37. "Of Keros, the children of ____" (Nehemiah 7:47)
38. Dir.
40. Box ____
41. Nation God called against Babylon (Jeremiah 51:27)
42. "The Princess and the ____" (classic fairytale)
43. "The border shall fetch a compass from ____" (Numbers 34:5)

44. It may stick out on Olive Oyl
45. Son of Bela (1 Chronicles 7:7)
49. Christmas tree
52. A city of Judah (Joshua 15:32)
53. Minor prophet (abbr.)
54. Church denomination (abbr.)
56. Masculine pronoun
57. "____ cannot serve God and mammon" (Matthew 6:24)

Puzzle 110

ACROSS

1. Shoe parts
6. Greek form of Uzziah
11. Son of Levi (Genesis 46:11)
12. Father of Baruch (Jeremiah 32:12)
14. Masculine nickname
15. Son of Adiel (1 Chronicles 9:12)
17. School subj.
18. Vote
19. Father of Darda (1 Kings 4:31)
20. Pronoun
21. Family of returned exiles (Ezra 2:57)
23. Pilot makes one
24. ____ change
25. Assign (arch.)
28. They come in flights
31. Slangy denial
32. It gives a hoot
33. Cauterized
36. Address
39. ____ blond
40. Construction necessity (abbr.)
42. Jane ____
43. Phonetic sound
44. Exhibits
46. Hospital inits.
47. "The kingdom of heaven is ____ hand" (Matthew 3:2)
48. Son of Elioenai (1 Chronicles 3:24)
50. Biblical exclamation
51. Catch one's eye
53. Glided
55. What Simeon was called at Antioch (Acts 13:1)
56. "The heifer...which is neither ____ nor sown" (Deuteronomy 21:4)

DOWN

1. Greek form of Sodom
2. Buckeye state (abbr.)
3. O.T. bk.
4. "He [Samson]...dwelt in the top of the rock ____" (Judges 15:8)
5. Son of Jahdai (1 Chronicles 2:47)
6. What the Israelites missed in the wilderness
7. Ardor
8. Son of Bela (1 Chronicles 7:7)
9. City near Bethel
10. "Pass ye away, thou inhabitant of ____" (Micah 1:11)
11. Early descendant of Adam (1 Chronicles 1:2)
13. What a good dog does
16. Pronoun for a seafaring vessel
22. Son of Asher (1 Chronicles 7:30)
24. Bribed
26. Wax or wig
27. Article
29. Big ____
30. Reverence
33. Antichrist
34. Son of Mehir (1 Chronicles 4:11)
35. Merchant
36. Contention
37. Became aloof
38. "When ____...had heard these things, he was troubled" (Matthew 2:3)
41. "Of Keros, the children of ____" (Nehemiah 7:47)
44. Visage
45. Father of Heber (Luke 3:35)
48. Verb for flower child
49. Mount where Aaron died (Numbers 20)

222

52. Polynesian woody plant
54. I (pl.)
    by Teri Grottke

ACROSS

1. Stop! (arch.)
3. Son of Tahath
   (1 Chronicles 6:24)
8. Father of Simon Peter
10. Assyrian god, which had a house
    in Nineveh (2 Kings 19)
13. Jealous gems?
15. Nephew of Abraham
17. Pronoun
18. Linking verb
19. Home of the brave (abbr.)
21. Postember state
22. Reproved
25. "In the night ____ of Moab is
    laid waste" (Isaiah 15:1)
27. Dir.
28. Where Miami University is (abbr.)
29. Hectare (abbr.)
31. Of starch (comb. form)
33. Pilfers (colloq.)
35. Musical abbr.
36. Where "The Music Man" was
    set (abbr.)
38. Figure on many TV crime shows
    (abbr.)
39. Hardwood
40. Son of Joktan (Genesis 10:26)
42. Son of Salah (Genesis 10:24)
44. Exclamation
46. Metric abbr.
47. Part of middle-school curriculum
    (abbr.)
48. Word in a command
50. Big ____, CA
51. Age of Jehoiachin when he
    began his reign
55. Deception
58. Too
59. Commanded
60. Strike

DOWN

1. Domicile
2. Chemical suffix
3. Except that
4. To free, with "of "
5. Assign
6. Hesitation sound
7. Biblical exclamation
8. "He is a ____, which is one
   inwardly" (Romans 2:29)
9. Son of Ulla (1 Chronicles 7:39)
11. Attired
12. O.T. minor prophet (abbr.)
14. First name of famed football
    coach
16. Symbol of thorium
20. "As ____ in summer...so honour
    is not seemly" (Proverbs 26:1)
22. ____, the Beloved Country
    (Paton book)
23. Preposition
24. Son of Benjamin
    (Genesis 46:21)
25. Eleventh letter of the Hebrew
    alphabet
26. Mischievous child
29. Was told, KJV style
30. Question
32. Untruth
33. Where Durban is (abbr.)
34. Nineteenth-century American
    writer
37. Prepare for battle
38. AL lineup abbr.
40. Assyrian king mentioned in
    Hosea
41. Alter
42. N.T. epistle (abbr.)
43. City where David took "exceed-
    ing much brass" (2 Samuel 8)
44. Snake

45. With Aaron, he held up Moses' arms
49. City built by descendants of Benjamin (1 Chronicles 8:12)
52. To cause to be (suffix, Brit.)
53. Bk. of the Torah
54. Father of Hophni
56. Note of the diatonic scale
57. Singer Ames

by Teri Grottke

ACROSS

1. Priestly garments
5. "Except your righteousness shall ____ the righteousness of the scribes" (Matthew 5:20)
7. Linking verb
8. Replied
10. "Give unto the Lord the glory ____ unto his name" (Psalm 29:2)
11. "Can a maid forget her ornaments, or a bride her ____?" (Jeremiah 2:32)
13. Of flying (comb. form)
14. Son of Seth
15. "Israel did ____ manna forty years" (Exodus 16:35)
17. "Yea, the ____ hath found an house" (Psalm 84:3)
19. "Employer" of Hagar
21. Oft-used abbr.
22. One (Ger.)
23. Rate of speed (abbr.)
24. Where Montauk is (abbr.)
25. "All they that cast ____ into the brooks shall lament" (Isaiah 19:8)
27. "They ____ in thee, and were not confounded" (Psalm 22:5)
29. "Agnus ___ "
30. Pay attention
31. "Yet will I bring ____ plague more upon Pharaoh" (Exodus 11:1)
32. "____ ye, and believe the gospel" (Mark 1:15)
34. "And Nathan said to David, Thou ____ the man" (2 Samuel 12:7)
35. End or line
36. John, to a Scot

37. "He made a ____ about the altar" (1 Kings 18:32)
39. "He shall be like a ____ planted by the rivers" (Psalm 1:3)

DOWN

1. Chopping tool
2. Public national library (abbr.)
3. "Upon these we ____ more abundant honour" (1 Corinthians 12:23)
4. "He hath put down the mighty from their ____" (Luke 1:52)
5. Before (poet.)
6. 502, according to Cicero
7. Charismatic atmosphere
9. God spoke in Bible times through these
10. Rely
11. Immediately (arch.)
12. Serving of corn
13. "All they which dwelt in ____ heard the word of the Lord Jesus" (Acts 19:10)
14. Great Lake
16. "I was afraid, and went and hid thy ____ in the earth" (Matthew 25:25)
18. Trusted, with "upon"
19. Potato
20. "I flee unto thee to ____ me" (Psalm 143:9)
23. "____ not thyself because of evildoers" (Psalm 37:1)
26. European lang.
27. "Leah was ____ eyed" (Genesis 29:17)
28. Ripped
30. "If thou seek him with all thy ____" (Deuteronomy 4:29)

33. Favorite
34. Sighing sound
36. "He casteth forth his ____ like morsels" (Psalm 147:17)
38. Compass dir.
    by Janet W. Adkins

ACROSS

1. Belonging to the Jairite who "was a chief ruler about David" (2 Samuel 20)
5. Lures
7. "Even of your lusts that ____ in your members" (James 4:1)
8. Name for a boy in Barcelona?
10. French export, to Emile
11. Really (arch.)
13. "Without the word be ____ by the conversation of the wives" (1 Peter 3:1)
14. New cars on the road
15. Person concerned with (suffix)
17. "But the righteous into life ____" (Matthew 25:46)
19. Advantage
21. City near Bethel
22. Electric ____
23. "But ____ thing is needful" (Luke 10:42)
24. Irish Pop
25. "And put a ____ to thy throat" (Proverbs 23:2)
27. "If he that cometh preacheth ____ Jesus" (2 Corinthians 11:4)
29. Ford model
30. Formerly Persia
31. Shem's home, for a while
32. Prayer
34. Hirt, and others
35. Region in NE Poland with many lakes (abbr.)
36. Like alt.
37. Person afflicted with tuberculosis (colloq.)
39. "Esau, who is ____ " (Genesis 36:1)

DOWN

1. Noun-forming suffix
2. Paper measure (abbr.)
3. "I ____ unto Caesar" (Acts 25:11)
4. "I will exalt my throne above the ____ of God" (Isaiah 14:13)
5. To M.D.s, summer scourge
6. Middle-school subj.
7. "Do not drink ____ nor strong drink" (Leviticus 10:9)
9. Bible mount
10. November activity
11. "Then Samuel took a ____ of oil" (1 Samuel 10:1)
12. Biblical exclamation
13. "All knees shall be ____ as water" (Ezekiel 21:7)
14. Joint
16. ____ of the Purple Sage (Z. Grey book)
18. Change for the better
19. In the very near future (arch.)
20. Whim
23. Second son of Judah (Genesis 38)
26. Certain California judge
27. In the vicinity
28. "How long ____ ye between two opinions" (1 Kings 18:21)
30. Release
33. Suitable for (suffix)
34. Farm science (comb. form)
36. "They might only touch the ____ of his garment" (Matthew 14:36)
38. Word in the Great Commission
   by Janet W. Adkins

Puzzle 114

ACROSS

1. Place which means "well of the oath" (Genesis 21)
6. Compass dir.
8. Prophet who advised David to go into the land of Judah (1 Samuel 22)
9. U.S. site of a Summer Olympics (abbr.)
10. Where Paul healed Publius' father (var., Acts 28)
11. Judah thought this woman was a prostitute (Genesis 38)
12. Electrical abbr.
13. City also known as Lydda (1 Chronicles 8:12)
16. Where one finds "the street which is called Straight"
17. "he is of ____; ask him" (John 9:21)
18. Esther's Shusan (var.)
20. Pot adjunct
21. City near Bethel (var.)
22. Coral reef
23. Consumed
25. The Great I ____
28. Site of Jesus' first miracle on earth
30. "The Nethinims dwelt in ____, unto the place over against the water gate" (Nehemiah 3:26)
31. "____ sharpeneth ____" [word repeated] (Proverbs 27:17)
34. Right-hand page (abbr.)
35. "For this Agar is mount Sinai in ____" (Galatians 4:25)
37. "David...escaped to the cave ____" (1 Samuel 22:1)
39. His two sons, Hophni and Phinehas, were priests of the Lord
41. Cape Cod state (abbr.)
42. After this Bible book, God did not speak to His people for 400 years (abbr.)
43. River of Egypt
45. "In so doing thou shalt ____ coals of fire on his head" (Romans 12:20)
46. Shammah was the son of this Hararite (2 Samuel 23)
47. Lion of ____ (name of Jesus)
48. "Arise ye, and let us go up to ____ unto the Lord our God" (var., Jeremiah 31:6)
51. Extremely agitated
52. Understand
53. Like a mom's day
54. "The Lord will cut off from ____ head and tail, branch and rush" (Isaiah 9:14)

DOWN

1. Where the handicapped waited "for the moving of the water"
2. Destination of two disciples, when they were joined by the risen Jesus Christ
3. One of seven cities addressed in early chapters of Revelation
4. "I was at Shushan...in the province of ____" (Daniel 8:2)
5. "Who passing through the valley of ____ make it a well" (Psalm 84:6)
6. Continent (abbr.)
7. Son of Shaphan (Jeremiah 29:3)
8. Paul stopped here on his third missionary journey, after Antioch (Acts 18)
10. Home of Gaius and Aristarchus, two of Paul's companions (Acts 19)
14. King who was a remnant of giants (Deuteronomy 3:11)

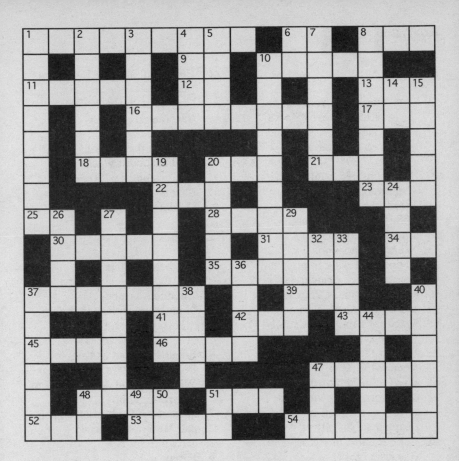

15. A city of Lycaonia, where Paul fled after Iconium (Acts 14)
19. "The field of blood" (Acts 1)
20. Where the city of Myra was located (Acts 27)
24. Famous seaport on the Mediterranean, in Bible days (var., Ezekiel 26)
26. Shape
27. City where Lydia was converted (Acts 16)
29. "All thy fortresses shall be spoiled, as Shalman spoiled Beth-____" (Hosea 10:14)
32. In parable, five virgins forgot this (Matthew 25)

33. Widow of ____
36. Where Paul's last days were spent
37. Site of Mars' hill
38. Wise men
40. Where Abraham built his second altar (Genesis 12)
44. ____ ink
47. N.T. book (abbr.)
48. Dir.
49. Branch of medicine (abbr.)
50. Greek letter
51. "Hearken unto the voice of ____ cry" (Psalm 5:2)
   by Michael J. Landi

ACROSS

1. "For they considered not the
   ____ of the loaves" (Mark 6:52)
7. "In the days of Noah, while the
   ____ was a preparing"
   (1 Peter 3:20)
10. "The sons of Carmi; ____"
    (1 Chronicles 2:7)
11. Word in a command
12. U.S. state named after
    Elizabeth I (abbr.)
13. Where the action is
14. "Those that walk in pride he is
    able to ____" (Daniel 4:37)
16. What the wife of Phinehas
    named their son (1 Samuel 4)
18. Father of Eliud (Matthew 1:14)
20. City near Bethel
22. "Thy right ____ shall save me"
    (Psalm 138:7)
23. Used to make powder
24. "Let tears run down like a
    river...give thyself no ____"
    (Lamentations 2:18)
26. Former name of Bethel
    (Genesis 28:19)
28. "The rock poured me out ____
    of oil" (Job 29:6)
32. "As he saith also in ____ "
    (Romans 9:25)
34. Waif, often
35. Compass dir.
36. Related to the camel
38. Forty-niner's destination (abbr.)
39. Father of Ahihud
    (Numbers 34:27)
41. ____ what?
42. State on the Pacific (abbr.)
43. Redact
44. Roger Williams's state (abbr.)

46. Reach out and touch someone
    (abbr.)
47. "I ____ hath sent me unto you"
    (Exodus 3:14)
48. Frustrate
50. "And on the wall of ____ he
    [Jotham] built much"
    (2 Chronicles 27:3)
52. "Yet had he the ____ of the spirit"
    (Malachi 2:15)

DOWN

1. "Is therefore Christ the ____ of
   sin? God forbid" (Galatians 2:17)
2. Chemical symbol
3. "I am glad of the coming of
   ...Fortunatus and ____ "
   (1 Corinthians 16:17)
4. Small fish used as bait
5. Political party in Great Britain
6. Where life and death decisions
   are made (abbr.)
7. As sons of God, what we can
   call Him (Galatians 4)
8. Stretch
9. Parent
12. "Surely there is a ____ for the
    silver" (Job 28:1)
15. Where the Emims were smote, in
    ____ Kiriathaim (Genesis 14)
17. "____ be thy name" (Luke 11:2)
19. Atlantic seaboard state (abbr.)
21. "And Phares begat ____"
    (Matthew 1:3)
25. Son of Japheth
    (1 Chronicles 1:5)
27. Simon ____ (Acts 1)
29. Exec.
30. "The Lord make the woman that
    is come into thine house like
    ____" (Ruth 4:11)

31. Slow goer
33. Shade tree
35. Son of Noah
37. "To meet the Lord in the ____"
    (1 Thessalonians 4:17)
40. "He that eateth of this bread
    shall ____ for ever" (John 6:58)
45. Borrower's woe
46. "In all matters of wisdom...the
    king...found them ____ times
    better" (Daniel 1:20)
47. Simile syntax
49. Greek letter
51. Part of middle-school curriculum
    (abbr.)

by Teri Grottke

ACROSS

1. "We have seen his _____ in the east" (Matthew 2:2)
5. Accepts, in a way
9. Atlantic seaboard state (abbr.)
11. "My _____ is in thee" (Psalm 39:7)
12. Warehouse
13. "Keep me as the _____ of the eye" (Psalm 17:8)
15. _____ de France
17. "My _____ shall praise thee" (Psalm 63:3)
19. Addiction to (suffix)
22. Affirmative (colloq.)
23. "Make thee a fiery serpent, and set it upon a _____" (Numbers 21:8)
24. Printer's measure
26. Secondborn of Adam
30. Cambridge college (abbr.)
31. "At thy word I will let down the _____" (Luke 5:5)
33. One source of evil
35. "The Lord is thy _____ upon thy right hand" (Psalm 121:5)
38. Soloist
39. Peter or Paul (abbr.)
41. Book or teller
42. "The sceptre shall not depart from _____" (Genesis 49:10)
44. "As light of foot as a wild _____" (2 Samuel 2:18)
45. Oft-used abbr.
46. "Put ye in the sickle, for the harvest is _____" (Joel 3:13)
48. Stay _____
50. "Thou hast been a _____ for me, and a strong tower" (Psalm 61:3)
52. _____ is condition
53. Unit of dry measure (abbr.)
54. Complete set of events
55. "Our word...was not yea and _____" (2 Corinthians 1:18)
56. Sauce made with fresh basil
57. Duly noted at a yearly physical (abbr.)

DOWN

1. Hone
2. Hat or heavy
3. "_____ thine heart to under standing" (Proverbs 2:2)
4. Depended upon
5. Second letter of the Hebrew alphabet (var.)
6. "They that wait _____ the Lord shall renew their strength" (Isaiah 40:31)
7. Thou, to a non-Quaker
8. Dismantle
10. Masculine nickname
14. Gov't. agency
16. "Consider the _____ of the field" (Matthew 6:28)
18. "Endured the cross, despising the _____" (Hebrews 12:2)
20. _____ cat
21. "A city that is _____ on a hill" (Matthew 5:14)
25. "As an eagle stirreth up her _____" (Deuteronomy 32:11)
27. One who takes to the rails (colloq.)
28. "Bread _____ and to spare" (Luke 15:17)
29. What a bank may do
32. Paul's _____ in the flesh
34. "For there is a _____ sacrifice there for all the family" (1 Samuel 20:6)
36. City on the banks of the Arnon River (Joshua 13:16)

37. Changed hues
40. "Over ____" (wartime favorite)
41. "Get thee behind me, ____"
    (Luke 4:8)
42. Prince of Peace
43. Wed, in Dogpatch
47. Throw things at
49. "Land of the free" (abbr.)
51. System or sphere
53. "____ of good cheer; I have
    overcome the world"
    (John 16:33)
    by Beverley Barnes

ACROSS

1. "There is nothing from without a man, that entering...can ____ him" (Mark 7:15)
4. "At home in the body, we are ____ from the Lord" (2 Corinthians 5:6)
8. Article
9. "____ your enemies" (Matthew 5:44)
11. "Thy rod and thy ____ they comfort me" (Psalm 23:4)
14. "The captain of his host was Abner, the son of ____" (1 Samuel 14:50)
15. "The Lord hath made bare his holy ____" (Isaiah 52:10)
16. "As a ____ doth gather her brood" (Luke 13:34)
17. Celebrated city of Asia Minor, visited by Paul more than once
18. ____ of Sharon (Song of Solomon 2)
20. "The ____ is not to the swift" (Ecclesiastes 9:11)
22. "At the name of Jesus every ____ should bow" (Philippians 2:10)
24. Denial (arch.)
26. Part of a castle
27. "Who can utter the mighty ____ of the Lord?" (Psalm 106:2)
28. King of Israel who was killed by Zimri (var., 1 Kings 16)
29. Linking verb
32. "If any of you lack wisdom, let him ____ of God" (James 1:5)
33. "If thou wilt ____ into life, keep the commandments" (Matthew 19:17)

34. From 1 Corinthians 13: faith, hope, and ____
36. Idol worshiped by Jezebel, among many others
37. Hard ____
40. Not B.C.
41. "Which he ____ on us abundantly through Jesus Christ" (Titus 3:6)
43. Judah's firstborn (Genesis 38:7)
44. Therefore

DOWN

1. "Lest at any time thou ____ thy foot against a stone" (Matthew 4:6)
2. "When thou prayest, ____ into thy closet" (Matthew 6:6)
3. ____ Al, airline known for its security measures
4. "____ not yourselves, but rather give place unto wrath" (Romans 12:19)
5. Son of Zophah (1 Chronicles 7:36)
6. "But let a man ____ himself" (1 Corinthians 11:28)
7. "The tongue can no man ____" (James 3:8)
10. City of Benjamin built or restored by Shamed (1 Chronicles 8:12)
12. "Arise, ye princes, and ____ the shield" (Isaiah 21:5)
13. How to describe Nebuchadnezzar's furnace
19. "The ____ for height, and the earth for depth" (Proverbs 25:3)
21. "Tarsus, a city in ____" (Acts 21:39)
22. Map info

23. "As also in all his ___, speaking in them of these things" (2 Peter 3:16)
25. Past somnolent
30. "For the ____ is red and lowring" (Matthew 16:3)
31. Gypsy ____ (sight in big city)
32. Father of Saul's concubine (2 Samuel 3)
35. "Be not ____ with thy mouth" (Ecclesiastes 5:2)
38. Neh. is part of this
39. Biblical pronoun

42. "Of all that Jesus began both to ____ and teach" (Acts 1:1)

by Michael J. Landi

PUZZLE 118

ACROSS

2. Metamorphosed
10. "He took ____ of his ribs" (Genesis 2:21)
11. Crasher or keeper
12. Partake
13. Missing ingredient in manna
14. Form of "drachma"
16. ____ Aviv
18. "But glory, honour, and ____, to every man that worketh good" (Romans 2:10)
20. Pal, to Philippe
21. ____ in (first point scored after deuce?)
22. Loan
24. "Burning ____ and a wicked heart" (Proverbs 26:23)
26. "He revealeth the ____ and secret things" (Daniel 2:22)
28. Conjunction
30. What April brings
32. "The ____ of all Israel are upon thee" (1 Kings 1:20)
34. One of David's men (1 Kings 1:8)
36. "Sow...in righteousness, ____ in mercy" (Hosea 10:12)
37. "Enter into the rock...for the glory of his ____" (Isaiah 2:10)
39. "But ____ wrought evil in the eyes of the Lord" (1 Kings 16:25)
40. What Isaac named the well at Gerar (Genesis 26:20)
42. Roman emperor with whom Paul had an audience
43. Not A.D.
44. Zaftig, but more bluntly perhaps?
45. "Call me not ____, call me Mara" (Ruth 1:20)

48. "Ye have made the heart of the righteous ____" (Ezekiel 13:22)
49. Aeries

DOWN

1. "Let not sin therefore reign in your ____ body" (Romans 6:12)
2. Do ____!
3. Meal shared by early Christians
4. Hub of a wheel
5. "We pray you in Christ's ____, be ye reconciled" (2 Corinthians 5:20)
6. "____ cities, with walls, gates, and bars" (2 Chronicles 8:5)
7. ____ Sea
8. Feminine name that means "bitter"
9. Rock where Samson lived after slaughter of Philistines (Judges 15)
15. "Come, buy wine and ____ without money" (Isaiah 55:1)
17. Enlighten
19. Head of a family of Gad (var., 1 Chronicles 5:13)
23. Runs swiftly
25. "For the ____ things are passed away" (Revelation 21:4)
27. "Learn first to show ____ at home" (1 Timothy 5:4)
29. "To every man that asketh you a ____ of the hope" (1 Peter 3:15)
31. "____, in all these things we are more than conquerors" (Romans 8:37)
32. Town of the tribe of Dan (Joshua 19:43)
33. Apostles and others
35. At ____-abarim, in the wilderness before Moab, Israelites pitched tents (Numbers 21:11)

38. Chief Philistine city
    (1 Samuel 6:17)
41. New Testament book
46. Its capital is Augusta (abbr.)
47. "For God ____ my witness"
    (Romans 1:9)
    by Michael J. Landi

ACROSS

1. Saul fought against them (1 Samuel 14)
6. "There shall they rehearse the righteous ____ of the Lord" (Judges 5:11)
9. "He shall ____ with his teeth, and melt away" (Psalm 112:10)
10. Actress McDaniel
11. "My ____ shall be joyful in my God" (Isaiah 61:10)
12. "Out of thine hand the ____ of trembling" (Isaiah 51:22)
14. Word heard on movie sets
15. Preposition
16. "By the rivers of Babylon, there we ____" (Psalm 137:1)
17. Land of Job
20. "____ unto you, scribes and Pharisees, hypocrites!" (Matthew 23:15)
22. Tenth part of one's income
23. ____ of the Chaldees
24. Town of the tribe of Benjamin (1 Chronicles 8:12)
26. "Go and ____ in the ears of Jerusalem" (Jeremiah 2:2)
27. Joshua, the son of ___
28. Gershwin
31. "The Lord make his ____ shine upon thee" (Numbers 6:25)
32. Word with grade or braid
33. Father of Ehud (Judges 3:15)
34. Scale unit (abbr.)
37. ____ Behind (LaHaye/Jenkins book)
38. "All we like ____ have gone astray" (Isaiah 53:6)

DOWN

1. Item worn by the high priest (Exodus 28)
2. "Because the Lord loved you,...he would keep the ____" (Deuteronomy 7:8)
3. "The tongue is a fire, a world of ____" (James 3:6)
4. Common abbr.
5. "As a jewel of gold in a swine's ____" (Proverbs 11:22)
6. Balaam's beast
7. "They hated knowledge, and did not ____ the fear of the Lord" (Proverbs 1:29)
8. "He went out, and departed into a ____ place" (Mark 1:35)
13. "To see thy ____ and thy glory" (Psalm 63:2)
18. "David took the strong hold of ___: the same is the city of David" (2 Samuel 5:7)
19. Without end
21. Languages (arch.)
23. Father of Michaiah (2 Chronicles 13:2)
25. Greek letter
29. "If ye have ____ as a grain of mustard seed" (Matthew 17:20)
30. "I ____ where I sowed not" (Matthew 25:26)
35. Nephew of Abraham, the son of Nahor (Genesis 22:21)
36. Biblical pronoun

by Michael J. Landi

ACROSS

1. "There sat a certain man at Lystra, ____ in his feet" (Acts 14:8)
7. Recurring chills
10. "When her branch is yet tender...ye know that summer is ____" (Mark 13:28)
11. At the age of (abbr.)
13. Naaman's illness (2 Kings 5)
14. Mischievous child
16. Study of art or science (pl. suffix)
18. Football position (abbr.)
19. Detail for a duffer
20. Stir up
21. Angry
22. Chicago's Lake Shore, for one (abbr.)
23. First name in life preservers?
24. ____ upsmanship
25. ____ Bravo
26. Possessive pronoun
27. "___, and Ammon, and Amalek; the Philistines" (Psalm 83:7)
30. Accountant's abbr.
32. In what state Churchill Downs is found (abbr.)
33. "____ said unto Samuel, Go, lie down" (1 Samuel 3:9)
35. What ___...? (worrywart's favorite question)
36. Small drink
38. "I will not drink henceforth of this fruit of the ____" (Matthew 26:29)
40. Sacrifice sitc
41. "Yesterday at the seventh hour the ____ left him" (John 4:52)
42. As stated
43. "But the wise took ____ in their vessels" (Matthew 25:4)

44. "Resist the devil, and he will ____ from you" (James 4:7)
45. Female deer (pl.)
46. Organization including Britain, France, and Germany (abbr.)
47. Bring legal action
48. "A certain man…had the ____" (Luke 14:2)
49. Egress

DOWN

1. "Himself took our ___, and bare our sicknesses" (Matthew 8:17)
2. "Come unto ___, all ye that labour" (Matthew 11:28)
3. "And many taken with ___, and that were lame, were healed" (Acts 8:7)
4. Rock worth mining
5. "The man took a golden ____ of half a shekel weight" (Genesis 24:22)
6. Describing a modern take on a classical style
8. Trotting, for one
9. Nero, for one
12. "They...fled unto ____ and Derbe, cities of Lycaonia" (Acts 14:6)
15. "A merry heart doeth good like a ____" (Proverbs 17:22)
17. ____ of many colors
28. Tournament privilege for number-one ranked team
29. Built to keep a river from overflowing
31. "And Lot dwelled in the ____ of the plain" (Genesis 13:12)
34. "Forsake not the Levite as long as thou ____" (Deuteronomy 12:19)

36. Rigged sailboat
37. Paralysis
39. "Which some professing have
    ____ concerning the faith"
    (1 Timothy 6:21)
41. Coming in of the tide
44. Assessment
45. "And whatsoever ye ____ in
    word or deed" (Colossians 3:17)
    by Janet Kennedy

PUZZLE 121

ACROSS

1. "Thou breakest the heads of _____ in pieces" (Psalm 74:14)
7. "Every one that lappeth of the water with his tongue, as a _____ " (Judges 7:5)
10. In on
11. Like an aria
12. "_____ it ever so humble"
13. Conjunction
14. "Behold behind him a _____ caught in a thicket by his horns" (Genesis 22:13)
17. Loathing
18. Feminine nickname
20. Brit. islands (abbr.)
22. Blue pencil pushers? (abbr.)
23. Printer's measure
24. Wisconsin, the _____ State
27. Catch sight of
30. "I _____ the true vine" (John 15:1)
31. "The hart, and the roebuck, and the fallow _____ " (Deuteronomy 14:5)
32. "All _____ like sheep have gone astray" (Isaiah 53:6)
34. Rooster's better half
35. Chicago sight
36. Dad, in Dublin
38. One of the 13 original states (abbr.)
39. "Your adversary the devil, as a roaring ___, walketh about" (1 Peter 5:8)
42. Stags
44. What to do with the frizzies and large felines
46. Greek letter
47. Iron (symbol)
48. Verb in primer's vocabulary
50. Director Lupino

52. Kind of engineer (abbr.)
53. TV network
54. "Shalt thou exalt like the horn of an _____ " (Psalm 92:10)

DOWN

1. Discovery zone? (abbr.)
2. "The poor man had nothing, save one little _____ lamb" (2 Samuel 12:3)
3. One of the 13 original states (abbr.)
4. "He shall rule...with a rod of _____ " (Revelation 2:27)
5. Expose to air
6. "And I saw heaven opened, and behold a white _____ " (Revelation 19:11)
7. Obstinate one, not too kindly
8. Chemical suffix
9. Rocky Mountain ___
15. Mosquito that carries yellow fever
16. Large quantity
19. Preposition
20. "Easier for a _____ to go through the eye of a needle" (Matthew 19:24)
21. Part of psyche
24. Requested (arch.)
25. "She maketh fine linen...and delivereth _____ unto the merchant" (Proverbs 31:24)
26. Harsh
28. Penn's pad? (abbr.)
29. "The king doth not fetch home again his _____ " (2 Samuel 14:13)
33. Exclamation of scorn
34. Tortoise's tormentor
37. City near Bethel
40. These may be yoked

244

41. Division of the United Kingdom (abbr.)
43. "And Peter followed ____ off" (Luke 22:54)
45. Fuss
49. Good or well (prefix)
50. Characteristic of (suffix)
51. Word in a command

by Janet Kennedy

ACROSS

1. Chop off
4. One of Hezekiah's overseers (2 Chronicles 31:13)
9. One's own turf?
12. Mother of Hezekiah (2 Kings 18:2)
13. Kind of finish
14. "The ____ appeareth, and the tender grass showeth itself" (Proverbs 27:25)
15. Atlantic seaboard state (abbr.)
16. Altar end of a church
17. "When I ____ the five loaves among five thousand" (Mark 8:19)
19. New churches, evangelically speaking
21. "As for ___, he made havock of the church" (Acts 8:3)
22. "I go my ___, and ye shall seek me" (John 8:21)
23. Paul or Peter or John or...
26. "A river went out of ____ to water the garden" (Genesis 2:10)
28. "Serve him in sincerity and in ____" (Joshua 24:14)
29. Masculine nickname
30. City in central Israel
31. "And Abram passed through the land...unto the plain of ____ " (Genesis 12:6)
32. In the ___
33. Jesus conversed in this language when on earth (abbr.)
34. "Eldad and ____ do prophesy in the camp" (Numbers 11:27)
35. "I will give thee a crown of ____" (Revelation 2:10)
36. Day of baptism (two words)
38. Kitchen implement

39. Vainly
40. Progenitor
43. Number of men who met Abraham at his tent, including the Lord (Genesis 18)
45. ____ in full
46. Conjunction
47. Consume
48. Desire strongly
50. Jane or John
51. "He planteth an ___, and the rain doth nourish it" (Isaiah 44:14)
52. Gluts
53. "For ye are all ____ in Christ" (Galatians 3:28)

DOWN

1. "Thy word is a ____ unto my feet" (Psalm 119:105)
2. "And Joktan begat...____ and Abimael and Sheba" (Genesis 10:28)
3. Greek letter
4. "The Lord hath brought me home again ____" (Ruth 1:21)
5. Girl in Glasgow
6. Resident (suffix)
7. ____ al
8. "And ___, and Shilhim...all the cities are twenty and nine" (Joshua 15:32)
9. Biblical verb
10. "Ye shall be as an ____ whose leaf fadeth" (Isaiah 1:30)
11. What to do with eggs?
16. One among the covenant sealers (Nehemiah 10:26)
18. Make haste
20. Held in fear
21. Flowed or gushed out (O.T. spelling)

23. "Women adorn themselves...not with...costly ____" (1 Timothy 2:9)
24. Gold ____
25. Life on the ____ (Dobson book)
26. Ardor
27. Feminine name
28. "Exhort one another daily, while it is called ____" (Hebrews 3:13)
31. Samplings of songs?
32. "Whoso breaketh an hedge, a serpent shall ____ him" (Ecclesiastes 10:8)
34. Darius the ____ (Daniel 11)
35. Master

37. "The voice of ____, and the voice of gladness" (Jeremiah 7:34)
38. Symptoms of malaise
40. "She shall shave her head, and ____ her nails" (Deuteronomy 21:12)
41. "I will cause the sun to go down at ____" (Amos 8:9)
42. The ____ of life (Revelation 22)
43. Prince of Wales, for example
44. Owns
45. Stand ___
49. Apiece (abbr.)
50. Accomplish
by Evelyn M. Boyington

ACROSS

1. Cry
4. Dream or organ
8. ____ team
12. Mouth (pl.)
13. "The children of ____ of Hezekiah, ninety and eight" (Ezra 2:16)
14. Jewelry setting, with no metal showing
15. By means of
16. Nurture
17. Great Lake
18. Masculine name that is an amalgam of Abraham and Noah
20. Make ____
22. Prim and proper
24. In Arthurian legend, the wife of Geraint
25. Writing ____ (what Zacharias asked for in Luke 1)
26. "____ thou not unto his [God's] words" (Proverbs 30:6)
27. Gazelle
30. Biblical exclamation
31. Possessive pronoun
32. "Thou hast enlarged my steps...that my feet did not ____" (Psalm 18:36)
33. Affirmative
34. Compass pt.
35. Obeys, to an AKC member
36. He was a prisoner on Patmos
37. Obliterate
38. Stick
41. Mentally acute
42. Not present and unaccounted for (abbr., pl.)
43. What commandos do
45. Anger
48. Parchment shade
49. "He...saw others standing ____ in the marketplace" (Matthew 20:3)
50. Not (prefix)
51. "And they straightway left their ___, and followed him" (Matthew 4:20)
52. Minister to
53. Our Father

DOWN

1. Absorb
2. Crude metal
3. He accompanied Paul on his first missionary journey
4. Procession
5. Article on a list
6. Legume
7. Missions
8. ____ trap
9. Give notice
10. Like many golfers?
11. What to wear when golfing? (pl.)
19. Nard, olive, et al.
21. Word that precedes day or air
22. Between check-in and check-out
23. "We spend our years as a ____ that is told" (Psalm 90:9)
24. All gone!
27. "Yet ____ grapes shall be left in it, as the shaking of an olive tree" (Isaiah 17:6)
28. Sesame, canola, et al.
29. Usually the east end of a church
31. "For such as be blessed of him shall ____ the earth" (Psalm 37:22)
32. Arid
34. Conjunction
35. Noticed
36. "Even so, come, Lord ____" (Revelation 22:20)

38. So be it
39. Prepare vegetables for cooking
40. "As the _____ panteth after the water" (Psalm 42:1)
41. Oven
44. Fruit drink
46. One of Pooh's pals
47. "And then shall the _____ come" (Matthew 24:14)
    by Evelyn M. Boyington

PUZZLE 124

ACROSS

1. Western state (abbr.)
3. "I gave Egypt for thy ransom, Ethiopia and ____ for thee" (Isaiah 43:3)
7. To do much better than another
12. ____ of the Chaldees
13. From ____ to stern
14. Fabric used to make an ephod
15. In law, an object
17. Preposition
18. "In the beginning was the ____" (John 1:1)
19. "The horse is prepared against the day of ____" (Proverbs 21:31)
21. "Stand in ___, and sin not" (Psalm 4:4)
22. "They fled before the men of ____" (Joshua 7:4)
24. Pres. Clinton's home state (abbr.)
25. Simile syntax
26. "The children of Israel be as the ____ of the sea" (Romans 9:27)
28. Administer the SAT again
31. Quaker pronoun
32. You, in the Yucatan
34. Start
36. Provincetown province (abbr.)
37. Grandfather of David, and son of Ruth
40. Means of communication
43. First word written on the wall (Daniel 5)
44. Linking verb
45. "Two of every ____ shalt thou bring into the ark" (Genesis 6:19)
48. Masculine nickname
49. Took a break
51. "It is as high as heaven...____ than hell" (Job 11:8)

53. Minuscule
54. Naval officer (abbr.)
55. Where one can perspire or be pampered
56. Portion
58. Used by the high priest to hold oil
60. Classified, for one
61. Spread around
62. Altar end of the church
63. Biblical pronoun

DOWN

1. Checks
2. ____ code
3. Christian ed. concern (abbr.)
4. Common abbr.
5. ____ noire
6. "I ____ God, even thy God" (Psalm 50:7)
7. "____ of speech" (how Moses described himself)
8. Employed, in Bible times
9. Conjunction
10. "This I know; for God is for ____" (Psalm 56:9)
11. Printer's measure
16. Day ___
18. "The field is ___, the land mourneth" (Joel 1:10)
20. Three, in Turin
22. "Ramoth with her suburbs, and ____ with her suburbs" (1 Chronicles 6:73)
23. Notion
25. "The ____ of Kish Saul's father were lost" (1 Samuel 9:3)
27. Sighing sound
29. Preposition
30. "The friendship of the world is ____ with God" (James 4:4)

32. Volume
33. Father of Gaal (Judges 9:30)
35. Note on diatonic scale
38. _____ passant (chess term)
39. "If any man _____ to be first, the same shall be last" (Mark 9:35)
41. "Pray for them which despitefully _____ you" (Luke 6:28)
42. Swabs
46. To reward
47. Barter
50. Once more
51. "Behold, the nations are as a _____ of a bucket" (Isaiah 40:15)

52. All _____ (attentive)
53. Pitch
56. Baseball player (abbr.)
57. Like alt.
58. Laughing sound
59. Quadrant in D.C.
by Evelyn M. Boyington

by Evelyn M. Boyington

ACROSS

1. Hoover, for example
4. "And I saw, and behold a white ____" (Revelation 6:2)
9. Auction action
12. "Beware of him, and ____ his voice" (Exodus 23:21)
14. "They gave him vinegar to drink mingled with ____" (Matthew 27:34)
15. Shoshonean tribe member
16. Scrambled scuffle
18. "And the Avims which dwelt in ____" (Deuteronomy 2:23)
20. Of considerable size
22. What a raconteur weaves?
23. "And in the fourth chariot ____ and bay horses" (Zechariah 6:3)
26. Cave dweller
27. Partner of rave
28. What Hebron was formerly called, and its namesakes (var., Genesis 35)
30. Preposition
32. ____ white
33. Bypass
34. Queen, for example
35. The royal ____
36. Teams
37. Melted, as a fuse
38. Deface
39. Bees in the bonnet?
41. One husband of Abigail
43. "Let the wicked fall into their own ____" (Psalm 141:10)
44. "God hath blessed thee ____" (two words, Psalm 45:2)
46. Aeries
49. "Manasseh made Judah and the inhabitants of Jerusalem to ____" (2 Chronicles 33:9)
50. "Unto Shem also, the father of all the children of ____" (Genesis 10:21)
52. Holding a grudge
53. ____ station
54. Packs away
55. Tatami (floor ____)

DOWN

1. Title of respect in Brazil and Portugal
2. Lincoln, to his nearest and dearest
3. "As when the ____ fire burneth" (Isaiah 64:2)
5. "Sihon king of the Amorites, and ____ king of Bashan" (Psalm 135:11)
6. Stadium sound
7. Smite
8. "____ the ninth" (1 Chronicles 12:12)
9. Charred
10. Inflammation (suffix)
11. Political partisan (abbr.)
13. Leaven
17. Building extension
19. Ages
21. "Intreat me not to ____ thee" (Ruth 1:16)
23. "The tree ___, and was strong" (Daniel 4:11)
24. "Why do the heathen ____" (Psalm 2:1)
25. Overcome with noise
29. Shaggy mammals
30. ____ there, done that
31. Coniferous trees
33. Achieves success
34. "Their root shall be as rottenness, and their ____ shall go up as dust" (Isaiah 5:24)

36. Bat's bailiwick
37. Pierces
38. "In the resurrection they neither _____ nor are given in marriage" (Matthew 22:30)
40. "Your father hath...changed my wages _____ times" (Genesis 31:7)
41. Feminine name
42. "The reward not reckoned of grace, but of _____" (Romans 4:4)
44. Handful
45. Automobile of a previous generation
47. Singing syllable

48. Jelled
51. Inits. accorded a member of the clergy

ACROSS

1. With Deborah, he confronted the army of Sisera
5. One of the sons of Merari (1 Chronicles 6:30)
12. Poems
14. Burn with anger
15. Contented comment
17. "And the Lord God caused a ____ sleep" (Genesis 2:21)
19. "Suffer the little children to come unto ____" (Mark 10:14)
20. Apiece (abbr.)
21. Perimeter
23. Farm implements
25. The ____ Pavilions (Kaye novel)
26. Son of Seth
28. "I took the little book...and ____ it up" (Revelation 10:10)
29. In the ____
30. Information
32. Balmy state (abbr.)
33. Spanish pronoun
35. "In the ____ God created" (Genesis 1:1)
37. Exclamation of surprise
39. Concerning, with "in"
40. Oppressed person
42. "I...was come nigh unto Damascus about ____" (Acts 22:6)
44. "The Lord that delivered me out of the ____ of the lion" (1 Samuel 17:37)
46. "Thou art not a ____ of the law, but a judge" (James 4:11)
48. "For the stone shall ____ out of the wall" (Habakkuk 2:11)
49. Mentions
51. Bide a ____ (Scottish phrase)
52. Printer's measure

53. Great Commission verb
54. "The first came out red...and they called his name ____" (Genesis 25:25)
56. Note on the diatonic scale
57. Abandon
60. "____ ye from your evil ways" (2 Kings 17:13)
62. "The God...who hath called us unto his ____ glory by Christ Jesus" (1 Peter 5:10)
63. Daniel's den mates

DOWN

1. Announce loudly
2. Right page (abbr.)
3. "Which of you...can ____ one cubit unto his stature?" (Matthew 6:27)
4. "If ye love me, ____ my commandments" (John 14:15)
6. Resident of the Far East (abbr.)
7. Certain rocks
8. Command to a horse
9. With ____
10. "Then I will give them ____ ____ to know Me" (2 words, Jeremiah 24:7, NKJV)
11. "____ unto me: I will teach you the fear of the Lord" (Psalm 34:11)
13. Actress Ward
16. "Naphtali is a ____ let loose" (Genesis 49:21)
18. "The blessed and only ___, the King of kings" (1 Timothy 6:15)
22. Ruth and Orpah were "women of ____" (Ruth 1)
24. Pronoun
25. Note on the diatonic scale
27. Cheerless

29. Ate out
31. "Strong meat belongeth to them that are of full ____" (Hebrews 5:14)
32. Old-fashioned hand towel message
34. Yield
36. Mature
38. "Moreover the Lord thy God will send the ____ among them" (Deuteronomy 7:20)
41. "My ____ did not slip" (Psalm 18:36)
43. Worried exclamation
44. Greek letter

45. Occident
47. Bridle part
49. ____ fields (what Jesus went through on the sabbath day, Mark 2)
50. Son of Kish
53. European tongue (abbr.)
55. Father of Bezaleel (Exodus 31:2)
58. Quadrant in D.C.
59. British 'bye
61. "And Abram said unto Lot, Let there be ____ strife" (Genesis 13:8)

by Evelyn M. Boyington

by Evelyn M. Boyington

ACROSS

1. Member of Congress (abbr.)
4. "Behold, ____ ____ is in thine own eye?" (2 words, Matthew 7:4)
9. Scheduled stopping place (abbr.)
12. Poetic preposition
13. "I will ____ thee seven years" (Genesis 29:18)
14. Handle roughly
15. "There is a friend that sticketh closer than a ____" (Proverbs 18:24)
17. Part of a book
19. Coop comment?
20. Nicholas, for one
21. "The children of Giddel, the children of ____" (Ezra 2:47)
23. "O thou ____ among women" (Song of Solomon 6:1)
26. Excuse me!
27. "Ehud the son of ____ , a Benjamite" (Judges 3:15)
28. Preposition
29. Measure of Everest (abbr.)
30. "This is ___, which was for to come" (Matthew 11:14)
31. "With the ____ of an ass have I slain a thousand men" (Judges 15:16)
32. Continent (abbr.)
33. Nonsense (Brit.)
34. Table or pike
35. "He...shall be called the son of the ____" (Luke 1:32)
38. "The birds of the air have ____" (Matthew 8:20)
39. Towel identification
40. Horned mammal
41. Describing a taskmaster

43. "A man of ____" (Isaiah's description of the Messiah)
46. Long, long time
47. "The sons of Shemidah were...Likhi, and ____" (1 Chronicles 7:19)
49. Greek form of Noah
50. You're all ___!
51. House of ____
52. Compass pt.

DOWN

1. "Will a man ____ God?" (Malachi 3:8)
2. Always (poet.)
3. "That a great ____ is risen up among us" (Luke 7:16)
4. One of the twelve tribes of Israel
5. Horn holler?
6. "Ye do ___, not knowing the scriptures" (Matthew 22:29)
7. Thoroughfare (abbr.)
8. "We have found the ____" (John 1:41)
9. Steeple
10. More than freckled
11. "Stand in ___, and sin not" (Psalm 4:4)
16. Five make one in b'ball
18. Average
20. Stopover on the journey from Egypt to Jordan (Numbers 33:27)
21. Where Joshua was buried: "on the north side of the hill ____" (Judges 2:9)
22. "And the children of Sheshan; ____" (1 Chronicles 2:31)
23. Small, snappish dog
24. Maze instruction
25. Boroughs

27. To cover up
30. "He became the author of _____ salvation" (Hebrews 5:9)
31. "They have slain them which showed before of the coming of the _____ _____" (2 words, Acts 7:52)
34. Rend
36. Belgian city
37. Pronoun
38. Standards
40. Pester continuously
41. "A time to rend, and a time to _____" (Ecclesiastes 3:7)
42. What a "piggy" is

43. Title of respect
44. "A brother offended is harder to be _____ than a strong city." (Proverbs 18:19)
45. Understand
48. Favorite first word
by Evelyn Boyington

ACROSS

1. To engrave with acid
4. Common contraction
7. Woodwind
11. Powerful lobby in D.C.
12. Erstwhile emerald?
14. "____ we like sheep have gone astray" (Isaiah 53:6)
15. Proximal's polar opposite
17. Central African nation
19. Gemstone comprising third foundation of wall of the New Jerusalem (Revelation 21)
21. To know (Scot.)
22. Spigot
24. Balaam's beast
25. Marble for marbles?
29. Scold constantly
31. "____ is finished" (John 19:30)
32. Gem in second row of high priest's breastplate (Exodus 28)
33. "I find ____ fault in him" (John 19:4)
34. "And on earth peace, good will toward ____" (Luke 2:14)
36. Bottom of the barrel?
37. "Some of them thought, because Judas had the ____" (John 13:29)
38. Familiar name of Brazilian port
40. Geographical abbr.
42. Gemstone comprising seventh foundation of wall of 19 across
47. Return to original speed (music)
49. Indian communal village
51. Zilch
52. Formerly known as the coney, in Bible times
54. Row
55. Gem in fourth row of 32 across
56. "Thou anointest my head with ____" (Psalm 23:5)
57. Cause disintegration of blood cells

DOWN

1. "But the ____ of all things is at hand" (1 Peter 4:7)
2. Practical joker
3. Converts into cold, hard currency
4. Soft mineral
5. Linking verb
6. To scatter or cluster
8. Tree found on Persian Gulf
9. Not a spring chicken
10. Character actor Jack, whose stock-in-trade was westerns
12. Cohort
13. Conscious self
16. Exposure in Ixtapa?
18. "Go to the ___, thou sluggard" (Proverbs 6:6)
20. Covers with a hard, glossy surface
23. Slender cigars
24. Aspire to
25. First ___
26. Needlefish
27. What to wear
28. Printer's measure
30. ____ and Magog (Revelation 20)
35. Well
37. Young Yankee employee?
39. Measure of resistance
40. Sodium hydroxide
41. One billionth (prefix)
43. Measure of rotations (abbr.)
44. Toy or turkey?
45. Gemstone

46. Light (Lat.)
48. _____ ear
50. Mineral resource
53. Eastern seaboard state (abbr.)
   by John H. Thornberg

ACROSS

1. Bashful
4. "Lest thou _____ thy foot against a stone" (Psalm 91:12)
8. "A glorious church, not having ___, or wrinkle" (Ephesians 5:27)
12. Sheltered from wind
13. Gnawing pain
14. Father of Ham, Shem, and Japheth
15. State that is bordered by Illinois (abbr.)
16. "Jesus saith unto them, Come and _____" (John 21:12)
17. Cattle or farm
18. Worship
20. Body parts between the waist and the knees
21. Ironic
22. Engage beforehand
25. Hard fat found in cattle and sheep
27. "The wisdom that is from above is...full of _____ and good fruits" (James 3:17)
28. Affirmative in Acapulco
29. "Your _____ men shall dream dreams" (Joel 2:28)
30. God worshiped by Jezebel, and its namesakes
31. Cotton ___
32. Article
33. Second planet from the sun
34. Small, headless nail
35. Qualities of a bishop: "_____, not a brawler" (1 Timothy 3:3)
37. Command to a horse
38. Killer whale
39. One foundation of Christian life
42. "O ye of little _____" (Matthew 8:26)

44. City in Normandy
45. Command word
46. Big blunder
47. "That ye _____ one another" (John 13:34)
48. United
49. Preposition
50. "Hear my voice, and _____ the door" (Revelation 3:20)
51. "That they may be ___, even as we are" (John 17:22)

DOWN

1. Make a mistake
2. "He that hath ears to _____" (Matthew 11:15)
3. Biblical pronoun
4. Jay's love in The Great Gatsby
5. Teen trauma
6. Pronoun
7. "Greater is _____ that is in you" (1 John 4:4)
8. Brisk and lively
9. Composure
10. Canoe component
11. "Hallowed be _____ name" (Matthew 6:9)
16. "Whose waters cast up mire and _____" (Isaiah 57:20)
17. Floppy ones?
19. Astonished
20. Feathered fishing lures
22. Real winner (colloq.)
23. Encompassing the Orient
24. "Charity suffereth long, and is _____" (1 Corinthians 13:4)
25. "For though thou wash thee with nitre, and take thee much_____" (var., Jeremiah 2:22)
26. Bone of the forearm
27. Bread from heaven

30. Hardwood tree
31. "The beauty of old men is the ____ head" (Proverbs 20:29)
33. "Add to your faith ____" (2 Peter 1:5)
34. Noggin
36. What the bread winner must do
37. "But her leaf shall be ____" (Jeremiah 17:8)
39. ____ the way
40. First home
41. "And he ____ upon a cherub, and did fly" (Psalm 18:10)
42. Airport abbr.
43. Vowel trio

44. To go back on a promise, with "out"
47. Biblical exclamation
48. Officer of the U.S. Army (abbr.) *by John H. Thornberg*

261

ACROSS

1. Shushan, per the NIV
5. ____ cake
9. "I therefore so ____, not as uncertainly; so fight I"
   (1 Corinthians 9:26)
12. Tore
13. The Syrians of ____
    (2 Samuel 10, hired by Ammon's heirs to fight David)
14. "Love ____ another"
    (1 John 4:7)
15. Brother of Jacob
16. Brother of Cain
17. Fuss
18. History
20. Moses' mouthpiece
22. Friendship
25. Alto ____ (jazz instrument)
26. O.T. major prophet (abbr.)
27. Melchizedek, king of ____
30. "O sole ___"
33. Seth's sire
34. Bridle part
35. Together
36. Time of revival (abbr.)
37. "City of David" (Luke 2)
39. What CBS, for one, would like to do: ___Fox?
40. Elemental particles
41. Shake violently
44. Window component
46. Crone
47. Like a funk
49. New Testament book
53. "Love worketh no ____ to his neighbour" (Romans 13:10)
54. Like a certain "ranger"
55. "But ____ found grace in the eyes of the Lord" (Genesis 6:8)
56. Two-____, as tissue

57. Loose ____
58. Times long past

DOWN

1. Compass dir.
2. Moments of elation
3. "Let the ____ roar, and the fulness thereof" (Psalm 96:11)
4. One who votes
5. Peter, for one
6. "And they put on him a purple ____" (John 19:2)
7. Honest one
8. Son of Beor (Numbers 22:5)
9. Deafening din
10. Let go
11. ____ tetra (tropical fish)
19. Yiddish exclamations
21. Get rid of
22. Slightly open
23. Darius the ____ (Daniel 11)
24. Middle Eastern country
25. Father of Enos (Luke 3)
28. Be a party to
29. American ____ (college course, abbr.)
30. Line that separates the earth's crust from its mantle (abbr.)
31. Thing to be done
32. Units of electrical resistance
35. City near Jerusalem
37. Collection
38. ____ Cruces, NM
39. Conjunction
41. Single snack
42. "Then led they Jesus...unto the ____ of judgment" (John 18:28)
43. Unsightly
44. "Here am I, ____ me"
    (Isaiah 6:8)
45. Mimics

48. Many moons
50. Dove ditty
51. Bituminous pitch
52. Pronoun
    by John H. Thornberg

ACROSS

1. Great amount
5. Lea denizen
8. "All ____ that we should be saved was...taken away" (Acts 27:20)
12. Son of Joah (1 Chronicles 6:21)
13. Gold, in Guatanamo
14. Grandson of Adam
15. "Neither count I my life____ unto myself" (Acts 20:24)
16. Bled, as fabric
17. Used to be
18. Usually 15 percent
20. To ____ for
22. Father of Rachel, and his namesakes
25. Cause great anger
29. Author of Tristram Shandy
30. 911 happy ending
31. Naval officer (abbr.)
32. Laughing syllable
33. "Make a great flame with smoke ____ ____ out of the city" (2 words, Judges 20:38)
37. Belonging to the first son of Eliphaz (Genesis 36:11)
41. "We who are Jews by ____" (Galatians 2:15)
42. "____ ____ Abana and Pharpar... better than all the waters of Israel?" (2 Kings 5:12)
43. Number of performances of a play
44. Day ____
45. Get out of
48. Former Mideast republic (abbr.)
50. Feminine name
54. "When ye ____ the harvest of your land" (Leviticus 23:22)
55. Hwy.
56. She was called "tender eyed"
57. Feminine name
58. Still
59. Writer Bombeck

DOWN

1. "I will ____ evil beasts out of the land" (Leviticus 26:6)
2. Netherlands metropolis
3. Feminine name
4. ____ board
5. "They came and took up his ____, and laid it in a tomb" (Mark 6:29)
6. Mouth (pl.)
7. "And there appeared another ____ in heaven" (Revelation 12:3)
8. "Let them live; but let them be ____ of wood" (Joshua 9:21)
9. Holy ____ of Israel
10. ____ favor (Sp.)
11. Compass pt.
19. "There was no room for them in the ____" (Luke 2:7)
21. Chemical suffix
22. Place of the seal (abbr.)
23. Entrance court (pl.)
24. Untamed one
26. Son of Carmi who was stoned by all of Israel (Joshua 7)
27. Fertilizer from sea birds
28. Shoe width
33. Hosp. employee
34. Continent which includes Italia
35. S.A. country
36. "But the talk of the lips tendeth only to ____" (Proverbs 14:23)
37. Musical instrument of the Old Testament (Isaiah 5)
38. Rather than
39. "____ not with him that flattereth with his lips" (Proverbs 20:19)

40. Elm, for one (abbr.)
45. Eastern state univ.
46. Uncle of Saul (1 Samuel 14)
47. Plug up
49. Consumed
51. Poetic preposition
52. Candidate for a burnt offering
53. Exclamation
    by Janet W. Adkins

ACROSS

1. Rouen repository
5. Douglas, for one
8. Father of Gaal (Judges 9:26)
12. Zest
13. Act or process (suffix)
14. "If a man _____ me, he will keep my words" (John 14:23)
15. City in western Germany
16. "Peter…_____ unto the sepulchre" (Luke 24:12)
17. Paradise
18. "There shall not be found among you...a charmer...or a _____" (Deuteronomy 18:10–11)
21. Lend an ___
22. Witticism
23. Maximum
26. "Trust in the Lord...and verily thou shalt be _____" (Psalm 37:3)
27. "A brother offended is harder to be _____ than a strong city" (Proverbs 18:19)
30. He was (Lat.)
31. _____ pottage (dish served in Genesis 25)
32. "And Judah and Israel dwelt safely...under his _____" (1 Kings 4:25)
33. Paving material
34. "A golden bell and a pomegranate, upon the _____ of the robe" (Exodus 28:34)
35. With fewer impurities
36. Son of Noah (var., Luke 3)
37. Wrongdoing
38. "He found them ten times better than all the..._____" (Daniel 1:20)
43. On a cruise
44. Mini_____

45. Pester
47. "God sent him forth from the garden...to _____ the ground" (Genesis 3:23)
48. Work unit
49. Server's advantage, in tennis
50. Unbelievable, as a story
51. Dentist's degree (abbr.)
52. Two nonconsecutive notes on the diatonic scale

DOWN

1. Community consumer org.
2. Elvis' middle name
3. Number of holes on a par-three course, usually
4. "Lest he be wise in his own _____" (Proverbs 26:5)
5. Hubbub
6. Last duke from the line of Esau (Genesis 36)
7. Appointed another appellation
8. "And I will bring forth a seed... and mine _____ shall inherit it" (Isaiah 65:9)
9. Augur
10. At any time
11. Where thieves dwell?
19. Tattle, with "on"
20. Where Cain dwelt (Genesis 4)
23. Rent out
24. Masculine name
25. Spoil
26. Not masc.
27. "I count all things but loss...that I may _____ Christ" (Philippians 3:8)
28. "When we are absent _____ from another" (Genesis 31:49)
29. Father of Abner (2 Samuel 3:23)
31. Separated

32. "Come thou hither...and dip thy morsel in the ____" (Ruth 2:14)
34. "Walk about Zion, and go round about ____" (Psalm 48:12)
35. "They sewed ____ leaves together" (Genesis 3:7)
36. Hesitate
37. "Thou shalt compass me about with ____ of deliverance" (Psalm 32:7)
38. Continent
39. Mimic a merchant
40. Ingredient definitely not found in low-fat recipes
41. Sat high in the saddle
42. "For Paul had determined to ____ by Ephesus" (Acts 20:16)
43. Corporate giant (abbr.)
46. Genetic material
   by Janet W. Adkins

ACROSS

1. Ancient Hebrew dry measure (pl.)
5. Fifteenth division of Psalm 119
7. Snare to trap game or fish
8. "And Samuel told him every ____" (1 Samuel 3:18)
10. Weak day? (abbr.)
11. "I am ____ at my very heart" (Jeremiah 4:19)
13. "Lucifer, ____ of the morning! how art thou cut down to the ground" (Isaiah 14:12)
14. "Speakest to ____ the wicked from his wicked way" (Ezekiel 3:18)
15. "La ____" (Debussy composition)
17. Omen; portent
19. Withhold nothing
21. Pronoun
22. Black ____
23. Pronoun for a seaworthy vessel
24. U.S. West Indies territory (abbr.)
25. "And David heard...that ____ did shear his sheep" (1 Samuel 25:4)
27. Knight's steed
29. O.T. book (abbr.)
30. Chinese canine breed
31. Age
32. Lot, to Abraham
34. Foot or footlike structure (zool.)
35. Fencer's gear
36. ____ France
37. "I am like an owl of the ____" (Psalm 102:6)
39. "And the veil of the temple was ____ in twain" (Mark 15:38)

DOWN

1. Give a pink slip
2. "____ I my brother's keeper?" (Genesis 4:9)
3. "____ of the leaven of the Pharisees" (Matthew 16:6)
4. Twenty-first division of Psalm 119
5. "If thou doest not well, ____ lieth at the door" (Genesis 4:7)
6. Liquid measure of ancient Hebrews
7. All ____!
9. To make suitable
10. Like all humans
11. This may be flipped
12. God (Lat.)
13. "They toil not, neither do they ____" (Matthew 6:28)
14. "Son of man, ____ for the multitude of Egypt" (Ezekiel 32:18)
16. "All the ____ run into the sea" (Ecclesiastes 1:7)
18. One who is warded off?
19. Author of Pygmalion
20. Money, in Milano
23. Demonstrate
26. David ____ Gurion
27. Stilton, for one
28. Late actor Will
30. "Be of good ____" (Matthew 9:2)
33. Catalog abbr.
34. "I am counted with them that go down into the ____" (Psalm 88:4)
36. Masculine nickname
38. Printer's measure
by Janet W. Adkins

ACROSS

1. Diva's defining moment
5. One who comes out, familiarly
8. Land measure
12. Preceding portrait or pity?
13. Mist (Scot.)
14. What every word in the Bible is
15. American playwright
16. Stadium sound
17. Actress Daly
18. Imitate
20. Linking verb
22. Birthplace of Saul
25. "The Lord knoweth the thoughts of man, that they are ____" (Psalm 94:11)
29. "In Damascus the governor under ____ the king" (2 Corinthians 11:32)
30. "For how can I ____ to see the evil that shall come unto my people?" (Esther 8:6)
31. Wrongly (prefix)
32. Twelve-step gp.
33. "In lowliness of mind let each ____ other better than themselves" (Philippians 2:3)
37. French painter Pierre Auguste ____
41. "____ my soul from their destructions" (Psalm 35:17)
42. "Ye were without Christ, being ____ from the commonwealth of Israel" (Ephesians 2:12)
43. Vacuum tube (abbr.)
44. Father of Saul, king of Israel
45. He offered "a more excellent sacrifice" than his brother
48. Exclamation of disbelief
50. Prophetess who awaited the Messiah

54. Used to be
55. Before (poet.)
56. "For thou art a ____ kinsman" (Ruth 3:9)
57. Corn quantity (pl.)
58. N.T. bk.
59. May be

DOWN

1. He succeeded his father, King Abijam (1 Kings 15)
2. Area (abbr.)
3. ____ de la Cite, in Paris
4. "But when thou makest ____ ____, call the poor, the maimed" (2 words, Luke 14:13)
5. Use of force or threats
6. Historical period
7. "Let us ____ ourselves valiantly for our people" (1 Chronicles 19:13)
8. Wait on
9. Wail
10. String of victories
11. Shoe width
19. "Of ____, the family of the Punites" (Numbers 26:23)
21. Sprinted
22. Less spicy
23. Bail out of bed
24. Musical notations
26. Measures used worldwide (abbr.)
27. "____ up a child in the way he should go" (Proverbs 22:6)
28. Parts of a century
34. O.T. bk. (abbr.)
35. Continent (abbr.)
36. ____-ammah, chief city of the Philistines (2 Samuel 8:1)
37. Jacob served Laban seven years for her

38. Father of Hophni and Phineas
39. Belonging to the first month, the month in which Pur was cast (Esther 3:7)
40. Whirlwind near the Faeroe Islands
45. "Stand in ___, and sin not" (Psalm 4:4)
46. Aunt ____ of TV's Mayberry
47. "To ____ is human"
49. Son of Jether (1 Chronicles 7:38)
51. Born (Fr.)
52. Not (Scot.)
53. "Thou hast scattered thine enemies with thy strong ____" (Psalm 89:10)

by Janet W. Adkins

271

ACROSS

1. Exclamation of sorrow
5. Catalog promise (abbr.)
8. "But ____ found grace in the eyes of the Lord" (Genesis 6:8)
12. Greek form of feminine name that means "princess"
13. ____ wife
14. ____-Lebanon (mountain range in W. Syria, which includes Mt. Hermon)
15. Not ready to turn pro (abbr.)
16. Bone
17. Cave dwellers
18. New Testament epistle
22. The green, green grass of home?
23. ____ of the above
24. Like a sprinter
27. 1/1000th of an inch
28. Exodus character
31. "For ____ be called, but few chosen" (Matthew 20:16)
32. Prevent
33. "Diana...should be destroyed, whom all ____...worshippeth" (Acts 19:27)
34. Employ
35. Biblical verb
36. "Let us ____ before the Lord our maker" (Psalm 95:6)
37. Greek letter
38. "And the ____ gave up the dead which were in it" (Revelation 20:13)
39. "The Lord hath given you the land,...all the ____...faint because of you" (Joshua 2:9)
44. Concept (comb. form)
45. Historical period
46. Tiny amount (colloq.)
48. Bereft; desolate (arch.)
49. Beam of light
50. Masculine name
51. Healing plant
52. Affirmative
53. "Simon ____..."

DOWN

1. Old Testament king whose name means "physician"
2. "For thou art my ____...the Lord will lighten my darkness" (2 Samuel 22:29)
3. Son of Ulla (1 Chronicles 7:39)
4. "O ____ us early with thy mercy" (Psalm 90:14)
5. Progenitor (colloq.)
6. With "down," way to meet the bed
7. "We are perplexed, but not in ____" (2 Corinthians 4:8)
8. Husband of Abigail (1 Samuel 25)
9. Second son of Judah (1 Chronicles 2:3)
10. Members of the bar (abbr.)
11. Possessive pronoun
19. His wife turned into a pillar of salt
20. Part of the psyche
21. Under the weather
24. Texas institute of higher learning (abbr.)
25. Had been
26. Suffix used to form feminine nouns
27. Welcome ___
28. Enzyme of vegetable origin (suffix)
29. Grain mentioned in the Old Testament (Isaiah 28)
30. Suitable for (suffix)

32. "And fire shall consume the tabernacles of ____" (Job 15:34)
33. Husband of Sapphira
35. "And there was war between ____ and Baasha king of Israel" (1 Kings 15:16)
36. Greek island in the Aegean
37. Single speech sound
38. Corset (Brit.)
39. Matinee ____
40. Notorious emperor of Rome
41. *Dies* ___
42. Brother of Job (Genesis 46:13)
43. Don't leave!
44. Longshoremen's org.

47. Solution (abbr.)

ACROSS

1. Don't just sit there
4. "I do __ my bow in the cloud" (Genesis 9:13)
7. Mightier than a machete?
10. Vast desert region (abbr.)
11. Of a certain Indochinese kingdom
12. Enthusiasm
13. "For whom he did foreknow, he also did ____" (Romans 8:29)
16. "Wound for wound, ____ for ____" (clue repeated) (Exodus 21:25)
17. Drunkard
18. Shows or does (suffix)
19. Epitome of wisdom
23. ____ au lait
25. Chums
26. Corrida cheer
27. "They lavish gold...hire a gold-smith; and he maketh it __ __" (2 words, Isaiah 46:6)
28. "They of Persia and of ____... were in thine army" (Ezekiel 27:10)
29. ____ code
30. "Lest I ____ mine own inheritance" (Ruth 4:6)
31. Ancient meeting place, in a city
32. Organ component
33. Omen
35. The Great ____
36. Half of 104, to Hadrian
37. "Ye were ____ with that holy Spirit of promise" (Ephesians 1:13)
40. "Ye are complete in him, which is the head of all ____ and power" (Colossians 2:10)
43. Helps

44. College entrance requirement (abbr.)
45. Three, in Turin
46. Not (Scot.)
47. Atlas, for one (abbr., pl.)
48. Well-spoken affirmative

DOWN

1. Cleopatra's instrument of death, and others
2. "They laid the ark of the Lord upon the ____" (1 Samuel 6:11)
3. "____ shall a man leave his father and his mother" (Genesis 2:24)
4. Drifted off
5. "Rise up, ye women that are at ____" (Isaiah 32:9)
6. Young one
7. Greek philosopher
8. Put on the feedbag
9. Compass dir.
12. Certain chemical compounds
14. Went out on the town
15. Tristran and ____, of the medieval legend
19. Prepare certain dishes
20. "For we...do groan...that ____ might be swallowed up of life" (2 Corinthians 5:4)
21. Oil (comb. form)
22. ____ tide
23. Become one with nature?
24. "For this ____ is mount Sinai in Arabia" (Galatians 4:25)
25. Of a sandy beach
29. "Set me as ____ ____ upon thine heart" (2 words, Song of Solomon 8:6)

31. "When her masters saw that the hope of their _____ was gone" (Acts 16:19)
34. Playground perennial
35. "Ye love the uppermost _____ in the synagogues" (Luke 11:43)
37. "He _____ on the ground, and made clay" (John 9:6)
38. To be (Fr.)
39. Colors
40. _____ fried
41. Long, narrow inlet
42. Doctrine or theory
by Janet W. Adkins

by Janet W. Adkins

ACROSS

1. Once more; again
5. Egyptian cobra, for one
8. "Launch out...let down your ____ for a draught" (Luke 5:4)
12. Feminine nickname (var.)
13. 1/1000th of an inch
14. "____, lama sabachthani?" (Mark 15:34)
15. With "off," visibly upset
16. Defined time of history
17. Bobbin of a weaver's shuttle
18. Have
20. U.S. medical research org.
22. Woman married (two words)
25. "The Lord is thy ____...thy shade upon thy right hand" (Psalm 121:5)
29. Doesn't pedal
30. "But to him that ____ righteousness shall be a sure reward" (Proverbs 11:18)
31. Assn.
32. Definite article
33. Depended upon
37. "____, which had kept his bed eight years, and was sick of the palsy" (Acts 9:33)
40. What the frontrunner will do
41. One of "the seven churches in Asia" (Revelation 1:11)
42. Long, undetermined time
43. Son of Noah (var., Luke 3:36)
44. Having to do with the community (abbr.)
47. Anger
49. Wood for a funeral rite
53. "____ was a great man among the Anakims" (Joshua 14:15)
55. Corn serving

56. "Not one ____ of his head fall to the ground" (1 Samuel 14:45)
57. Gossip (colloq.)
58. Promotion for a police officer (abbr.)
59. They attend Promise Keepers events

DOWN

1. Corporate giant (abbr.)
2. Jacqueline Kennedy, ____ Bouvier
3. Before (poet.)
4. "But the younger ____ refuse... they will marry" (1 Timothy 5:11)
5. Make ____
6. Title of respect
7. "So Solomon...covered the floor of the house with ____ of fir" (1 Kings 6:14–15)
8. "He shall neither have son nor ____ among his people" (Job 18:19)
9. High priest who raised Samuel
10. High, rocky hill
11. Wrongdoing
19. ____ paint
21. Vowel trio
22. Prepare meat for grilling
23. One of the fenced cities of Naphtali (Joshua 19:38)
24. "Though thou shouldest make thy nest as high as the ____" (Jeremiah 49:16)
26. His name literally means "a stone"
27. Leader Allen of the Green Mountain Boys
28. Father of Joanna (Luke 3:27)

34. Wrath
35. Part of the psyche
36. "The cock shall not crow, till thou hast ____ me thrice" (John 13:38)
37. Express one's opinion
38. Crony (arch.)
39. Maiden in mythology
44. Possessed with a devil
45. Eastern state univ.
46. Where an inch is really an inch (abbr.)
48. Feminine name
50. Sweet potato
51. Grain mentioned in the Old Testament (Isaiah 28)

52. Sea eagle
54. "Then said I, ____ Lord God" (Jer. 1:6)

ACROSS

1. _____ water
4. One of Shem's children (Genesis 10:22)
8. Business correspondence abbr.
12. That (Sp.)
13. Latvian monetary unit
14. Composer Stravinsky
15. Becoming slower, in music (abbr.)
16. Layer
17. _____ of the above
18. "_____ not at the matter: for he that is higher...regardeth" (Ecclesiastes 5:8)
20. _____ culpa
22. Person concerned with (suffix)
23. Evergreen tree of the cypress family, known for its berries
27. "Thou shalt be missed, because thy _____ will be empty" (1 Samuel 20:18)
29. Source of poi
30. Norma ___, Oscar-winning movie
31. "So Manasseh made Judah and the inhabitants of Jerusalem to _____" (2 Chronicles 33:9)
32. "So will I do for my servants' _____ that I may not destroy them all" (Isaiah 65:8)
33. Carbohydrate (suffix)
34. Resinous substance of South Asia
35. Canned (colloq.)
36. Not brand new
37. Son of Uzziah (Nehemiah 11:4)
39. One (Scot.)
40. Mountain stat.
41. "He is _____ of death" (Matthew 26:66)

44. He helped build the towns of Ono and Lod (1 Chronicles 8:12)
47. Steel beam used in construction
49. Biblical exclamation
50. Presidential power
51. Alley Oop's girlfriend
52. Paving substance
53. "The land is as the garden of _____ before them" (Joel 2:3)
54. Joyeux _____ (holiday greetings in Grenoble?)
55. Sea eagle

DOWN

1. Time in an elected office
2. "All they which dwelt in _____ heard the word of the Lord Jesus" (Acts 19:10)
3. "Let me freely speak unto you of the _____ David" (Acts 2:29)
4. Amend slightly
5. Complain bitterly
6. Gobbled up
7. "But their scribes and Pharisees _____ against his disciples" (Luke 5:30)
8. _____ Peninsula
9. Time past
10. "Unto us a child is born, unto us a _____ is given" (Isaiah 9:6)
11. Before (poet.)
19. Profession of the late James Herriot (colloq.)
21. Son of Seth
23. Father of Agur (Proverbs 30:1)
24. "Woe unto you, scribes and Pharisees...ye compass sea and land to make one _____" (Matthew 23:15)
25. At _____ (heard at boot camp)
26. Bane of oboist?

27. Actress Ward
28. He was (Lat.)
29. "He exacted the silver and... gold...of every one according to his _____" (2 Kings 23:35)
32. Breeze along
36. Iowa institute of higher learning (abbr.)
38. "And Moses told _____ all the words of the Lord" (Exodus 4:28)
39. Related to the sense of hearing
41. Strong wind
42. Speed along
43. Seafarer's woolly tale?

44. Whom the serpent beguiled, ever so subtly
45. Hotel room requirement
46. Summer on the Seine
48. Startling sound
by Janet W. Adkins

PUZZLE 139

ACROSS

1. And so on (abbr.)
4. Describing nonclergy
8. "This ____ Jesus, which is taken up from you into heaven" (Acts 1:11)
12. Gala event, to Gabrielle
13. ____ Domini
14. "The Lord be a ____ and faithful witness" (Jeremiah 42:5)
15. Poetic contraction
16. Welcome benefit or blessing
17. Transportation (colloq.)
18. "All the land of Canaan fainted by ____ of the famine" (Genesis 47:13)
20. "The children of Keros, the children of ____" (Nehemiah 7:47)
22. Uncle of Saul (1 Samuel 14)
23. Fortified rampart
27. Hit TV show
29. "And his ____ went throughout all Syria" (Matthew 4:24)
30. Busy one
31. Untried, as talent
33. "Beggar named Lazarus, which was laid at his gate, full of ____" (Luke 16:20)
34. Singleton, in Strasbourg
35. Doctors' support group (abbr.)
36. Mythological god of war
37. KJV word for "bud," as on a flower (Exodus 25)
38. "I will utter dark ____ of old" (Psalm 78:2)
40. "Lord, if it be thou, ____ me come unto thee on the water" (Matthew 14:28)
41. The year 1501, to Flavius
42. Son of Levi (Numbers 3:17)
45. Continent
48. Change direction slightly
50. Land where Cain dwelt (Genesis 4)
51. What is unfurled
52. Fencing sword
53. Food fish
54. Actress Daly
55. Actress Talbott
56. WWII milieu (abbr.)

DOWN

1. Father of Peleg and Joktan (Genesis 10:25)
2. Noxious weed (Matthew 13)
3. "Create in me a ____ heart, O God" (Psalm 51:10)
4. Apply some elbow grease
5. Therefore (arch.)
6. Ending for many words in Italian
7. Devours
8. "She [Rebekah] said...We have both ____ and provender enough" (Genesis 24:25)
9. Onassis
10. Miry clay
11. Shoe width
19. "I will ____ no wicked thing before mine eyes" (Psalm 101:3)
21. The Philippines, for example, to Rene
23. Uncovers
24. "And he brought forth the spoil of the city in great ____" (2 Samuel 12:30)
25. Nevada city
26. "Thou wilt ____ him in perfect peace" (Isaiah 26:3)
27. Times of historical significance
28. "In ____ was there a voice heard, lamentation, and weeping" (Matthew 2:18)

29. "Be of good cheer; thy sins be _____ thee" (Matthew 9:2)
32. "After the _____ which they call heresy, so worship I the God" (Acts 24:14)
33. "A foolish man, which built his house upon the _____" (Matthew 7:26)
37. "In the night _____ of Moab is laid waste, and brought to silence" (Isaiah 15:1)
39. Another word for idol
40. City of Macedonia where Paul preached

42. "With them in the clouds, to _____ the Lord in the air" (1 Thessalonians 4:17)
43. "For he shall grow up...as a _____ out of a dry ground" (Isaiah 53:2)
44. _____ the seer (2 Chronicles 12:15)
45. Rear of a ship
46. Cunning
47. John (Scot.)
49. On or upon (prefix)
by Janet W. Adkins

ACROSS

1. Juliette Low's organization (abbr.)
4. Depot (abbr.)
7. ____ reliever
11. "The ____ state of that man is worse than the first" (Luke 11:26)
13. Desire
14. Competent
15. Theory
16. Old auto
17. Wild goat
18. Stinging comment
19. Welfare; benefit
21. "And ____ also the Jairite was a chief ruler about David" (2 Samuel 20:26)
23. Part of a day (abbr.)
24. One-____ is a tithe
27. Righteous, symbolical name of Israel (var.)
32. One of Lamech's two wives (Genesis 4:19)
33. Conjunction
34. Late folk singer Laura
35. David's nephew (2 Samuel 13:3)
38. "Yet through the ____ of water it will bud, and bring forth boughs" (Job 14:9)
39. Certain therapist (abbr.)
40. Kitchen necessity
41. "Can two walk ____" (Amos 3:3)
46. "____ it Romantic?"
49. Inter ____
50. On or upon (prefix)
51. Unit of weight in the Middle East
52. Practices fabrication
53. ____ Perce, North American Indian tribe

54. Heads
56. Center; source
57. Understand; realize
58. "____ unto you, scribes and Pharisees" (Matthew 23:14)

DOWN

1. Speaking too easily
2. Actress Thompson
3. Tribe to which Anna the prophetess belonged (Luke 2)
4. Mideast country
5. Problem child?
6. "And he [Samson] said...then shall I be weak, and be as ____ man" (Judges 16:11)
7. Matched set
8. French clergy member
9. Channel, Solomon, Hawaiian, et al., to Christophe
10. ____! (word heard in a queue)
12. Aka Dorcas (Acts 9)
20. Sounds of hesitation
22. ____ factor (group of antigens)
24. ____ Mahal
25. People living in southern Nigeria
26. Feminine nickname
27. Patient and faithful sufferer
28. "But ye have an ____ from the Holy One, and ye know all things" (1 John 2:20)
29. Deli loaf
30. Footed vase
31. ____ a chance
36. Period
37. Site of Mars' hill
38. Thus
40. "In a race run all, but one receiveth the ____" (1 Corinthians 9:24)
41. Bath powder

42. Highly spiced stew
43. The _____ eagle (fowl not to be
    eaten; Leviticus 11:18)
44. "Among these nations shalt thou
    find no _____"
    (Deuteronomy 28:65)
45. Fencer's adjunct
47. Garbage _____
48. Mount _____, in the land of
    Moab, gateway to Canaan
    (Deuteronomy 32)
55. Compass point
by Janet W. Adkins

ACROSS

1. "For ____ have sinned, and come short of the glory of God" (Romans 3:23)
4. ____ Miner's Daughter (Loretta Lynn film biography)
8. ____ California
12. Misery
13. "He died unto sin ___: but in that he liveth" (Romans 6:10)
14. Son of Shobal (Genesis 36:23)
15. "Angels which kept not their first ____" (Jude 6)
17. In close proximity
19. "Kiss the Son, ____ he be angry, and ye perish" (Psalm 2:12)
21. Alaskan outpost
22. Extinct creatures
25. Upper ____
27. Calm; tranquil
28. Where Stephane keeps his savings
29. Young man
32. "Thou shalt dwell in the land of Goshen, and thou shalt ____ ____ unto me" (2 words, Genesis 45:10)
34. "Thy ___, O God, is for ever and ever" (Psalm 45:6)
36. What old colleges do?
37. Hand (Sp.)
39. The Thin Man's (of moviedom) best friend?
40. Simon ___
41. "____ ye in at the strait gate" (Matthew 7:13)
42. Son of Eliphaz (Genesis 36:11)
45. What crowed thrice (Matthew 26)
47. "The governor under ____ the king kept the city of the Damascenes" (2 Corinthians 11:32)

49. One like Mr. Dithers (of the comics), and others
53. With 20 Down, singing syllables
54. First murder victim
56. Retirement acct.
57. Printer's measure
58. Darius the ___, ruler of Babylon
59. See ___

DOWN

1. "Stand in ___, and sin not" (Psalm 4:4)
2. ____ Alamos
3. "____ all the earth fear the Lord" (Psalm 33:8)
4. Shelters for farm animals
5. Individuals
6. Dog days demand (abbr.)
7. Where the cedars were acclaimed (abbr.)
8. "____ Buddies" (short-lived 80s TV sit-com)
9. City in southern Judah (Joshua 15:50)
10. Color of green
11. Church denomination (abbr.)
16. "He sitteth ____ and keepeth silence" (Lamentations 3:28)
18. He "walked with God"
20. With 53 Across, singing syllable
22. "Him that worketh is the reward not reckoned of grace, but of ____" (Romans 4:4)
23. Preposition
24. "If any man will come after me, let him ____ himself" (Matthew 16:24)
26. Aware of what's really happening (colloq.)
28. "Doth the wild ass ____ when he hath grass?" (Job 6:5)

29. "For the Son of man is come to save that which was ____" (Matthew 18:11)
30. To pay one's share (colloq.)
31. "Neither count I my life ____ unto myself" (Acts 20:24)
33. ____ Colonies, Iowa historic communities
35. Holds a certain position
38. Group that advises the President (abbr.)
40. God allowed him to harm Job
41. School (Fr.)
42. "We spend our years as a ____ that is told" (Psalm 90:9)

43. Head of the Eranites (Numbers 26:36)
44. Honey, in the pure, clarified form
46. Father of Jesse
48. Masculine nickname
50. Title of respect
51. Poetic contraction
52. Got the blues
55. "____ sober" (1 Peter 5:8)
by Janet W. Adkins

ACROSS

1. Rascal
4. Le Cote ____ (W. Africa region)
7. Son of Enoch (Genesis 4:18)
11. Woman was made from ____ ____ (2 words)
13. Her name means "life"
14. Spy (colloq.)
15. ____ de soie (rich, silken material)
16. Fall flower, for short
17. "A flattering mouth worketh ____" (Proverbs 26:28)
18. Of considerable size, as a drink
19. "And Israel dwelt in all the cities of the ____" (Numbers 21:25)
21. Used to be
23. WWII red-letter day (abbr.)
24. "A virtuous ____ is a crown to her husband" (Proverbs 12:4)
27. "And Saul smote the Amalekites from ____ until...Shur" (1 Samuel 15:7)
32. "And Israel...spread his tent beyond the tower of ____" (Genesis 35:21)
33. "Therefore God...hath anointed thee with the ____ of gladness" (Psalm 45:7)
34. One conquered by Persia
35. Stringed instrument resembling a lyre, in the Bible
37. Aussie tennis great
38. And (Fr.)
39. ____ Harbor, NY
40. "Lest...when I have preached to others, I...should be a ____" (1 Corinthians 9:27)
45. ____ the Terrible, Russian czar
49. Ancient Hebrew dry measure
50. Broadcast
51. Mount ____, in the land of Moab (Deuteronomy 32)
52. Bill of fare
53. Louis XV, par exemple
54. First name in murder mysteries (and Perry's creator)
55. ____bellum South (period following Civil War)
56. Gov't. drug prevention org.
57. Affirmative

DOWN

1. Like Queeg or Bligh (abbr.)
2. ____ code
3. Popular soap
4. "Luke, the beloved physician, and ___, greet you" (Colossians 4:14)
5. Mature female cell
6. Dismissal
7. Son of Bani (1 Chronicles 9:4)
8. Defeat utterly
9. "When he speaketh ____ ___, he speaketh of his own" (2 words, John 8:44)
10. Cubs' "cribs"?
12. Fortress
20. N.T. book (abbr.)
22. Article
24. NBA great Unseld
25. Harem room
26. Son of (Scot., prefix)
27. Used physical force
28. "How long will ye ____ mischief against a man?" (Psalm 62:3)
29. O.T. book (abbr.)
30. Summer drink
31. Pronoun
33. "For which cause we faint not;... though our ____ man perish" (2 Corinthians 4:16)

36. Feminine nickname
37. Calif. city
39. Mideast country
40. Unconscious condition
41. "So be it"
42. Faxed
43. Factual and actual
44. Vowel quartet
46. "Every thing that he had made...
    was ____ good" (Genesis 1:31)
47. Skilled; competent
48. Greek form of father of Shem,
    and his namesakes
    by Janet W. Adkins

ACROSS

1. Father, by another name
5. Possesses
9. "Why make ye this ___, and weep?" (Mark 5:39)
12. Idol worshiped
13. "How beautiful are the ____ of them that preach the gospel" (Romans 10:15)
14. Receptacle
15. Summers on the Seine
16. "Lest he ____ my soul like a lion, rending it in pieces" (Psalm 7:2)
17. Shakespearean sonnet, perhaps
18. "Let us therefore come boldly unto the ____ of grace" (Hebrews 4:16)
20. "The spirit truly is ___, but the flesh is weak" (Mark 14:38)
22. School subj.
24. "Therefore if thine ____ hunger, feed him" (Romans 12:20)
26. Stern, nautically speaking
28. Tennis call
30. ____ of the Chaldees
31. Simon ___-Jona
32. Preposition
33. Sibling, for short
35. "____ will not forsake thee" (Deuteronomy 4:31)
36. "Unto Shem also, the father of all the children of ____" (Genesis 10:21)
38. Big ___
39. "For his ____ endureth but a moment" (Psalm 30:5)
41. Biblical exclamation
43. The witch of ____ (visited by Saul)
45. Prophet of God who convicted David of his sin

50. Organization similar to 4-H (abbr.)
51. Hardy cabbage
53. Vigorous
54. Brand name to "dye" for
55. "Feed me...for I am faint: therefore was his name called ____" (Genesis 25:30)
56. Feminine name
57. ____ a girl!
58. Like most gossips
59. Sea mammal

DOWN

1. Aid in wrongdoing
2. Noted hot springs locale
3. TV's "Beverly Hillbillies" actor
4. Besides
5. "O Jerusalem, Jerusalem...how ____ would I have gathered thy children" (Matthew 23:37)
6. Tiny
7. Not too far away
8. "Arise, and go into the ____ which is called Straight" (Acts 9:11)
9. Dwelling
10. Greek form of Thomas
11. Bill of currency
19. Take-home pay
21. Article
23. "The ____ of the Lord shone round about them" (Luke 2:9)
25. Part of a century (abbr.)
26. Twelve-step group (abbr.)
27. "For he that is dead is ____ from sin" (Romans 6:7)
29. Sound of hesitation
31. "They are faithful and beloved, partakers of the ____" (1 Timothy 6:2)

32. Iron (abbr.)
33. "____ habla Espanol"
34. Preposition
35. Laughing syllable
37. "The sacrifices of God are a ____ spirit" (Psalm 51:17)
38. Sheep's comment
40. Irritating insects
42. "Thou hast been...a strong tower from the ____" (Psalm 61:3)
44. Famed watchmaker
46. "____ same Jesus, which is taken up from you into heaven" (Acts 1:11)
47. Tortoise's tormentor
48. Egyptian dancing girl
49. Actress Patricia
50. Day of the wk.
52. ____ Alamos

by Janet W. Adkins

ACROSS

1. Singer Garfunkel
4. WWII fliers (abbr.)
7. Poet Teasdale
11. "Serve him with all your heart and with all your ____" (Deuteronomy 11:13)
13. Actress Gardner
14. Freshman at West Point (var.)
15. Father (Aramaic)
16. Not mentioned in another place (abbr.)
17. Opposite of windward
18. "For rebellion is as the sin of ____" (1 Samuel 15:23)
21. Nineteenth U.S. president
23. Vowel trio
24. "____ and friend hast thou put far from me" (Psalm 88:18)
25. Take a ___
26. Article
29. Ancient Hebrew dry measure
30. ____ ear
31. Win, place, or ___
32. ____ capita
33. Form a lap?
34. "The Lord make his face ____ upon thee" (Numbers 6:25)
35. Masculine nickname
36. "Heal the sick, cleanse the lepers, ____ the dead" (Matthew 10:8)
37. "He smote his neighbour unwittingly, and hated him not ____" (Joshua 20:5)
41. Once more; again
42. Used to be
43. "Do good, and ___, hoping for nothing again" (Luke 6:35)
47. Animal shelter
48. Linking verb
49. "He being not a forgetful hearer, but a ____ of the work" (James 1:25)
50. Tribe of the prophetess Anna
51. ____ of man
52. Beans or sauce

DOWN

1. King of Judah, after his father Abijam (1 Kings 15)
2. Embezzle
3. Vat
4. Carries on
5. Opposite of sans
6. "They were all amazed,...saying, We never saw it on this ____" (Mark 2:12)
7. Show mercy
8. ____ breve (music)
9. Sand bar
10. Be a party to mischief
12. One who's passed the bar?
19. Person concerned with (suffix)
20. Lea denizen
21. Base in baseball
22. State unequivocally
24. Cut off
25. Bridle part
26. Not that
27. Sharpen
28. "Hey, ___!" bleated the goat
30. "Now the ____ ____ the time of the firstripe grapes" (2 words, Numbers 13:20)
31. "But thou, O Lord, art a ____ for me" (Psalm 3:3)
33. Title of respect
34. Uncle ___
35. Ivory ____ (where a prof resides, maybe)
36. "He is ___!" (Easter exultation)

37. "Who passing through the valley
of ____ make it a well"
(Psalm 84:6)
38. Son of Seth
39. Treat like the guest of honor
40. Poi source
44. Identified with the Roman
Aurora (Gr. myth.)
45. Latest (comb. form)
46. "My flesh longeth for thee in a
____ and thirsty land"
(Psalm 63:1)
by Janet W. Adkins

ACROSS

1. King of the Amalekites, whose life Saul spared
5. Sibling, familiarly
8. French cleric
12. ____ 18 (Uris novel about Warsaw Ghetto)
13. Unfortunate occurrence (arch.)
14. Father of Eliasaph (Numbers 3:24)
15. Contemporary
16. When this org. meets, there are plenty of doctors in the house
17. "The ____ are a people not strong" (Proverbs 30:25)
18. "Give thanks at the ____ of his holiness" (Psalm 97:12)
21. Poetic contraction
22. "I will ____ you out of their bondage" (Exodus 6:6)
23. In a line
26. Preposition
27. Tell on (colloq.)
30. Soft fabric
31. "If any man be in Christ, he is a ____ creature" (2 Corinthians 5:17)
32. San ___, CA
33. Masculine nickname
34. Work outside the home?
35. One of Japheth's sons (Genesis 10:2)
36. First name in Exodus, Uris novel
37. Mother ____
38. "Are they not all ____ spirits, sent forth...for them who shall be heirs" (Hebrews 1:14)
43. "The Lord is my strength and ____" (Exodus 15:2)
44. Row

45. Yearn for
47. Rabbit relative
48. Mine (Ital.)
49. Cowboy portrayer Jack
50. Son of Salah (Genesis 10:24)
51. Church officer (abbr.)
52. Soaks flax

DOWN

1. Measure of electrical power
2. Inedible fowl (Leviticus 11:18)
3. Toward the sheltered side, nautically
4. "And when I heard this thing, I rent my ____" (Ezra 9:3)
5. "The nations have heard of thy ____, and thy cry hath filled the land" (Jeremiah 46:12)
6. Poetic foot
7. "Yea, the ____ hath found an house" (Psalm 84:3)
8. "____ ____ flowing with milk and honey" (2 words, Exodus 3:8)
9. Where interest accrues, in France
10. ____ noire
11. They loop the Loop
19. Work unit
20. Broadcast on TV
23. Toward the stern of the ship
24. He surrendered at Appomattox
25. Not a spring chicken
26. "The harvest truly is great, but the labourers are ____" (Luke 10:2)
27. "Will a man ____ God?" (Malachi 3:8)
28. "And ____ did that which was right in the eyes of the Lord" (1 Kings 15:11)

29. _____ Aviv
31. "There fell a _____ and grievous sore upon the men which had the mark of the beast" (Revelation 16:2)
32. "[Elijah] sat down under a _____ tree: and he requested...that he might die" (1 Kings 19:4)
34. High-tech medical test (abbr.)
35. Province (abbr.)
36. "And the _____ of the Lord was kindled against Moses" (Exodus 4:14)
37. King of Judaea at Christ's birth
38. Ruth and Orpah's homeland

39. Concerning
40. Canine emotional barometer
41. River formed at Khartoum
42. Pesky insect
43. Pronoun
46. Printer's measures
    by Janet W. Adkins

ACROSS

1. "He [Jesus] went into the synagogue...and stood up for to ____" (Luke 4:16)
5. ____ Sea
8. Become wan
12. Inter ____
13. Mother lode
14. "For this ____ is mount Sinai in Arabia" (Galatians 4:25)
15. "Thou shalt lend unto ____ nations, and thou shalt not borrow" (Deuteronomy 28:12)
16. More, in Managua
17. Showy flower
18. Be quiet!
20. Where Esther lived, but not Mordecai
22. ____ Pan Alley
23. Belonging to a town near Bethel (Joshua 7)
24. Father of Jeroboam (1 Kings 16:3)
27. Drug prescription abbr.
28. Tore
31. Sixth month of the Jewish year
32. Mideast alliance (abbr.)
33. ____ it!
34. French possessive pronoun
35. Feminine name
36. "But let us watch and be ____" (1 Thessalonians 5:6)
37. Work unit
38. Summer home staple
39. Where Jesus delivered "The Olivet Discourse"
46. Goofs
47. Patriotic org.
48. Sacred vow
49. Brand name in sauces
50. Pot adjunct
51. She sailed in 1492
52. Born (Fr.)
53. Parts of a century (abbr.)
54. Hidden obstacle

DOWN

1. Candidates for offerings, as in burnt
2. King of Israel, while Asa reigned over Judah (1 Kings 16)
3. Indigenous, ethnic group of Japan
4. "Until the...dawn, and the ____ ____ arise in your hearts" (2 words, 2 Peter 1:19)
5. CD____ (computer adjunct)
6. Historical time period
7. "We are perplexed, but not in ____" (2 Corinthians 4:8)
8. Old-fashioned fire fighters' needs
9. Site of the Taj Mahal
10. Describing nonclergy
11. Gaelic
19. Direct ____
21. First ____
24. War zone, of the not too distant past (colloq.)
25. Netherlands city
26. ____ relief
27. Catch some rays
28. "To turn aside the needy...that they may ____ the fatherless!" (Isaiah 10:2)
29. Fifth or Madison, e.g.
30. Uncle of Saul (1 Samuel 14:50)
32. "Blessed is the man that walketh not in the counsel of the ____" (Psalm 1:1)
33. Parts of parliamentary procedure
35. Biblical verb

1
2
3
4
5
6
7
8
9
10
11
12
13
14
15
16
17
18
19
20
21
22
23
24
25
26
27
28
29
30
31
32
33
34
35
36
37
38
39
40
41
42
43
44
45
46
47
48
49
50
51
52
53
54

36. Costa del ___
37. "Let him seek peace, and ____ it" (1 Peter 3:11)
38. "He had made a scourge of small ____" (John 2:15)
39. Body of water, in Boulogne
40. Algerian seaport
41. Encourage
42. Not biased
43. "For ____ is the help of man" (Psalm 60:11)
44. Sicilian volcano
45. Carpet quality

by Janet W. Adkins

ACROSS

1. She played Nora to Powell's Nick
4. Balaam's bane
7. Father of Saul (Acts 13)
10. Mimic
11. O.T. book (abbr.)
12. "Through faith also ____ ...received strength to conceive" (Hebrews 11:11)
13. One quality of God
16. Like blustery, cold weather
17. First manners lesson word
18. Grain
20. Title given to Italian monk
21. "Blessed are they whose...sins are ____" (Romans 4:7)
25. Depressed
27. "I ____ on the work of thy hands" (Psalm 143:5)
28. Christmas ____
29. Girl (Scot.)
30. Found in veins?
31. ____ canto, singing style
32. Shoshonean
33. ____ Scott decision, landmark legal case
34. Roll call answer
35. "who hath ____ of eyes?" (Proverbs 23:29)
37. Seasoning (Fr.)
38. Shoe width
39. Heats to almost boiling
42. "The Lord said unto him [Solomon], I have heard thy prayer and thy ____" (1 Kings 9:3)
45. Retirement accts.
46. Its members trace their ancestors to the Mayflower (abbr.)
47. Plain of ____ (Nehemiah 6:2)
48. Kin (abbr.)
49. Consumed
50. ____ Paltz, NY

DOWN

1. "Thy word is a ____ unto my feet" (Psalm 119:105)
2. European auto maker
3. "Because I have called, and ____ ____" (2 words, Proverbs 1:24)
4. Feminine name (var.)
5. Ump's call
6. Texas college (abbr.)
7. ____ blanche
8. Gershwin
9. Maxim; proverb
14. "Lest at any time your hearts be overcharged with...____ of this life" (Luke 21:34)
15. Let free
19. Park, for one (abbr.)
21. "Behold, I cast out devils, and I do ____" (Luke 13:32)
22. "For ____ is as the sin of witchcraft" (1 Samuel 15:23)
23. At any time
24. Editor's mark
25. To obscure
26. Fashionably ____
27. "Let me set a ____ of bread before thee" (1 Samuel 28:22)
33. "Praise the Lord from the earth, ye dragons, and all ____" (Psalm 148:7)
34. Miami pro team
36. Himalayan country
37. Give goosebumps
39. Scram!
40. Finished
41. "Drought and heat consume the ____ waters" (Job 24:19)

42. Title of respect
43. Actress Mary
44. Director Lupino
   by Janet W. Adkins

PUZZLE 148

ACROSS

1. Feminine name
4. "All the trees of the field shall ____ their hands" (Isaiah 55:12)
8. State, Main, etc.
11. Johnny ___
12. Lucifer
13. Biblical exclamation
14. First name of Greek magnate
15. One (comb. form)
16. Confederate general Jubal
18. Easter time
20. Civil rights activist Guinier
21. O.T. book
22. Aloof
25. Geometrical shape
26. Main part of the church building (pl.)
27. Buckeye state (abbr.)
28. "Stand in ___, and sin not" (Psalm 4:4)
29. Linking verb
30. "Asahel was as light of foot as a wild ____" (2 Samuel 2:18)
31. Quadrant in D.C.
32. Brother of Rebekah
34. "Yet he abideth faithful: he cannot ____ himself" (2 Timothy 2:13)
35. "When I shall send ____ unto thee, or Tychicus" (Titus 3:12)
37. "Cursed be every ____ that curseth thee" (Genesis 27:29)
38. "I am weak: O Lord, ____ me; for my bones are vexed" (Psalm 6:2)
39. Reveal
41. "Ye ask, and receive not, because ye ask ____" (James 4:3)
43. Father of Saul
44. Pale

47. "I count all things but loss...that I may ____ Christ" (Philippians 3:8)
48. Son of Enan (Numbers 1:15)
50. Compass dir.
51. Record of progress
52. Replied
53. Moisture

DOWN

1. Retirement acct.
2. German article
3. Texas town
4. Metric measure (abbr.)
5. 28 x 2, to Tiberius
6. "And Joshua sent men from Jericho to ____" (Joshua 7:2)
7. Aim to satisfy
8. Mideast country
9. ____ Aviv
10. ____ what?
12. Grayish brown color
17. "The ____ are a people not strong" (Proverbs 30:25)
19. "As the serpent beguiled ____ through his subtlety" (2 Corinthians 11:3)
20. Bring cheer
21. "For thou hast made him a little ____ than the angels" (Psalm 8:5)
22. Belonging to the fifth son of Zerah (1 Chronicles 2:6)
23. "____ ____ comes to the Father except through Me" (2 words, John 14:6, NKJV)
24. Not we
25. "And...there was a marriage in ____ of Galilee" (John 2:1)
26. "David heard in the wilderness that ____ did shear his sheep" (1 Samuel 25:4)

298

30. "Thy youth is _____ like the eagle's" (Psalm 103:5)
32. Sheltered place (pl.)
33. Belonging to Absalom's captain of the host (2 Samuel 17:25)
34. Of gold (Fr.)
36. Object
39. Coach of the Indiana Pacers
40. Good king of Judah (1 Kings 15)
41. Hole-making tool
42. Mine (Ital.)
43. Ripe old age, in Rome
45. Chemical suffix
46. "And he hath put a _____ song in my mouth" (Psalm 40:3)

49. Laughing sound
by Janet W. Adkins

Puzzle **149**

ACROSS

1. Dr. Zhivago heroine
5. Metric land measure (abbr.)
8. Bone or breaker
11. Ancient Hebrew dry measure
12. Feminine name
14. N.A. country
15. "Avenge not yourselves, but rather ____ ____ unto wrath" (2 words, Romans 12:19)
17. Knight's form of address
18. Actress Ullmann
19. "____ hath desired to have you, that he may sift you" (Luke 22:31)
21. "Shall seven years of ____ come unto...thy land?" (2 Samuel 24:13)
24. Indian princess
25. Southern state (abbr.)
26. Turmoil
28. "Give not that which is holy unto the ____" (Matthew 7:6)
30. Shoe width
31. Bog
33. Provide the means
35. Compass dir.
36. Thing on a list
37. "And your children shall ____ in the wilderness forty years" (Numbers 14:33)
40. Like an ump
42. Circular ____ (junk mail repository?)
43. Formerly Clay
44. "Dearly beloved, ____ ____ yourselves...I will repay" (2 words, Romans 12:19)
49. "But as the days of ____ were, so shall also the coming of the Son of man be" (Matthew 24:37)

50. Telephoned
51. "For a good man some would even ____ to die" (Romans 5:7)
52. Acted
53. At loose ___
54. "We have seen his ____ in the east" (Matthew 2:2)

DOWN

1. Ship's record
2. Boyfriend for Babette?
3. N.T. book
4. Son of Gad (Genesis 46:16)
5. Share equally
6. In the manner of
7. "Render therefore unto ____" (Matthew 22:21)
8. "And by him all that believe are ____ from all things, from which ye could not be...by the law of Moses" (Acts 13:39)
9. Continent
10. Sound an alarm
13. Akin to a ringmaster (abbr.)
16. Individual number, for ATMs and credit cards
20. City in southern Judah (Joshua 15:50)
21. Bell bottoms or hula-hoops
22. Healing plant
23. "And let thy name be ____ for ever" (2 Samuel 7:26)
24. Hwy.
26. "Stand still, and ____ the salvation of the Lord" (Exodus 14:13)
27. Sea eagle
29. Formed a lap
30. Small town street name
32. Poetic contraction
34. "Take heed, ____ of the leaven of the Pharisees" (Mark 8:15)

37. "Oh that I had _____ like a dove!" (Psalm 55:6)
38. Required H.S. math
39. Obligations
40. Author Ayn
41. "_____, lama sabachthani?" (Mark 15:34)
42. Ward off
45. Actor Johnson
46. Masculine nickname
47. Mouth (pl.)
48. Like a patio (abbr.)
    by Janet W. Adkins

ACROSS

1. Hand or season
4. "____ things are lawful for me... but I will not be brought under the power" (1 Corinthians 6:12)
7. ____ the bill
11. Very (Fr.)
13. Medic's abbr.
14. King of Israel (1 Kings 16)
15. Bye-bye, to Brits
16. Canadian prov.
17. The act of (suffix)
18. Biblical measurement
19. "Redeem us from all iniquity, and purify unto himself a ____ people" (Titus 2:14)
21. Put on the feedbag
23. Pronoun
24. "They defile not their ___, in the midst whereof I dwell" (Numbers 5:3)
27. "For the ____ of this people cause them to err" (Isaiah 9:16)
32. To braid
33. "And the anger of the Lord was ____ against Israel" (Judges 2:20)
34. Great Lake
35. "Send me also cedar trees, fir trees...out of ____" (2 Chronicles 2:8)
37. Land measure (pl.)
38. That hurts!
39. Boring tool?
40. "____ now thy Creator in the days of thy youth" (Ecclesiastes 12:1)
45. "Neither do the ____ understand judgment" (Job 32:9)
49. Great-grandfather of Lamech (Genesis 4:18)
50. Within (prefix)

51. Partner of rant
52. Virginia ___, first English child born in America
53. Possessive pronoun
54. Tied
55. Father of Ahira (Numbers 2:29)
56. Article
57. Golfer Ernie

DOWN

1. King of Germany, and Holy Roman Emperor
2. Oil filter maker
3. Honor, as at a banquet
4. Use as one's own
5. Single
6. "Nor the ____ of their shoes be broken" (Isaiah 5:27)
7. Young farm animal
8. All, everywhere (comb. form)
9. Killer whale
10. Arena area
12. "Unto none of them was Elias sent, save unto ___, a city of Sidon" (Luke 4:26)
20. Vowel trio
22. Simile syntax
24. Army rank (abbr.)
25. ____ wife
26. Fairy queen of English folklore
27. Actor Chaney
28. "Sing praises to the Lord...____ among the people his doings" (Psalm 9:11)
29. Mess up
30. Bible grain (Isaiah 28:25)
31. French possessive pronoun
33. Nevertheless (arch.)
36. ____ de plume
37. Exclamation of protest
39. Was resurrected, as Jesus Christ

40. To stay afloat, with "out"
41. One of the sons of Shuthelah (Numbers 26:36)
42. "Call me ___: for the Almighty hath dealt very bitterly with me" (Ruth 1:20)
43. Idyllic setting
44. O.T. book
46. Contributed
47. First name in "daredeviltry"
48. Cubs' "cribs"?
    by Janet W. Adkins

ACROSS

1. KJV verb
5. Mouthfuls of chewing gum
9. Linking verb
12. Tribe of Israel
(var., N.T. spelling)
13. Son of Rehoboam
(1 Chronicles 3:10)
14. Body of water, in Boulogne
15. "Can any understand the _____ of
the clouds?" (Job 36:29)
18. Note on the diatonic scale
19. Parched
20. Diminutive ending (pl.)
22. "The Lord is thy _____ upon thy
right hand" (Psalm 121:5)
25. Printer's measure
27. Of flying (prefix)
28. "The lot is cast into the _____"
(Proverbs 16:33)
29. Misplace
31. Subject of Kilmer poem
33. "That through your mercy they
also may _____ mercy"
(Romans 11:31)
35. Boat ends
37. "The _____ of God is eternal life"
(Romans 6:23)
38. It can be cold and hard
40. When Columbus is feted (abbr.)
41. Stagger
43. "_____ with thine adversary
quickly" (Matthew 5:25)
45. "They could not drink of the
waters of _____" (Exodus 15:23)
46. "It is a _____ thing that the king
requireth" (Daniel 2:11)
48. Workout zone (sing.)
49. The act of washing out or
flushing
54. Crafty

56. Roof edge
57. _____ Bator (Mongolian capital)
58. Three (comb. form)
59. Lea languishers
60. Part of *la famille*

DOWN

1. Used to be
2. "The child shall play on the hole
of the _____" (Isaiah 11:8)
3. Sunday speech (abbr.)
4. "I give unto you power to _____
on scorpions" (Luke 10:19)
5. Dry valley or ravine, except in
the rainy season
6. "The one who says he _____ in
Him ought himself to walk in the
same manner as He walked"
(1 John 2:6, NAS)
7. Loud, continuous noise
8. Wise man
9. "I _____ he that liveth"
(Revelation 1:18)
10. Adjunct to a resume
11. Historical periods
16. Son of Gad (Genesis 46:16)
17. Aver
21. "Thou shalt not be afraid for the
_____ by night" (Psalm 91:5)
22. Trudge
23. In move-in condition
24. "All that were strong and _____
_____ [2 words] war"
(2 Kings 24:16)
26. Promontory; headland
30. Fairy-tale beginning
32. This (Sp.)
34. Grandson of Sheshan
(1 Chronicles 2:35)
36. Father of Abraham
(Luke 3:34)

39. Realize success
42. Number of months baby Moses was hidden before his mother put him in an ark (Exodus 2:2)
44. Elaborate dress
45. "Thou shalt be...as he that lieth upon the top of a _____" (Proverbs 23:34)
47. Matures
50. Not polished
51. _____ de la Cite, in Paris
52. "All that handle the _____, the mariners" (Ezekiel 27:29)
53. Compass dir.
55. Part of a century (abbr.)

by Evelyn Boyington

ACROSS

1. "I will come in to him and will ____ with him" (Revelation 3:20)
4. "The foxes have ____" (Matthew 8:20)
9. Isaac, to Abraham
12. ____-la-la
13. Pole vault or high jump, for example, in a track meet
14. "____ of every sort shalt thou bring into the ark" (Genesis 6:19)
15. Went in
17. Alter, hopefully for the better
19. "And he shall rule them with a rod of ____" (Revelation 2:27)
20. Celestial sign, to Magi
21. Remnant of a broken pot (KJV var.)
23. "Nor silver, nor brass...nor scrip for your ____" (Matthew 10:9, 10)
26. Fowl creatures
27. Nonsense
28. In ____ (concerning)
29. Consume
30. Certain collectibles
31. Age
32. Title used when not on a first-name basis (abbr.)
33. "You're So ____" (C. Simon hit)
34. Confirm
35. "If any man ____, let him come unto me" (John 7:37)
37. Drops pounds
38. Act as accomplice
39. Actor Orson, for one
40. "Ye are not in darkness, that that day should overtake you as a ____" (1 Thessalonians 5:4)
42. Pasture activity
45. Rowing implement
46. Chief son of Kohath (1 Chronicles 15:5)
48. Born (Fr.)
49. Twisted strand in rope
50. "Make a joyful noise unto the Lord, all ye ____" (Psalm 100:1)
51. Came into possession

DOWN

1. Jeanne d'Arc, e.g.
2. Vase
3. "Rejoicing in hope, ____ in tribulation" (Romans 12:12)
4. "For ____ feared John, knowing that he was a just man" (Mark 6:20)
5. Appliance
6. "He was ____ as a sheep to the slaughter" (Acts 8:32)
7. Half an em
8. Icons, perhaps
9. Far from cracking a smile
10. Possess
11. "And Cain...dwelt in the land of ____ on the east of Eden" (Genesis 4:16)
16. Blunders
18. One betrothed to Joseph
20. In the near future
21. Son of Noah
22. "A merry ____ maketh a cheerful countenance" (Proverbs 15:13)
23. Elbow, for one
24. "Who concerning the truth have ____, saying that the resurrection is past" (2 Timothy 2:18)
25. "For I have laid upon thee the ____ of their iniquity" (Ezekiel 4:5)
27. Raise up
30. "Be ____ for nothing" (Philippians 4:6)

31. After dusk
33. Emotional reaction (colloq.)
34. Son of Jotham, king of Judah
    (2 Kings 16:1)
36. Hirsute
37. What the Lamb opens, in the
    Book of Revelation
39. Partner of born
40. Over the ___
41. Masculine nickname
42. Cotton ___
43. New (comb. form)
44. "___ thee behind me, Satan"
    (Matthew 16:23)
47. Chemical element (abbr.)

by Evelyn Boyington

ACROSS

1. Collected prose or poetry of a particular time period (abbr.)
4. TV newsman Sevareid
8. Egg ____ soup, Chinese classic
12. Epoch
13. Beginning of refreshing brand name that "spells" summer to kids
14. Land measure
15. Ancient musical instrument, mentioned in Isaiah 5:12
17. "The Lord God will come with a strong hand, and his ____ shall rule" (Isaiah 40:10)
19. Where Sherman marched (abbr.)
20. "There is a ____ here, which hath five barley loaves" (John 6:9)
21. El ___
22. Deface
23. "Children, ____ your parents in the Lord" (Ephesians 6:1)
25. Sports venue
26. Prohibits
27. "Cast the ____ on the right side of

   the ship" (John 21:6)
28. Total
29. ____ Auerbach, famed NBA coach
30. Masculine nickname
31. "Praise him with the ____ and dance" (Psalm 150:4)
33. Continent (abbr.)
35. "Take, ____: this is my body" (1 Corinthians 11:24)
36. Fare poorly
37. Possessed
38. "I will sing a new ____ unto thee, O God" (Psalm 144:9)
40. Popular street name

41. "All things were ____ by him" (John 1:3)
42. "I am too ____ to have an husband" (Ruth 1:12)
43. "The word ____ God" (John 1:1)
44. Chum
45. Atlantic state (abbr.)
46. Broadcast
47. "One jot or one __ shall in no wise pass from the law" (Matthew 5:18)
50. At any time
52. "For ____ Christ pleased not himself" (Romans 15:3)
54. Corn serving
55. "We shall all stand before the judgment ____ of Christ" (Romans 14:10)
56. Feast fashionably
57. Hair to ____ for (salon slogan)

DOWN

1. Tennis call
2. Gershwin
3. Pill, perhaps
4. Got by, barely, with "out"
5. Go bad
6. Vowel duo
7. ____ check
8. Hoover, for one
9. Cola brand name
10. Liver or lung, for example
11. Bosc and Anjou
16. Oz scarecrow Bolger
18. Byway (abbr.)
21. "They lifted up their voice with the trumpets and ____" (2 Chronicles 5:13)
22. Insane
23. United
24. "Rise, take up thy ____, and walk" (John 5:8)

25. Adhesive
26. ____ canto, singing style
28. Make a lap
29. Kin (abbr.)
31. Game where someone is "it"
32. "Over the ____" (goal of hoopsters)
33. "When ye fast, be not...of a ____ countenance" (Matthew 6:16)
34. Fruit drink
35. "The ____ of all things is at hand" (1 Peter 4:7)
37. Brought to a stop
38. "There was a certain beggar named Lazarus...full of ____" (Luke 16:20)

39. Item found in groves
40. Dog-____ (like the pages of a book)
41. Tatami, commonly
43. Midwest state (abbr.)
44. Yearn for
46. "____ thou the Christ?" (Luke 22:67)
47. Perfect score, to some
48. "I will both __ me down in peace, and sleep" (Psalm 4:8)
49. Poetic contraction
51. Apiece (abbr.)
53. Caribbean island group (abbr.)
by Evelyn Boyington

ACROSS

1. "I will go before thee, and...cut in sunder the ____ of iron" (Isaiah 45:2)
4. "For now we see through a ____, darkly" (1 Corinthians 13:12)
8. Optometrist's degree (abbr.)
10. "There followed ____ and fire mingled with blood" (Revelation 8:7)
12. "It is appointed unto men once to ____" (Hebrews 9:27)
13. One of twenty-six
14. Printer's measure
16. "____ for them that despitefully use you" (Matthew 5:44)
18. "They that sow in tears shall ____ in joy" (Psalm 126:5)
20. Slangy negative reply
22. First garden
24. "The nations are as a ____ of a bucket" (Isaiah 40:15)
26. Relative of 911
28. Was a pathfinder
30. "It is a people that do ____ in their heart" (Psalm 95:10)
31. Cream of the crop
32. Courtroom verb
34. Note in diatonic scale
35. "The ____ of mine apostleship are ye in the Lord" (1 Corinthians 9:2)
37. "Who is this that cometh from Edom, with ____ garments?" (Isaiah 63:1)
39. Simile syntax
41. "Let them learn first to shew ____ at home" (1 Timothy 5:4)
43. "Father, glorify thy ____" (John 12:28)
45. Sault ____ Marie

47. Chafed, as skin
48. Feminine nickname
49. Tattled, with "on"
51. Become bored
54. Cave dweller
56. Presummertime priority
58. Partner of dear
60. Dr. ____ (I. Fleming work)
61. Land-grant college department (abbr.)
62. Hula-Hoop, for one
64. Epochs
66. Western state (abbr.)
67. "____ yourselves unto God, as those that are alive from the dead" (Romans 6:13)
68. Created

DOWN

1. "____ there, done that"
2. Blood factor
3. "The trees of the Lord are full of ____" (Psalm 104:16)
4. Bag or rags
5. Classified, for one
6. Title of address
7. "He that goeth forth and weepeth, bearing precious ____, shall doubtless come again" (Psalm 126:6)
8. Send home
9. Beast of burden
11. Anger
15. Win by a ____
17. Give a holler
19. Linking verb
21. Coin ___
23. "Open thy hand wide unto...thy ____" (Deuteronomy 15:11)
25. Conceit
27. "There is but a ____ between me and death" (1 Samuel 20:3)

29. "A ____ in thy courts is better than a thousand" (Psalm 84:10)
31. "Every ____ of the forest is mine" (Psalm 50:10)
32. Fold
33. Cubs' coves
36. Tune, melody
38. To coat with slime and pitch, as Moses' mother did with his ark (Exodus 2:3)
40. Uninteresting
42. Jacob, to Esau
44. "A Jew of Tarsus... a citizen of no ____ city" (Acts 21:39)
46. Father of Hophni and Phineas

50. "The Philistine said, I ____ the armies of Israel" (1 Samuel 17:10)
52. "A bruised ____ shall he not break" (Isaiah 42:3)
53. "Incline thine __ unto me and hear my speech" (Psalm 17:6)
55. Sped like the wind
57. ____ chi, ancient Asian art of controlled exercise
59. What Abraham saw caught in a thicket (Genesis 22)
61. Exclamation of disappointment
63. Bethany Beach state (abbr.)
65. Continent (abbr.)
by Evelyn Boyington

ACROSS

1. "But the very ____ of your head are all numbered" (Matthew 10:30)
6. Throws a fit
11. Twilight
12. Changes the subject
14. California time (abbr.)
15. "Carry neither ____, nor scrip, nor shoes" (Luke 10:4)
17. A tree's blood
18. Buckeye bailiwick (abbr.)
19. "Prove me now...if I will not...____ you out a blessing" (Malachi 3:10)
20. Note on the diatonic scale
21. "____ it, even to the foundation thereof" (Psalm 137:7)
24. "Go, sell the ____ and pay thy debt" (2 Kings 4:7)
25. One of Jezebel's gods
27. "The stone shall cry out...and the beam out of the ____ shall answer it" (Habakkuk 2:11)
29. "And I was afraid, and went and hid thy ____ in the earth" (Matthew 25:25)
31. Long, long time
32. Thing, in legalese
33. Positions
36. Getaway destination
39. Adjective or adverb that is the equivalent of an exclamation mark
40. Take advantage of
42. Incite, with "on"
43. Printer's measure
44. A transparent body used to refract light
46. Quadrant in D.C.
47. Conjunction
49. Eagle abode
50. "There was no room for them in the ____" (Luke 2:7)
51. Escargots
53. "David ____ before the Lord with all his might" (2 Samuel 6:14)
55. Touching, as a gesture
56. Member of church hierarchy

DOWN

1. Friend of David (2 Samuel 15:32)
2. "Go to the ____, thou sluggard" (Proverbs 6:6)
3. Linking verb
4. Agent, slangily
5. Kin to comatose state
6. Outcome
7. To declare positively
8. Peachy place (abbr.)
9. Manuscript refiners (abbr.)
10. One who takes to the seas
11. "Be a ____!"
13. "We...are as water ____ on the ground" (2 Samuel 14:14)
16. Like Louis XIV, *par exemple*
22. Libel, slang
23. Pioneer African American periodical
25. "My soul may ____ thee before I die" (Genesis 27:4)
26. Fabled author
28. "Be sober, and hope to the ____ for the grace" (1 Peter 1:13)
30. Linking verb
33. In Sverige, you may meet more than a few
34. "Two ____ shall there be in one board" (Exodus 26:17)
35. Most certain
36. Hang one's hat
37. Messenger

	1	2	3	4	5		6	7	8	9	10	
11							12					13
14				15		16				17		
18					19					20		
21		22	23		24			25	26			
27				28			29	30				
					32							
36								37	38			
					42							
		45				46						
					50							
53		54										
56												

The Ten Commandments

I. Thou shalt have no other God before me.

II. Thou shalt not make unto thee any graven image.

III. Thou shalt not take the name of the Lord thy God in vain.

IV. Remember the Sabbath day, to keep it holy.

V. Honor thy father and thy mother.

VI. Thou shalt not kill.

VII. Thou shalt not commit adultery.

VIII. Thou shalt not steal.

IX. Thou shalt not bear false witness against thy neighbor.

X. Thou shalt not covet.

ACROSS

1. "____ no man any thing, but to love one another" (Romans 13:8)
4. "His enemy came and sowed tares among the ____" (Matthew 13:25)
9. Greek letter
12. Benign skin tumor
13. "Let your laughter be turned to mourning, and your joy to ____" (James 4:9)
15. United ____
17. "Woe to them that are at ____ in Zion" (Amos 6:1)
18. Actor Buttons
19. "Ye shall no more give the people ____ to make brick" (Exodus 5:7)
22. Lets go
24. Article
25. Explorer Johnson
28. Preposition
29. Warns, ominously
31. Exclamations of disappointment
32. "Another angel came...having a golden ____" (Revelation 8:3)
34. Rouses, sometimes repeatedly
36. Entertaining troops is org.'s forte
37. One or the other
39. Half an em
40. Compass pt.
41. By means of
42. Acclaimed TV miniseries
44. Religion that has a claim in Jerusalem
46. Tribe of Israel
47. *My Name Is* ____ (W. Saroyan novel)
50. "He shall give thee the ____ of thine heart" (Psalm 37:4)
53. Those who trust in the Lord find this (Proverbs 16:20)
56. Continent (abbr.)
57. One that builds hills
58. "Shall I go and call to thee a ____ of the Hebrew women?" (Exodus 2:7)
59. Within (prefix)

DOWN

1. "His ____ received him not" (John 1:11)
2. "Much study is a ____ of the flesh" (Ecclesiastes 12:12)
3. "____ into his gates with thanksgiving" (Psalm 100:4)
4. Reporter's question
5. Brooding bunch
6. ____ *of Eden* (J. Steinbeck novel)
7. Madison, for one (abbr.)
8. Note on the diatonic scale
9. Orange pckoe, for one
10. "With the jaw of an ____...have I slain a thousand men" (Judges 15:16)
11. "He shall be a vessel...meet for the master's ____" (2 Timothy 2:21)
14. "What thing is this? what ____ doctrine is this?" (Mark 1:27)
16. Creative impulses
20. Where Saul abode: in Gibeah under a tree in ____ (1 Samuel 22:6)
21. Solution
22. Zero in on
23. Gets some shut-eye
25. "An angel of the Lord...sat under an ____" (Judges 6:11)
26. "This roll...was in my mouth as honey for ____" (Ezekiel 3:3)
27. Organizations (abbr.)

30. Israeli politician Sharon
33. Not "in a little while"
35. Son of Gad (Genesis 46:16)
38. _____Vic's (former restaurant chain)
43. Rower
44. Mischievous one
45. Army repast
47. Exclamation of discovery
48. Bled, as madras might
49. Likely to
51. Compass pt.
52. _____ Paulo
54. Preposition
55. Greek letter

by Evelyn Boyington

ACROSS

1. Linking verb
4. Prophets, such as Samuel and Isaiah
9. Occupy; control
12. Suitable; apt
13. Doctrine or belief held as truth
14. Poetic before
15. "____ ____ ____ [3 words]; and blessed be my rock" (Psalm 18:46)
18. Status in a group, slang
19. Decay
20. Loiters or lingers (colloq.)
22. Gets ready to face the day
25. Exclamation of dismay
26. Referred to
28. Greek letter
29. Unit equal to 1/1,000 inch
30. "One load of bread, and one cake of ____ bread" (Exodus 29:23)
31. "If we say that we have no ____, we deceive ourselves" (1 John 1:8)
32. Fifth or Park, e.g.
33. "When thou prayest, ____ into thy closet" (Matthew 6:6)
34. Act stubbornly
35. Orderly
37. Puts aside
38. Option at car dealership
39. City near Bethel
40. "____ ____ ____ [3 words], O my soul. While I live will I praise" (Psalm 146:1, 2)
48. Owns
49. "The house was filled with the ____ of the ointment" (John 12:3)
50. Western Native American
51. Chemical ending
52. Memos
53. Button on the VCR (abbr.)

DOWN

1. "The servant of the Lord must...be...____ to teach" (2 Timothy 2:24)
2. Stadium sound
3. "The ____ God is thy refuge" (Deuteronomy 33:27)
4. Organ options
5. Poetic contraction
6. "Mark the perfect man...for the ____ of that man is peace" (Psalm 37:37)
7. Kin (abbr.)
8. "They ____ up the people, and the elders, and the scribes" (Acts 6:12)
9. Certain sports competitions
10. "Rabbi, thou ____ the Son of God" (John 1:49)
11. O.T. minor prophet (abbr.)
16. "The ____ of the lame are not equal" (Proverbs 26:7)
17. "The earth was without form, and ____" (Genesis 1:2)
20. In the Book of Esther, Mordecai's nemesis
21. "In Christ shall all be made ____" (1 Corinthians 15:22)
22. Son of Hezekiah (Ezra 2:16)
23. John on Patmos, for example
24. Is unable to swim
26. Bigger than a borough
27. Destination *pour les vacances*
30. "There was a dead man carried out, the ____ ____ [2 words] of his mother" (Luke 7:12)

31. "My spirit hath rejoiced in God my ____" (Luke 1:47)
33. Ornamental case
34. Idol of the Phoenicians and Tyrians
36. "Those that walk in pride he is able to ____" (Daniel 4:37)
40. Greek letter
41. Tore
42. Tokyo, formerly
43. Young one
44. Tint
45. Sounds of hesitation
46. Highway (abbr.)

47. "They shall wet thee with the ____ of heaven" (Daniel 4:25)

by Evelyn Boyington

ACROSS

1. Insect indicated in Deuteronomy 1:44
4. Clothes
8. Book division
12. Son of Abijam and good king of Judah
13. Medicinal plant
14. One of David's valiant men: ____ the Ahohite (1 Chronicles 11:29)
15. Affirmative
16. Blue or White
17. Sets goals
18. "For he is Lord of lords, and ____ ____ ____ [3 words]" (Revelation 17:14)
21. Members of conger family
22. "His bones are like bars of ____" (Job 40:18)
23. Debris
25. African antelope
26. Apiece (abbr.)
28. "The ____ are a people not strong" (Proverbs 30:25)
29. Child's play
30. Fine-feathered filler
32. Empire state (abbr.)
33. Reporter's question
34. Pulled along
35. "The day dawn, and the day ____ arise in your hearts" (2 Peter 1:19)
37. Horse or brake
38. Powerful acclamation of Jesus [3 words] (1 Timothy 6)
41. Add to the payroll
42. Father of Amos (Luke 3:25)
43. Shanty
45. Before (prefix)
46. Priest who "brought the law" (Nehemiah 8)
47. Wrath
48. Postparty scene
49. Quadrant of D.C.
50. "Be strong, and quit yourselves like ____" (1 Samuel 4:9)

DOWN

1. Hudson, for one
2. "He called the name of the well ___; because they strove with him" (Genesis 26:20)
3. Most direct, as a route
4. To make a knot
5. Medleys
6. Volkswagen vehicle
7. "I come ____ fruit on this fig tree, and find none" (Luke 13:7)
8. ____forte
9. Straighten, as a column
10. Drives into
11. Poetic contraction
19. New Jersey pros
20. Son of Caleb (1 Chronicles 4:15)
23. Pale
24. "If ____ of you lack wisdom, let him ask of God" (James 1:5)
25. Enola ___
26. Nathan told David the story of the ____ lamb
27. Conjunction
29. "By him were all things created... whether they be ____, or dominions" (Colossians 1:16)
30. "Behold, the judge standeth before the ____" (James 5:9)
31. "One was brought unto him, which ____ ____ [2 words] ten thousand talents" (Matthew 18:24)
33. Lump sum
34. Doubting disciple

35. Sifts, like socks
36. Ash, and others
37. Disparaging remark
38. "Their _____ is gone out through all the earth" (Psalm 19:4)
39. Bother
40. "Be ye _____ of this, that the kingdom of God is come nigh unto you" (Luke 10:11)
41. Son of Noah
44. "Your father hath deceived me, and changed my wages _____ times" (Genesis 31:7)
    by Evelyn Boyington

ACROSS

1. Deface
4. A seal or official stamp
8. Like a black pearl
12. Poetic before
13. Aesop's foolish fellow
14. Great Lake
15. Masculine nickname
16. Son of Jerahmeel (1 Chronicles 2:25)
17. Darius the _____, one-time ruler of Babylon
18. Far ___
20. Bane of insomniacs (pl.)
22. Grammar-school essay
24. Liquid measure
25. "They may teach the young _____ to be sober" (Titus 2:4)
26. Sheltered side
27. FBI agent, familiarly
30. Symbolic sign
31. Owns
32. Harsh breathing
33. Meditation by preacher (abbr.)
34. "My house shall be called the house of prayer; but ye have made it a _____ of thieves" (Matthew 21:13)
35. "Thou shalt not bear _____ witness" (Exodus 20:16)
36. Trench surrounding fortified place
37. "So I sware in my wrath, They shall not _____ into my rest" (Hebrews 3:11)
38. "Except ye _____, ye shall all likewise perish" (Luke 13:3)
41. Make a judgment
42. "The fire shall _____ be burning upon the altar" (Leviticus 6:13)
43. "Father, save me from this _____" (John 12:27)

45. River or Sea
48. Close by
49. Ultimatum word
50. Blunder
51. "I beseech thee, look upon my son: for he is mine _____ child" (Luke 9:38)
52. "For ye have _____ of patience" (Hebrews 10:36)
53. Actress Laraine

DOWN

1. "They...found the colt tied by the door...where two ways _____" (Mark 11:4)
2. Linking verb
3. "I know that my _____liveth" (Job 19:25)
4. "A good name is rather to be _____ than great riches" (Proverbs 22:1)
5. "Then shall the lame man leap as an _____" (Isaiah 35:6)
6. Mine find
7. Common cents
8. Forgive or pardon
9. Greek god of war
10. Let it ___
11. Shoe sizes
19. "For all the promises of God in him are yea, and in him _____" (2 Corinthians 1:20)
21. "One thousand shall flee at the rebuke of _____" (Isaiah 30:17)
22. Jesus sent His disciples out by _____ (Mark 6:7)
23. Base in baseball
24. "They shall _____ vineyards, but not drink the wine thereof" (Zephaniah 1:13)
27. Wavered

28. In addition
29. *The ____ Slayer* (J. F. Cooper novel)
31. "The idols of the ____ are silver and gold" (Psalm 135:15)
32. Throw a fit
34. Puzo's Corleone
35. "The Lord...is to be ____ above all gods" (1 Chronicles 16:25)
36. "A ____ heart maketh a cheerful countenance" (Proverbs 15:13)
38. First woman to be U.S. Attorney General
39. "Let me be weighed in an ____ balance" (Job 31:6)
40. Ring out
41. Masquerade of sorts
44. Corrida cry
46. Age
47. "He turneth...the watersprings into ____ ground" (Psalm 107:33)
by Evelyn Boyington

ACROSS

1. "Except I shall see in his hands the print of the ____" (John 20:25)
6. "Bring forth...every living thing...that they may ____ abundantly" (Genesis 8:17)
11. "Take heed and beware of the ____ of the Pharisees" (Matthew 16:6)
12. Occupied an apartment
14. More than a kernel
15. Wife of Abram
17. Tavern brew
18. Mideast dialect (abbr.)
19. "____ up a child in the way he should go" (Proverbs 22:6)
20. Buffalo college
21. "The ____ of the temple was rent in twain" (Matthew 27:51)
24. "This gospel...shall be preached in all the world...and then shall the ____ come" (Matthew 24:14)
25. 1,061, to Claudius
27. Bloopers
29. "Ye shall appoint you cities...of refuge...that the ____ may flee thither" (Numbers 35:11)
31. Cereal grain
32. Son of Bela (Numbers 26:40)
33. Grouped together
36. Claudius ____, who wrote a letter to Felix on Paul's behalf (Acts 23:26)
39. ____ is more
40. The Gilded Age, for one
42. Say "whoa"
43. Printer's measure
44. Shasta ____
46. Hawkeye state (abbr.)
47. Red, for one

49. "I am ____ and Omega" (Revelation 22:13)
50. Put it in writing
51. English or western, in the tack room
53. Item to do
55. "The angels shall come forth, and ____ the wicked from among the just" (Matthew 13:49)
56. Tizzies

DOWN

1. "Now is our salvation ____ than when we believed" (Romans 13:11)
2. Rhine tributary
3. Patient adjunct, in hospital (abbr.)
4. For fear that
5. "But they [other nations] shall be ____ and traps unto you" (Joshua 23:13)
6. "French" is one style of these
7. Slow down or stop
8. Fourteenth letter of the alphabet
9. Greek letter
10. Super-duper
11. "For thou wilt not ____ my soul in hell" (Psalm 16:10)
13. King of Eglon (Joshua 10:3)
16. Headed for the hills
22. Golfer's gear
23. Large quantities
25. Mystery writer Ngaio
26. Seller of purple from Thyatira
28. Highway (abbr.)
30. "Now I ____ me down..."
33. "I will ____ thy name for ever and ever" (Psalm 145:1)
34. Man sick with the palsy for eight years (Acts 9)
35. Wheeler follower

36. Speaks angrily, with "out"
37. Not citizens
38. "Put on the whole armour of God, that ye may be able to _____ against the wiles of the devil" (Ephesians 6:11)
41. Tear
44. Roy's partner
45. Storyteller's specialty
48. Summer drink
50. Almost too reasonable, as an excuse
52. Wounded ex-soldier (abbr.)
54. Eastern U.S. state
by Evelyn Boyington

PUZZLE 161

ACROSS

1. Linking verb
4. Makes like the sun
9. Possesses
12. Insane
13. Lovable nerd on TV's "Family Matters"
14. Honest one
15. French conjunction
16. Land from which the Lord will recover the remnant of His people (Isaiah 11:11)
18. Live for the moment
19. Like food and clothing
21. Held with a certain tool
23. Frost, for one
25. Pitch in
26. High priest in Shiloh
28. More reliable
30. Director Lupino
33. Poetic contraction
34. "Then _____ brought out silver and gold out of the treasures of the house of the Lord" (2 Chronicles 16:2)
35. Spat
36. Likely
37. TV's "Get ___"
39. Frozen water
40. "Thy word is a _____ unto my feet" (Psalm 119:105)
42. "And he...cast him into prison, till he should pay the _____" (Matthew 18:30)
44. At a certain location
46. Organic substance from plants
49. Concerning
50. "While the bridegroom _____ they all slumbered and slept" (Matthew 25:5)
54. Therefore
55. Vein contents
57. What hobos rode
58. In the manner of
59. Benign skin tumor
60. Lacking originality
61. O.T. book (abbr.)

DOWN

1. So be it
2. Per diem, for one
3. Before PCs, one who used a blue pencil (abbr.)
4. Particular potato
5. April correspondent (abbr.)
6. TV's "_____ King"
7. Poetic contraction
8. Splinter
9. Half a laugh
10. French cleric
11. "He that goeth forth and weepeth, bearing precious _____" (Psalm 126:6)
16. "Why make ye this _____, and weep?" (Mark 5:39)
17. To pain, discomfort, or trouble
20. Letter from Paul
22. "Who maketh his angels _____; his ministers a flaming fire" (Psalm 104:4)
24. Trudge along
25. "I cannot hold my peace, because thou hast _____, O my soul, the sound of the trumpet" (Jeremiah 4:19)
26. Greek letter
27. _____ service
29. Team _____, e.g., at the Olympics
31. Halliday, for one
32. Reverence
37. Rips one's reputation

38. Feminine name (var.)
41. Masculine nickname
43. "Arise, take up thy _____, and go unto thine house" (Matthew 9:6)
44. Believe or think (arch.)
45. In or at this place
47. Man, for one
48. Father of Japheth
51. Tell on
52. Inlet
53. Feeling poorly
56. ___-Gedi, city of Judah (Joshua 15)
58. Article

by Evelyn Boyington

ACROSS

1. When a rooster rouses
5. Air (comb. form)
8. A. Hitchcock film classic
12. Operatic solo
13. Busy one
14. First garden
15. Tree house
16. Under the weather
17. Center
18. Was wary, with "away"
20. "When ye blow an _____, then the camps...on the east shall go forward" (Numbers 10:5)
22. "But _____ thing is needful: and Mary hath chosen" (Luke 10:42)
23. Jesus likens the kingdom of God to _____ virgins (Matthew 25)
24. Makes payment for, as Jesus' sacrifice on the cross
27. "And as they were _____, Jesus took bread" (Matthew 26:26)
31. "A brother offended is harder to be _____ than a strong city" (Proverbs 18:19)
32. ___classical style
33. Let go
37. Saul's exit "vehicle" out of Damascus (Acts 9)
40. Body part of priest on which the ram's blood was sprinkled (Exodus 29:20)
41. Employ
42. Times to "catch the worm"
44. Experienced labored breathing
47. Experience ennui
48. Where the good Samaritan left the wounded man
50. Lions' den
52. Sheltered side, nautically
53. "Deliver thyself as a _____ from the hand of the hunter" (Proverbs 6:5)
54. Firstborn of Isaac
55. Held or kept in, with "up"
56. "Be sober, and hope to the _____ for the grace" (1 Peter 1:13)
57. Niece and nephew, e.g. (abbr.)

DOWN

1. Tribe of Israel
2. Greek counterpart of Mars
3. "Let them be...put to shame that _____ me evil" (Psalm 40:14)
4. "Let us cut it [Moab] off from being a _____" (Jeremiah 48:2)
5. Awaits; stays close to
6. Conger
7. Feel a kinship toward
8. Retract
9. Aroma
10. Salon service
11. Chemical suffix
19. Compass dir.
21. Grassy field
24. A piercing tool
25. "Is any thing _____ hard for the Lord?" (Genesis 18:14)
26. "The sons of...Shamed, who built _____, and Lod" (1 Chronicles 8:12)
28. "He pronounced all these words...and I wrote them with _____ in the book" (Jeremiah 36:18)
29. Born (Fr.)
30. Purchased
34. Mulberry, for one
35. Ages and ages
36. "I _____ to be present with you now" (Galatians 4:20)

37. "The bush_____ with fire, and the bush was not consumed" (Exodus 3:2)
38. Good king of Judah
39. Lydia was a _____ of purple
42. Burrowing mammal
43. "_____ me first" (former Kodak come-on)
45. "His soul shall dwell at _____" (Psalm 25:13)
46. _____ tone
47. Cartographer's product
49. Forget it, to Philippe
51. Masculine nickname (var.)
by Evelyn Boyington

ACROSS

1. Director Peckinpah
4. Understands
8. "Thou liftest me up to the wind; thou causest me to ____ upon it" (Job 30:22)
12. Ripen
13. Secular person
14. SW Ohio city
15. "Blessed be the God and ____ of our Lord Jesus Christ" (1 Peter 1:3)
17. "Whosoever shall exalt himself shall be ____" (Matthew 23:12)
19. "I ____ not from thy precepts" (Psalm 119:110)
20. "Let us run with patience the ____ that is set before us" (Hebrews 12:1)
21. "To do" tasks
24. Crone
27. So much, so great
29. New Jersey, to Noelle
31. ____ shirt
32. Dolly's domain (abbr.)
33. "We should be holy and without ____ before him in love" (Ephesians 1:4)
34. Administrator of TLC
35. Fruity drink
37. To be (Fr.)
38. University of Michigan's Schembeckler, familiarly
40. "He [Judah] couched as a lion... who shall ____ him up?" (Genesis 49:9)
42. Where Saul encountered a witch
44. Son of Melchi (Luke 3:27)
46. Blot out

49. "The Lord said, My ____ shall not always strive with man" (Genesis 6:3)
51. Does the hora
52. Act or result (suffix)
53. "____ was a tiller of the ground" (Genesis 4:2)
55. Meadow
56. Masculine nickname
57. Disapproving sound
58. Flightless bird

DOWN

1. "The king said, Is the young man Absalom ____?" (2 Samuel 18:29)
2. "For this ____ is mount Sinai in Arabia" (Galatians 4:25)
3. ____ system
4. Animal not to be eaten (Deuteronomy 14:13)
5. It contains a hammer and a stirrup
6. Note on diatonic scale
7. To mark permanently
8. "Then saith he to Thomas, ____ hither thy finger" (John 20:27)
9. Place inside
10. Stag's mate
11. Bitter or dead
16. Abraham and Sarah were buried in field purchased from sons of ____ (Genesis 25)
18. Tend to a turkey
22. "The heart of Egypt shall ____ in the midst of it" (Isaiah 19:1)
23. "I may tell all my bones: they look and ____ upon me" (Psalm 22:17)

25. Poetic contraction
26. Benign tumors
27. "There fell a great____ from heaven" (Revelation 8:10)
28. Disentangle
30. "Let all the people say, ____" (Psalm 106:48)
33. Father of Hosea (Hosea 1:1)
36. Mother of Timothy (2 Timothy 1:5)
38. "Unto you is ____ this day...a Saviour" (Luke 2:11)
39. Kin to a prophet
41. Son of Zebulun (Genesis 46:14)
43. College officials
45. Restless desire
47. Appear likely
48. "____ despised his birthright" (Genesis 25:34)
49. Game, ____, match
50. Like an IOU, only more specific
51. Show no respect (colloq.)
54. "I have given into thy hand the king of ____, and his people" (Joshua 8:1)

by Evelyn Boyington

ACROSS

1. Places for the accident prone (abbr.)
4. Things to do
9. "Festus said...much learning doth make thee ____" (Acts 26:24)
12. "The trees of the Lord are full of ____" (Psalm 104:16)
13. First letter of Hebrew alphabet
14. Hullabaloo
15. "The Lord had prepared a great fish to ____ up Jonah" (Jonah 1:17)
17. Consumed
19. Noise or disturbance
20. "Have ____ in yourselves, and have peace one with another" (Mark 9:50)
21. Star of Gigi
23. "The ____ beguiled me, and I did eat" (Genesis 3:13)
26. In a short time (arch.)
27. Swift mammals
28. Conjunction
29. Girl Scouts of America founder
30. ____ girl
31. Actor Vigoda
32. Maxwell Perkins, to F.S. Fitzgerald (abbr.)
33. "For whosoever will ____ his life shall lose it" (Luke 9:24)
34. "I...am persuaded that he is ____ to keep that which I have committed" (2 Timothy 1:12)
35. Edible bugs, according to Leviticus 11:22
37. "The ____ of them which have reaped are entered into the ears of the Lord" (James 5:4)
38. Feminine nickname
39. House or hog

40. Motif
42. Old Testament book
45. "____ ____ [2 words] the Rose of Sharon" (Song of Solomon 2:1)
46. "The good shepherd giveth his life for the ____" (John 10:11)
48. Ascot, for one
49. Less than desirable abode
50. Certain amphibians
51. Stolen (colloq.)

DOWN

1. Type of curve
2. Unrefined
3. "Yea, the ____ hath found an house" (Psalm 84:3)
4. Bird claw
5. Oodles
6. "Woe to the women that ____ pillows to all armholes" (Ezekiel 13:18)
7. Mess duty (abbr.)
8. "Like a lamb dumb before his ____" (Acts 8:32)
9. Dull finish
10. Summer quaff
11. Actor Ameche
16. "The first beast was like a ____" (Revelation 4:7)
18. European mountain range
20. Dried up; withered
21. One of the twelve spies sent by Moses into Canaan (Numbers 13)
22. Positively charged electrode
23. Jesus ____ our souls
24. Duke or earl, for example
25. Isaiah describes these as clapping their hands
27. Shanty; hut
30. "Why ____ thou me good?" (Matthew 19:17)

31. "Like unto the Son of God; _____ a priest continually" (Hebrews 7:3)
33. "There shall come forth a rod out of the _____ of Jesse" (Isaiah 11:1)
34. Mideast resident
36. "How long shall mine _____ be exalted?" (Psalm 13:2)
37. Graduate degree tests (abbr.)
39. Regretted
40. Poetic contraction
41. _____ trick
42. Teachers' organization (abbr.)
43. _____ Grande

44. Jelled
47. "_____, every one that thirsteth" (Isaiah 55:1)

by Evelyn Boyington

ACROSS

1. "They came to the threshing-floor of ____, which is beyond Jordan" (Genesis 50:10)
5. Highway (abbr.)
8. Bargain events
10. ____ apple (candy flavor)
11. "After the same manner also he took the cup, when he had ____" (1 Corinthians 11:25)
13. Beyond compare
15. Paddle
16. Momentous sign
17. ___-Eglaim, near the Salt Sea (Ezekiel 47)
18. Wight, for one
19. *King* ____ (J. Clavell novell)
20. Went golfing
21. "The Lord is good to ____" (Psalm 145:9)
24. Compass dir.
25. Like some numbers
26. ____ bargain
27. "These shall ye not eat of them that chew the ____" (Leviticus 11:4)
28. Minor prophet
29. Conjunction
30. "For we are saved by ____" (Romans 8:24)
34. "He it is, to whom I shall give a ____, when I have dipped it" (John 13:26)
35. "They shall lay hands on the sick, and they shall ____" (Mark 16:18)
37. Entrapped
40. "So be it"
41. "When he had made a scourge... he ____ them all out of the temple" (John 2:15)

42. David ___-Gurion
43. Action

DOWN

1. Was in agreement
2. Greek letter
3. Mount Blanc is one
4. "He [Nebuchadnezzar] was ____ from his kingly throne" (Daniel 5:20)
5. Stronger than string
6. "Whosoever shall smite thee on thy right cheek, __ to him the other" (Matthew 5:39)
7. Poetic before
9. "Ye were ____ with that holy Spirit of promise" (Ephesians 1:13)
10. "How precious also are thy thoughts...how great is the ____ of them" (Psalm 139:17)
12. ____ Scott, subject of landmark legal case
13. Hence
14. Dry or liquid
18. Judge Lance
19. Taped
21. "I see a rod of an ____ tree" (Jeremiah 1:11)
22. "The ____ shall lie down with the kid" (Isaiah 11:6)
23. ____ Cruces, NM
26. Bridge response
30. "Whilst we are at ____ in the body, we are absent from the Lord" (2 Corinthians 5:6)
31. "God so clothe the grass... which to day is, and to morrow is cast into the ____" (Matthew 6:30)

32. "I will not with ink and ____ write unto thee" (3 John 13)
33. Hesitation sound
36. NYC sight
38. "Let her be as the loving hind and the pleasant ____" (Proverbs 5:19)
39. First female
    by Evelyn Boyington

ACROSS

1. "Will a man ____ God?"
   (Malachi 3:8)
4. Moon or mast
8. German physicist
11. Son of Seth (Genesis 4:26)
13. Bread spread
14. Dramatic feathery wrap
15. Israel seaport
16. "For thus saith the high and lofty
    One that inhabiteth ____"
    (Isaiah 57:15)
18. Time on the religious calendar
19. Note on the diatonic scale
20. Playwright's direction
24. "Is Israel a servant? is he a
    homeborn ____?"
    (Jeremiah 2:14)
28. Measure of journey
30. Small space
32. Jellylike substance
33. Son of Abijam; king of Judah
34. "And supper being ____, the
    devil having now put into the
    heart of Judas Iscariot"
    (John 13:2)
36. "Above the ____" (goal of b'ball
    players)
37. Yes, in Yokohama
38. Saline drop
39. Golfer Ernie
40. Like some egg yolks
43. ____ scheme
45. Many-tome resource (abbr.)
47. Ancient Hebrew dry measure
50. "Minister the same one to another,
    as good ____" (1 Peter 4:10)
55. Tractor-trailer, to many (colloq.)
56. Person who has to do with
    (suffix)
57. Protest, with "against"
58. Cut off
59. "He that hath a bountiful ____
    shall be blessed" (Proverbs 22:9)
60. Hold ___
61. Three, in Turin

DOWN

1. Camino ___
2. "God hath spoken ___; twice
   have I heard this" (Psalm 62:11)
3. "Being ____ ____ [2 words], not
   of corruptible seed" (1 Peter 1:23)
4. Tend to the garden
5. Mountain measure (abbr.)
6. Beloved general of Virginia
7. Creates from nothing
8. Japanese sash
9. Like dog days
10. Feminine name
12. Complete collections
17. Nothing
21. "He casteth forth his ____ like
    morsels" (Psalm 147:17)
22. Impression
23. Pliny the ____ (Roman writer)
25. "And what ____ hath the temple
    of God with idols?"
    (2 Corinthians 6:16)
26. "And, behold, the ____ of the
    temple was rent in twain"
    (Matthew 27:51)
27. Shade trees
28. Wizard of Oz actor
29. "Jacob have I loved, but ____
    have I hated" (Romans 9:13)
31. "Tender-eyed" woman of the
    Old Testament
35. Parched
41. Partner of then
42. "The ____ of the wicked shall be
    shortened" (Proverbs 10:27)

44. Playwright Hart
46. "No man can come to me, except the Father which hath sent me _____ him" (John 6:44)
48. Arab chieftain
49. "The harvest of the earth is _____" (Revelation 14:15)
50. "O taste and _____ that the Lord is good" (Psalm 34:8)
51. Mystery writer Josephine
52. Poetic before
53. Throughout; across (prefix)
54. Wily; conniving

by Evelyn Boyington

ACROSS

1. Spelunker's domain
5. "Out of his belly shall ____ rivers of living water" (John 7:38)
9. Majorette's must
10. "Ye are all children of ____" (1 Thessalonians 5:5)
12. Tendon
13. "I will come in to him, and will ____ with him" (Revelation 3:20)
14. At present
16. Chemical suffix
17. Off one's rocker
18. "There is none righteous, ____, not one" (Romans 3:10)
19. Biblical exclamation
20. ____ Western Reserve University
21. VCR button
23. "Lo, I am with you alway, even unto the ____ of the world" (Matthew 28:20)
25. Orthopedists' org., and many others (abbr.)
26. "They were swifter than eagles, they were stronger than ____" (2 Samuel 1:23)
27. Latest fad
29. "Yet ____ of you keepeth the law" (John 7:19)
30. Stock in trade
32. Family room, formerly
33. "A time to rend, and a time to ____" (Ecclesiastes 3:7)
36. Mammoth
37. Meat paste
38. Bar Harbor state (abbr.)
39. Preposition
40. "Dear ____:"
41. "____ up the gift of God, which is in thee" (2 Timothy 1:6)
43. Summer, en Paris
45. Coop denizen
46. For ____!
47. Ancestor of Jesus; father of Achim (Matthew 1:14)
49. Tows away
50. Cantered
51. "The coast turneth to Ramah, and to the strong city ____" (Joshua 19:29)

DOWN

1. Sugar, for one
2. Gobbled up
3. "____, and pay unto the Lord your God" (Psalm 76:11)
4. Printer's measure
5. James Galway's forte
6. "My ____ shall utter praise" (Psalm 119:171)
7. King of Bashan (1 Kings 4:19)
8. *Pourquoi*, to Pete
9. Before the West was won, they were plentiful
11. Partner of mortise
12. White ____
13. Capital of ancient Elam, now a city in ruins in Iran
15. A-one
17. "Father, glorify thy ____" (John 12:28)
20. Canary coop
21. "For the wages of ____ is death" (Romans 6:23)
22. Appendages
24. Bore (colloq.)
26. Unattached
28. Linking verb
29. "They straightway left their ____, and followed him" (Matthew 4:20)

30. If the _____ fits....
31. Pursues with a vengeance
32. Mend a sock
34. "The _____ dwelt therein in times past, a people great" (Deuteronomy 2:10)
35. Existed
37. _____ de resistance
40. "Your feet _____ with the preparation of the gospel of peace" (Ephesians 6:15)
41. "Abraham journeyed...and dwelled between Kadesh and _____" (Genesis 20:1)

42. "We spend our years as a _____ that is told" (Psalm 90:9)
44. What the high priest's servant lost in the Garden of Gethsemane, temporarily
46. Have one's _____
48. "Let him eschew evil, and _____ good" (1 Peter 3:11)
49. Kin to alt.

by Evelyn Boyington

ACROSS

1. Have Midas' touch
5. "God is...a very present ____ in trouble" (Psalm 46:1)
9. Unit with several rooms (abbr.)
12. ____ code
13. State one's case
14. Certain princess' veggie villain
15. "When he had found one ____ of great price, went and sold all" (Matthew 13:46)
17. Debussy's "Le ___"
18. High school subject (abbr.)
19. Kind of gloves
21. Escalator alternative
23. Unlikely hit
27. Take-home pay
28. Between a rock and a hard place
29. Lion ____
31. "Unto whom he said, ____, such a one!" (Ruth 4:1)
33. Employ
34. Title in Tijuana
35. "Yet ____ is born unto trouble" (Job 5:7)
36. Exist
37. Kind of watercraft
38. What it's better to be
39. Fire
40. Defies detention
42. Tide, Crest, and others
45. Sympathetic sound
46. "Give ____ unto the law of our God" (Isaiah 1:10)
47. Detergent name
49. Purple peddler of Philippi
53. Linking verb
54. Den of beasts
56. Many, many moons (pl.)
57. Buttons or Auerbach
58. "Consider the lilies...they toil not, they ____ not" (Luke 12:27)
59. Descartes

DOWN

1. "Stand in the ____ before me for the land" (Ezekiel 22:30)
2. Anger
3. Idyllic setting
4. "I will ____ the earth in the clear day" (Amos 8:9)
5. Initials of electronics giant
6. Small-town America street
7. Actress Grant, and others
8. "Whoso is ____ with a thief hateth his own soul" (Proverbs 29:24)
9. Divide asunder, familiarly
10. On a ___
11. Vittles
16. Sass
20. Prevent
22. Air (comb. form)
23. Broadway souvenir
24. Don't win some
25. Poetic before
26. Songdom's "home"
30. One of the "3 Stooges," and others
31. "Do good to them which ____ you" (Luke 6:27)
32. Addition column
34. "But be shod with ____; and not put on two coats" (Mark 6:9)
35. It usually has a key
37. Prohibit
38. "And, behold, a certain ____ stood up and tempted him" (Luke 10:25)
39. Was concerned about
41. Masculine nickname

42. "In their hands they shall ____ thee up" (Matthew 4:6)
43. "It is a ____ thing that the king requireth" (Daniel 2:11)
44. Smite, more familiarly
48. Weeks in a year, Roman style
50. Stag's mate
51. Bed and breakfast, for example
52. Chemical suffix
55. Hospital employee (abbr.)
   by Evelyn Boyington

ACROSS

1. Heavenly being (Fr.)
5. "____ gave names to all cattle" (Genesis 2:20)
9. Get equipped
12. "Who shall ____ us away the stone from the door of the sepulchre?" (Mark 16:3)
13. By the side of (prefix)
14. Talk baby talk
15. Made footprints
16. Arab chieftain
17. Classic auto
18. Looks at a book
20. Bureau
22. On the ____ day Jesus rose from the dead
24. Pronoun for an ocean liner
25. ____ Grande
26. Have a ___
29. Minor prophet
33. "So the wall was finished in the twenty and fifth day of the month ____" (Nehemiah 6:15)
35. Like henna
36. "Take also of the tree of life... and ____ forever" (Genesis 3:22)
37. "I am, and none ____ beside me" (Isaiah 47:8)
38. Ruby, and others
40. Born (Fr.)
41. "I took the little book...and ____ it up" (Revelation 10:10)
43. "For I know the thoughts that I ____ toward you" (Jeremiah 29:11)
45. Rhombus or rectangle, for example
48. Dashes off
50. Poetic contraction
51. Solo for Dame Sutherland
53. "They came to the threshing-floor of ____" (Genesis 50:10)
56. Force to be accepted
57. Sacrifice
58. Singer McIntire
59. "I the Lord search the heart, I ____ the reins" (Jeremiah 17:10)
60. Table d'____
61. High school course (abbr.)

DOWN

1. "Our Father which ____ in heaven" (Matthew 6:9)
2. Conjunction
3. "The light of the ____ gospel of Christ" (2 Corinthians 4:4)
4. "Rebuke not an ____, but entreat him as a father" (1 Timothy 5:1)
5. Mimicked
6. Hoover, and others
7. Exodus hero
8. The ____ sisters of Little Women
9. Seaport in Israel
10. European deer
11. ____ point
19. Classified material
21. "____ the sick, cleanse the lepers" (Matthew 10:8)
22. "I give to eat of the ____ of life" (Revelation 2:7)
23. "I set my king upon my holy ____ of Zion" (Psalm 2:6)
24. Flower part
27. Boundary
28. Popeye's short answer
30. "Thou shalt be a good ____ of Jesus Christ" (1 Timothy 4:6)
31. "The day cometh, that shall burn as an ____" (Malachi 4:1)
32. "____ ye first the kingdom of God" (Matthew 6:33)

34. ____ year
39. Female saint (Fr. abbr.)
42. "I will...____ thee in the way which thou shalt go" (Psalm 32:8)
44. "The law of his God is in his ____" (Psalm 37:31)
45. Kind
46. Understand, in a way
47. Arnie's ____ (golfer's gallery)
48. Make a ___
49. With "of," recently
52. Milne marsupial
54. Daughter of Zachariah (2 Kings 18:2)
55. Hammarskjold, to friends

by Evelyn Boyington

ACROSS

1. ____ canto (singing style)
4. Queen of ____
9. "The ____ of the Lord is at hand" (Joel 1:15)
12. Mirror
13. Instrument board
14. "The wheat and the ____ were not smitten" (Exodus 9:32)
15. "Blessed is the man that walketh not...nor standeth in the way of ____" (Psalm 1:1)
17. "They that dwell in my house, and my ____, count me for a stranger" (Job 19:15)
19. Prong
20. "____ not sleep, lest thou come to poverty" (Proverbs 20:13)
21. Milk that doesn't require tears
23. "Isaac loved Esau, because he did eat of his ____" (Genesis 25:28)
26. Stubborn sort
27. Holds; restrains
28. One of the Kettles
29. Golfer Ernie
30. Alights
31. "And beneath upon the ____ of it [ephod] thou shalt make pomegranates of blue" (Exodus 28:33)
32. Simile syntax
33. Skin afflictions
34. Wise man
35. Shrinks
37. Fathers, familiarly
38. Burden
39. ___meet (a spouse)
40. Onionlike vegetables
42. "I will ____ the lovingkindnesses of the Lord" (Isaiah 63:7)
45. Reply (abbr.)
46. "____ up a child in the way he should go" (Proverbs 22:6)
48. Before
49. Understand, really
50. Popular Parker Bros. game
51. Saw ___

DOWN

1. ____-relief (sculpture technique)
2. Upon; over (prefix)
3. Old World legumes
4. Exhausted
5. Rabbit's relative
6. Naval rank (abbr.)
7. Exist
8. What Aaron's rod yielded (Numbers 17)
9. Takes away moisture
10. First ___
11. Affirmative
16. Blue or White
18. Hertz competitor
20. Loans money
21. Smudge
22. ____ rate
23. Climbing vegetation
24. Greek letter
25. "Rather rejoice, because your ____ are written in heaven" (Luke 10:20)
27. Reveals, as one's soul
30. "His meat was ____ and wild honey" (Matthew 3:4)
31. More satisfied
33. "The stone ____ into his forehead" (1 Samuel 17:49)
34. "Let your speech be alway with grace, seasoned with ____" (Colossians 4:6)
36. KJV verb

37. "He had agreed with the labourers for a _____ a day" (Matthew 20:2)
39. Bequeathed one
40. Fall behind
41. Compass dir.
42. Scratch or stain, for example
43. It runs in veins
44. Masculine nickname
47. Right-hand page (abbr.)

by Evelyn Boyington

ACROSS

1. "Sing unto him, sing _____ unto him" (1 Chronicles 16:9)
7. Father of Abraham (Luke 3:34)
12. Hangs one's hat
14. Has a fit
15. Mount. measure
16. "When even was come, he _____ down with the twelve" (Matthew 26:20)
17. Nicklaus's needs
18. "You've got _____" (computer memo)
20. "I have _____ thee with an ever-lasting love" (Jeremiah 31:3)
22. Atlantic state (abbr.)
23. One who requires taming
25. Cast out
26. "These _____ times have ye reproached me" (Job 19:3)
27. "They call their lands after their own _____" (Psalm 49:11)
29. Gossip (colloq.)
30. San _____, NM
32. "Manasseh...hath made Judah also to sin with his _____" (2 Kings 21:11)
34. "_____ tu": how Juan would say, "It's you."
35. Loose
37. French seasoning
38. Before (prefix)
39. Tribe of Israel
43. Energy unit (abbr.)
44. Rector's residence
46. Raconteur's revelation
47. Dromedary, to Bismarck
49. Nicotine's no-good partner
51. Chemical suffix
52. Emulate Daniel Webster
53. Moved, emotionally
55. What Naaman was (2 Kings 5:1)
56. "Owls shall dwell there, and _____ shall dance there" (Isaiah 13:21)

DOWN

1. Hyde Park sight (pl.)
2. Hebrew term, found in Psalms
3. Just waking up
4. Chinese measure of distance
5. AMA members
6. "Shut up the words, and _____ the book" (Daniel 12:4)
7. "When he hath _____ me, I shall come forth as gold" (Job 23:10)
8. "Is any thing too _____ for the Lord?" (Genesis 18:14)
9. Time past
10. Gives; pays
11. Go along with
13. "Laying up in _____ for them-selves a good foundation against the time to come" (1 Timothy 6:19)
19. Loans
21. "O _____ me with thy salvation" (Psalm 106:4)
24. _____ and Remembrance (H. Wouk novel)
26. Up to the time of
28. "Woe unto you that laugh now! for ye shall _____ and weep" (Luke 6:25)
29. KJV verb
30. "I go to _____ a place for you" (John 14:2)
31. Conger
33. Through (prefix)
34. Israeli statesman Levi
36. Aeries
38. More wan
40. Hirsute

41. Church leader
42. Bassoon, and others
44. "With what measure ye ____, it shall be measured to you" (Matthew 7:2)
45. The one who ____ blood shall bear his iniquity (Leviticus 17:14, 16)
48. Cartographer's triumph
50. ____ Novosti, Russian news agency
54. Not left (abbr.)
by Evelyn Boyington

ACROSS

1. "Behold the ____ of God, which taketh away the sin" (John 1:29)
5. "From the blood of ____ unto the blood of Zacharias" (Luke 11:51)
9. Afternoon repast
12. ____ code
13. Haircare name
14. Lacking polish
15. "Thou hast strengthened the ____ hands" (Job 4:3)
16. "The kingdom of heaven is like unto ____ hid in a field" (Matthew 13:44)
18. Parts of a tennis match
20. "I will ____ mine arrows upon them" (Deuteronomy 32:23)
21. Earthy
23. Greek letter
25. Broadcast
26. "And they came to the threshing-floor of ____" (Genesis 50:10)
28. "He ____ on the ground, and made clay" (John 9:6)
32. Party necessity
33. More pink
35. Avenue, in Avignon
36. Cozy place
38. Turner, for one
39. "The harvest is the ____ of the world" (Matthew 13:39)
40. This means business (abbr.)
42. ETS output (pl.)
44. One of the twelve cities of the tribe of Benjamin (Joshua 18:24)
47. "Let them sing aloud upon their ____" (Psalm 149:5)
48. "The Lord taketh ____ in his people" (Psalm 149:4)
51. Aden, for one
54. Poetic contraction
55. "They...were forbidden of the Holy Ghost to preach the word in ____" (Acts 16:6)
56. Great Lake
57. Arrest
58. "Our end is ____, our days are fulfilled" (Lamentations 4:18)
59. We should love in word, in ____, and in truth (1 John 3:18)

DOWN

1. Before grace there was the ____
2. Linking verb
3. "Make ready quickly three ____ of fine meal" (Genesis 18:6)
4. Soaked up too much sun
5. "Many of them...which used curious ____ brought their books...and burned them" (Acts 19:19)
6. "Crossing the ____" (Tennyson work)
7. Christmas ____
8. "He that is ____ in the kingdom of heaven is greater than he" (Matthew 11:11)
9. Not fictional
10. Succeed the old-fashioned way
11. Speechless
17. De rigeur at resorts (pl.)
19. Thing to be shed
21. "Whosoever slayeth ____, vengeance shall be taken on him" (Genesis 4:15)
22. Texas university
23. Silents star Theda
24. Utopia
27. Chalky substance
29. Steady but unrelenting weight

30. "Thou shalt not approach to his wife: she is thine _____" (Leviticus 18:14)
31. Williams, and others
34. Assess
37. Feminine name
41. Hebrew month (Nehemiah 2:1)
43. "Out of his mouth went a sharp two_____ sword" (Revelation 1:16)
44. U.S. _____ (sports event)
45. _____ bargain
46. "Your bones shall flourish like an _____" (Isaiah 66:14)

47. "I will meet them as a _____ that is bereaved" (Hosea 13:8)
49. "Teach the children of Judah the _____ of the bow" (2 Samuel 1:18)
50. Miss. Riv. arsenal
52. "He maketh me to _____ down in green pastures" (Psalm 23:2)
53. G-man

ACROSS

1. Kitchen measure (abbr.)
4. "Let her ____: against the day of my burying hath she kept this" (John 12:7)
9. Baden-Baden is one
12. Titian's medium
14. "I have set before thee an ____ door" (Revelation 3:8)
15. Possesses
16. Evening wrap
18. "The ear trieth words, as the mouth ____ meat" (Job 34:3)
20. Strive for dominance
21. Rows
22. Hardly worth commenting on
26. "Leah said a troop cometh: and she called his name ____" (Genesis 30:11)
27. Actor Auberjonois
28. "They were swifter than eagles, they were stronger than ____" (2 Samuel 1:23)
30. Preposition
32. Univ. subj.
33. Collect collectibles
34. Verses to a Grecian urn
35. French conjunction
36. Diagram
37. Author unknown (abbr.)
38. Exclamation of achievement
39. "Thou ____ up the sum, full of wisdom" (Ezekiel 28:12)
41. Live like a longhorn
43. Leave out
44. Where ship is secured
46. Lake ____ (outdoor playground)
49. Hosp. facilities (pl.)
50. Affirm or attest to
52. Delhi "to go" garb
53. Born (Fr.)
54. African scavenger
55. Author Amy

DOWN

1. Basketball blunders (abbr.)
2. Portraitist's command
3. "He was ____ with twelve yoke of oxen" (1 Kings 19:19)
5. KJV exclamation
6. Elect
7. Spiffy
8. Certain sailors
9. Broken piece of pottery, KJV style
10. Touches lightly
11. Tree type
13. Demetrius, in *The Robe*
17. The family of ____, descendants of Gad (Numbers 26:16)
19. Prince of Wales, and others
22. "I give to eat of the ____ of life" (Revelation 2:7)
23. Torn apart
24. Feminine name
25. Ananias and Sapphira, to name two
29. Bones (comb. form)
30. Big deals
31. Abraham's abode
33. Son of Ahab (1 Kings 22:40)
34. "He that...meddleth with strife... is like ____ ____ [2 words] taketh a dog by the ears" (Proverbs 26:17)
36. Scorch
37. Witness Protection Program gift
38. Was no longer supine
40. Quantity (abbr.)
41. Former senator from Tennessee
42. Green monster
44. Door designation

45. Command to a horse
47. Mouth (pl.)
48. German article
51. TLC provider
    by Evelyn Boyington

ACROSS

1. Kind of walker
4. One that sends hisses
7. What the diseased woman touched on Jesus' garment
10. "____ no man any thing, but to love one another" (Romans 13:8)
11. Capture, in a way
12. Son of Seth
14. Chicken, in Dodge City
16. Accomplished
17. Laughing syllable
19. ___head
20. "They ____ my path, they set forward my calamity" (Job 30:13)
21. Like 911
22. "The ____ enemy that shall be destroyed is death" (1 Corinthians 15:26)
24. Son of ___
25. Oil or water
26. King of Bashan (1 Kings 4:19)
27. "Arise, take up thy ____, and go unto thine house" (Matthew 9:6)
28. "Write in it with a man's ____" (Isaiah 8:1)
29. "I saw seven ____ candlesticks" (Revelation 1:12)
32. "Lord, they have killed thy prophets, and ____ down thine altars" (Romans 11:3)
35. Potato part
36. ____ potato
37. Bible language (abbr.)
38. "Jesus saith unto them, Come and ____" (John 21:12)
40. Funny person
41. "This is the whole ____ of man" (Ecclesiastes 12:13)

43. Masculine nickname
44. Knock
45. Sample
46. Revere(d) state (abbr.)
47. Douglas is one
48. Thing to be controlled
51. Average
53. ___-Gurion
54. Sprightly one
55. "He walketh through ____ places, seeking rest" (Luke 11:24)
56. Breadcrust, for example
57. Throw away

DOWN

1. "They rejoiced with exceeding great ____" (Matthew 2:10)
2. ____ struck
3. Painful cries
4. In a short time (arch.)
5. "A time to rend, and a time to ____" (Ecclesiastes 3:7)
6. Liquid measure (abbr.)
7. Son or daughter, most likely
8. "He that keepeth my works unto the ____, to him will I give power" (Revelation 2:26)
9. "Show Me" state (abbr.)
13. "Their tongue is as an arrow ____ out" (Jeremiah 9:8)
15. Put a match to
16. Tribe of Israel
18. Furniture wood
20. Consumed by, with "for"
21. Paul and Silas prayed and ____ in prison
22. Captain's journal
23. Times past
24. "Whom do ____ say that I am?" (Mark 8:27)

25. "Therefore shall he _____ in harvest, and have nothing" (Proverbs 20:4)
27. "The Lord shall hiss...for the _____ that is in the land of Assyria" (Isaiah 7:18)
28. Seed
30. Part of church calendar
31. Tie-_____
32. "A living _____ is better than a dead lion" (Ecclesiastes 9:4)
33. Mother's advice concerning broccoli
34. _____ run
36. Chance (arch.)

38. Item on an AKC document
39. Duke of Edom (Genesis 36:43)
40. Rage against
41. Far from brainy
42. "He shall show you a large _____ room furnished" (Luke 22:12)
44. Tim, for one
45. Post
47. _____ cry
48. Perfect score, sometimes
49. Father of Hophni (1 Samuel 1:3)
50. "Mayberry _____" (former TV show)
52. Publishing person (abbr.)
53. Live

by Evelyn Boyington

ACROSS

1. Holiday symbol
4. "The ____ of the wicked shall be put out" (Proverbs 13:9)
8. Not as much
12. ____ reliever
13. Object of worship
14. Press
15. "____ far from me vanity and lies" (Proverbs 30:8)
17. Linking verb
19. KJV exclamation
20. Reverence
21. Pantry pest
22. What Nebuchadnezzar was washed with, in the wilderness
23. As thin as a ____
25. Fitting
26. "For my yoke is ____, and my burden is light" (Matthew 11:30)
27. Vase
28. Take in a little at a time, literally
29. Low island
30. State of the Southwest (abbr.)
31. "Thou ____ my wanderings: put thou my tears into thy bottle" (Psalm 56:8)
33. "Look!" to King James
35. Cow sound
36. Gershwin
37. "Man that is born of a woman is of ____ days and full of trouble" (Job 14:1)
38. Pump
40. Understand
41. "Then shall the ____ man leap as an hart" (Isaiah 35:6)
42. SRO show
43. Like a bassett hound's expression
44. ____ hen
45. Of Middle Eastern ancestry (abbr.)

46. "Make thee an ____ of gopher wood" (Genesis 6:14)
47. "Such ____ works are wrought by his hands" (Mark 6:2)
50. Very special
52. "Thou hast been in ____ the garden of God" (Ezekiel 28:13)
54. Kind of lamb in Nathan's symbolic story to David
55. Redact
56. "The Lord is my strength and ____" (Psalm 118:14)
57. Become soft

DOWN

1. "The Son of man is as a man taking a ____ journey" (Mark 13:34)
2. Put on ____
3. "That my joy might ____ in you" (John 15:11)
4. Animate
5. Summer drink
6. Detective's quest (abbr.)
7. Put down roots
8. Fabrication
9. Sound of hesitation
10. Shoe parts
11. Unsoiled; spotless
16. "I am like an ____ of the desert" (Psalm 102:6)
18. Not left (abbr.)
21. "I ____ mine heart to know...and to seek out wisdom" (Ecclesiastes 7:25)
22. "To proclaim...the ____ of vengeance of our God" (Isaiah 61:2)
23. "Ye did ____ well; who did hinder you" (Galatians 5:7)
24. Get equipped
25. Be in distress
26. Take a nibble

28. Baste
29. Jeff Davis's org.
31. Digit
32. Before
33. Haw's partner
34. Be in debt
35. "The ____ fell on Matthias; and he was numbered" (Acts 1:26)
37. God is our ____
38. "The Lord is thy ____ upon thy right hand" (Psalm 121:5)
39. "Paul dwelt two whole years in his own ____ house" (Acts 28:30)
40. "All things are for your ____" (2 Corinthians 4:15)
41. Journey jaunt
43. Dad might be one (abbr.)
44. Annex
46. "____ thou he that should come?" (Luke 7:19)
47. Fathers and uncles, for example
48. "____ of every sort shalt thou bring" (Genesis 6:19)
49. "Though he slay me, ____ will I trust in him" (Job 13:15)
51. "Gibeon...was greater than ____ and all the men...were mighty" (Joshua 10:2)
53. Act

by Evelyn Boyington

PUZZLE 176

ACROSS

1. "Every one could sling stones at an hair breadth, and not____" (Judges 20:16)
5. "In their hands they shall ____ thee up lest...thou dash thy foot against a stone" (Matthew 4:6)
9. Before
12. Duke or duchess, for example
13. Word in a threat
14. Disagreement
15. Tribe of Israel
17. "So then they that are in the flesh cannot ____ God" (Romans 8:8)
19. This cookie didn't crumble (it's a success)
21. Lets up
22. Outgrowth
25. Linking verb
26. Canola, for one
27. "Joy that was set before him, endured the ____, despising the shame" (Hebrews 12:2)
29. Unit of weight (abbr.)
31. Behold's partner
32. "Behold an Israelite indeed, in whom is no ____" (John 1:47)
33. "They fled before the men of ____" (Joshua 7:4)
34. French conjunction
35. "This he said, not that he ____ for the poor" (John 12:6)
36. Consumed
37. With Aaron, he held up Moses' hands (Exodus 17)
38. "But ____ us from evil" (Matthew 6:13)
41. Maritime occurrence
43. "The third day he shall ____ again" (Matthew 20:19)
44. "Fallen ____ in Christ" (Christians who have already died) (1 Corinthians 15:18)
46. Stop on the journey from Egypt to Jordan (Numbers 33:27)
49. Tribe of Israel
50. "Hallowed be thy ____" (Matthew 6:9)
53. Continent
54. Hospital facility (abbr., pl.)
55. Sheet size
56. Ancient European

DOWN

1. Baby lamb's cry
2. April addressee
3. Take to ____ (or defeat handily, colloq.)
4. Pottery remains (arch.)
5. "How can these things ____?" (John 3:9)
6. It loops the Loop (abbr.)
7. Serpent
8. "Whom will ye that I ____ unto you, Barabbas or Jesus?" (Matthew 27:17)
9. Wipe away
10. "The desert shall...blossom as the ____" (Isaiah 35:1)
11. Part of the pasture populace (pl.)
16. Son of Peleg (Genesis 11:18)
18. Corn servings
20. Happen
22. "Make thee a fiery serpent and set it upon a ____" (Numbers 21:8)
23. Uproar
24. True's partner
28. Longer in the tooth
29. "It is vain for you to rise up early, to sit up ____" (Psalm 127:2)

354

30. Coffin and platform
32. Item of clothing
35. Find a solution
36. Disinclined
37. What are not barred (colloq.)
39. Illuminated
40. Ishmael's half-brother
41. Wise man
42. Peter, for one
45. "The Lord that delivered me out of the _____ of the lion" (1 Samuel 17:37)
47. To be under the weather
48. Panama, for one
51. Note on the diatonic scale

52. Printer's measure
by Evelyn Boyington

ACROSS

1. They give a hoot
5. Smite, modern style
9. Time of personal testing
10. "Every kind of beasts...hath been _____ of mankind" (James 3:7)
12. Rio ___
13. Officer of David who "was over the tribute" (2 Samuel 20:24)
15. Cereal grain
16. "He cannot _____ himself" (2 Timothy 2:13)
18. Trigonometric ratio
19. Healing plant
21. Put two and two together
23. Middle-school subj.
24. Egg size
26. One who grinds his teeth
28. "Stand in the _____ before me" (Ezekiel 22:30)
30. Cotton ___
31. God _____ those who honestly seek Him
35. Earl, for one
39. Ancient Scandinavian war horn
40. _____ de France
42. Dandelion, for one
43. To be (Fr.)
45. "I will...that men _____ every where, lifting up holy hands" (1 Timothy 2:8)
47. One beguiled by the serpent
48. Scoundrel (colloq.)
50. "Looking up to _____ he blessed them" (Luke 9:16)
52. Garden or grass, for example
53. Amend
54. What club coffers contain
55. Lunch orders (abbr.)

DOWN

1. "The Lord...doth take away from Jerusalem...the eloquent_____" (Isaiah 3:1, 3)
2. "I count all things but loss...that I may _____ Christ" (Philippians 3:8)
3. Actor Alan
4. "Now I lay me down to ___"
5. _____ power
6. Young boy
7. Minor prophet
8. "_____ the thought"
9. Singing syllables
11. "Praise him with the timbrel and _____" (Psalm 150:4)
12. Paul's was the high calling of God in Jesus Christ
14. Gutsy Golda
17. What husbands don't want wives to do
20. Served shirred, perhaps
22. "The Lord God had not caused it to _____ upon the earth" (Genesis 2:5)
25. Whence the wise men came
27. _____on-the-mountain
29. "Thou must prophesy again before many _____" (Revelation 10:11)
31. Played certain instruments
32. Old stringed instruments
33. Task to do
34. French preposition
36. "And levy a tribute unto the Lord...both of the persons, and of the _____" (Numbers 31:28)
37. Bar used to pry
38. "All the trees of _____, the choice and best of Lebanon" (Ezekiel 31:16)

41. "They...came into an harlot's house, named ____" (Joshua 2:1)
44. Firstborn of Isaac and Rebekah
46. Make oneself heard
49. Make ends meet, with "out"
51. Memo abbr.
by Evelyn Boyington

ACROSS

1. Polite word (pl.)
5. Seaport of Israel
9. Nocturnal creature
12. David or Solomon, perhaps
13. London's Abbey is one
14. Nineteenth-century American author
15. Prophetess and daughter of Phanuel
16. They respond to 911 (abbr.)
17. Like food or water
18. "Or if he shall ask an ____, will he offer him a scorpion?" (Luke 11:12)
20. Former P.M. of Israel
22. "____ not at all; neither by heaven" (Matthew 5:34)
24. Period
25. Simile syntax
27. One hundred fifty-one, to Livy
28. Hoover, for one
30. Large group
32. Trite phrase
34. Like one who "hath a devil" (John 10:20)
36. Always
37. "Be ye ____, and sin not" (Ephesians 4:26)
39. Regret
41. Before
42. Movie rating (abbr.)
43. Texas Tech's ____ Raiders
45. Like a foyer
47. Room's partner
49. Just a ___
50. Asaph the ____ (2 Chronicles 29:30)
52. Have a bite
54. After the crucifixion, the soldiers gambled for Jesus' ___
57. Hole-making tool
58. "His clothes shall be rent and his head ____" (Leviticus 13:45)
59. Prophet who follows Joel
60. Still
61. Former British P.M. Anthony
62. It comes with the territory, in the kitchen

DOWN

1. Retreat, perhaps
2. Electrically charged atom
3. "Be ye transformed by the ____ of your mind" (Romans 12:2)
4. ___struck
5. Linking verb
6. Search thoroughly
7. Demolished (as in Psalm 137:7)
8. Sullivan, for one
9. Pull to ___
10. "One ____ is past and behold there come two" (Revelation 9:12)
11. "He was ____ as a sheep to the slaughter" (Acts 8:32)
17. "As vinegar upon ____, so is he that singeth songs to an heavy heart" (Proverbs 25:20)
19. Tribe of Israel
21. "There is but one ____" (1 Corinthians 8:6)
22. "His ____ was in his hand: and he drew near the Philistine" (1 Samuel 17:40)
23. Slam against
25. _____ Fisher Hall, in NYC
26. Withered
27. "O ____ your hands, all ye people" (Psalm 47:1)
29. Deface

1 2 3 4 5 6 7 8 9 10 11
12 13 14
15 16 17
18 19 20 21
22 23 24 25 26
27 28 29 30 31
32 33 34 35 36
37 38 39 40 41
42 43 44 45 46
47 48 49
50 51 52 53 54 55 56
57 58 59
60 61 62

31. "But be of good cheer; I have ____ the world" (John 16:33)
33. "He is risen from the dead: so the last ____ shall be worse than the first" (Matthew 27:64)
35. Date ____ (library logo)
38. KJV affirmative
40. Naval officer (abbr.)
44. "Fear and ____ shall fall upon them" (Exodus 15:16)
46. Father of Abram
47. Update of biblical girdle
48. "For I will not ____ to speak of any of those things which Christ hath not wrought" (Romans 15:18)
50. " ____ what?"
51. Lea dowager
53. "Praise the Lord with...an instrument of ____ strings" (Psalm 33:2)
55. Flamboyant wrap
56. NYC time
58. Exist

by Evelyn Boyington

ACROSS

1. Iowa city
5. Apple variety
9. Thirty Years' ___
12. "I will bring again the captivity of ___" (Jeremiah 49:39)
13. Levitical city of refuge (1 Chronicles 6:73)
14. Samuel's mentor
15. Continent (abbr.)
16. Wired, with "on"
18. "They shall ___ the whirlwind: it hath no stalk" (Hosea 8:7)
19. "My Father giveth you the ___ bread from heaven" (John 6:32)
20. Where the prodigal son dined out
22. Live; realize one's potential
23. "The ___ of wisdom is above rubies" (Job 28:18)
25. "If the good man...had known what hour the ___ would come" (Luke 12:39)
27. Deceased
28. Facade
29. Kind of number
32. Ember residue
33. Trunk "tenant"
34. KJV deer
35. Born (Fr.)
36. Pitchfork hazard
37. Winter plague
38. Adhere
40. Fish or fight
41. Hush!
43. Linking verb
44. "I was an hungred and ye gave me no ___" (Matthew 25:42)
45. ___ and Gown
47. Unplanned information channel (colloq.)

48. Son of Judah (Genesis 38)
50. Used to row the boat
51. Opera solo
53. "At ___" (heard at certain camps)
55. Meddle
56. Be introduced
57. "I am instructed...both to abound and to suffer ___" (Philippians 4:12)

DOWN

1. Number of lepers in Samaria who were healed by Jesus (Luke 17)
2. In the manner of
3. One of the Kettles
4. "And they shall ___ him in an hundred shekels of silver" (Deuteronomy 22:19)
5. "The chariots shall ___ in the streets" (Nahum 2:4)
6. Number of lepers in Samaria who praised God (Luke 17)
7. Bar Harbor state (abbr.)
8. Auntie ___ (L. F. Baum character)
9. Tiny and young
10. Southern state (abbr.)
11. Ready
17. "Let us not be weary...for in ___ season we shall reap" (Galatians 6:9)
18. Deli staple
19. "Bring ye all the ___ into the storehouse" (Malachi 3:10)
20. Lion's portion
21. Horologist's concern, in a way
23. ___ of action
24. Level, as a building (Brit.)

25. "First, I ____ my God through Jesus Christ for you all" (Romans 1:8)
26. Didn't remember
28. ____ Islands
30. Dreary
31. "Let us not love in word...but in ____" (1 John 3:18)
33. Agitate
37. Become aware of
39. Ecru
40. The Great ____
41. Organ option
42. "As small as the ____ frost on the ground" (Exodus 16:14)

44. "I have ____ to eat that ye know not of" (John 4:32)
46. Droll
47. ____ low
48. Compass dir.
49. Buttons
51. Exist
52. In ____
54. One (Scot.)
by Evelyn Boyington

PUZZLE 180

ACROSS

1. "God clave an hollow place that was in the ____, and there came water thereout" (Judges 15:19)
4. Prepare fruit
8. Whatever ____ you
12. Jurist Fortas
13. Black
14. Dagger
15. "He ____ my strength in the way" (Psalm 102:23)
17. Permanent mark
18. Evidence of beating
19. Sesame, for one
20. Northwest ____ (abbr.)
21. "Shoot out thine ____, and destroy them" (Psalm 144:6)
24. Ate out
27. Linking verb
28. Comprehend
29. Son of Zeus
30. "How can a man be born when he is ___?" (John 3:4)
31. *Dead* ____ (Dick Francis classic)
32. French pronoun
33. Hole-making tool
34. Amusement park amusements
35. Begin a conversation
37. Wager
38. Hurry (arch.)
39. Punish (arch.)
43. Steakhouse selection, perhaps
45. "Though they would have cast anchors out of the ____" (Acts 27:30)
47. Cary Grant, once
48. Father of Azariah (2 Chronicles 15:1)
49. Paris summer
50. Challenge
51. Whirlpool
52. Affirmative vote

DOWN

1. Spielberg film
2. Aid's partner
3. ____ thin
4. "There was none that moved the wing or opened the mouth, or ____" (Isaiah 10:14)
5. Son of Ner (2 Samuel 2:8)
6. "Asahel was as light of foot as a wild ____" (2 Samuel 2:18)
7. Like omega
8. Son of Kohath (1 Chronicles 6:22)
9. "And they wrought onyx stones ____ in ouches of gold" (Exodus 39:6)
10. Bucolic locale
11. Indian weight
16. Unclean birds (Deuteronomy 14:13)
19. Pay dirt
21. Son of Bela (Numbers 26:40)
22. Used to be
23. Cupboard collections, as in dishes
24. Fruit of the palm
25. Smooth
26. One close by
27. Cheer competitor
30. "____ no man any thing, but to love" (Romans 13:8)
31. Refers to
33. Mature
34. "The wrath of the Lord arose against his people, till there was no ____" (2 Chronicles 36:16)
36. Seat location
37. Told all
40. Feminine name

41. Bethlehem: _____ of David
42. Fencing gear
43. Exterminate
44. Lupino
45. Nemesis
46. "The _____ number...is to be redeemed" (Numbers 3:48)
    by Evelyn Boyington

ACROSS

1. This admits attorneys
4. Tribe of Israel
9. Son of King Abijam
12. KJV verb
13. "The last ____ of that man is worse than the first" (Luke 11:26)
14. Atlantic state (abbr.)
15. Exist
16. "Abstain from ____ lusts which war against the soul" (1 Peter 2:11)
18. Apiece (abbr.)
19. Golf goal
21. Golf bag contents
23. "I will not give sleep to mine ____" (Psalm 132:4)
25. Aerie
26. Prophetic O.T. book (abbr.)
28. Entreat
30. What may be let out
33. Linking verb
34. "____ yourselves likewise with the same mind" (1 Peter 4:1)
35. "As it was in the days of ____, so shall it be" (Luke 17:26)
36. Del ____, CA
37. Fades
39. "There was no room for them in the ____" (Luke 2:7)
40. In short order (arch.)
42. ____ man (jazz player)
44. King of the Moabites (Numbers 22:4)
46. Dinner table favorites, especially with children
49. Linking verb
50. Populates
54. Twelve Step gp.
55. Under-____ (beach hazard)

57. Hebrew month
58. ATM number
59. "It will be fair weather: for the ____ is red" (Matthew 16:2)
60. Undergarments
61. What Hophni and Phineas took into battle

DOWN

1. Bunyon's ox
2. ____ code
3. Correct (abbr.)
4. "Where is the promise of his coming? for since the fathers fell ____" (2 Peter 3:4)
5. Sault ____ Marie
6. Possesses
7. Ordinal suffix
8. Depended on
9. Classified info
10. "God hath ____ mine affliction" (Genesis 31:42)
11. Exclamation of dismay
16. Summer pest
17. Time period (abbr., pl.)
20. "To the ____ assembly and church of the firstborn" (Hebrews 12:23)
22. First judge of Israel
24. "In the midst of the elders, stood a Lamb as it had been ____" (Revelation 5:6)
25. "Your ____ are written in heaven" (Luke 10:20)
26. Flood preventer, sometimes
27. Former NFL coach Parseghian
29. "Ye do ____, not knowing the scriptures" (Matthew 22:29)
31. Many moons

32. "Let no man glory in ___. For all things are yours" (1 Corinthians 3:21)
37. "Who sent ____ and wonders into the midst of thee, O Egypt" (Psalm 135:9)
38. Mythological nymphs
41. Part of fabric
43. PC operating system
44. Cavern dwellers
45. Lose control, with "run"
47. Hideaway
48. Went down
51. What was poured on Saul's head
52. Greek letter

53. Sitting down, you get this
56. Western state (abbr.)
58. State College state (abbr.)

by Evelyn Boyington

ACROSS

1. White, for one
5. "For I have no man...who will naturally ____ for your state" (Philippians 2:20)
9. Kind of truck
12. Minor prophet
13. So be it
14. Female lea dweller
15. 3.1416
16. Sixties-style dress
18. "They compassed me about like ____" (Psalm 118:12)
19. "She shall shave her head and ____ her nails" (Deuteronomy 21:12)
20. Greek letter
22. NY or CA
23. Greek isle
25. "Do ye think that the scripture ____ in vain" (James 4:5)
27. Definitely pink
28. Nick Charles, aka *The* ____ *Man*
29. Exclamation of discovery
32. ____ *on parle francais*
33. "For if ye love them which love you, what ____ have ye?" (Luke 6:32)
34. ____ fried
35. Barbara ____ Geddes
36. Baby and bath, to name two
37. "And he ____ and touched his tongue" (Mark 7:33)
38. "Is the Lord's hand waxed ___?" (Numbers 11:23)
40. Prophets
41. Athens is here (abbr.)
43. "Joseph...was the son of his ____ age" (Genesis 37:3)
44. ____ there, done that

45. "The workman is worthy of his ____" (Matthew 10:10)
47. Come together; touch
48. "Arise, go up to ____" (Joshua 8:1)
50. Mess up
51. Shut's partner
53. Apparent one
55. Asiatic deer
56. Accustomed
57. "I'm all ___"

DOWN

1. "The trees of the Lord are full of ____" (Psalm 104:16)
2. French friend
3. Biblical exclamation
4. "He hath regarded the low ____ of his handmaiden" (Luke 1:48)
5. Hawaiian product, for short
6. Quantity (abbr.)
7. Concerning
8. ___-gedi (where David dwelt for a time)
9. To a ___
10. Is beholden to
11. Author Nathanael
17. Before
18. Bridle part
19. Pauline's adventures of filmdom
20. "Whom God hath raised up, having loosed the ____ of death" (Acts 2:24)
21. Kind of hole
23. "Where no oxen are, the ____ is clean" (Proverbs 14:4)
24. 3 K or 5 K, for example
25. "Thou ____ love thy neighbor" (Romans 13:9)

26. "He...began to tell them what things should _____ unto him" (Mark 10:32)
28. "The Lord called Samuel again the _____ time" (1 Samuel 3:8)
30. Absalom's stunning feature
31. "The _____ are a people not strong" (Proverbs 30:25)
33. Hand or power
37. Rage inside
39. Salsa choice
40. Jurisdiction of a bishop
41. Ancient Hebrew dry measure
42. Deli order

44. "He hath _____ his bow, and made it ready" (Psalm 7:12)
46. Linking verb
47. "I will...that _____ pray everywhere" (1 Timothy 2:8)
48. Broadcast
49. Government agency (abbr.)
51. Ouch!
52. River in Italy
54. Per person (abbr.)
by Evelyn Boyington

ACROSS

1. "Until the day dawn, and the day ____ arise" (2 Peter 1:19)
5. "Believe not every spirit, but ____ the spirits" (1 John 4:1)
8. Some circles
12. "Take thine ____, eat, drink, and be merry" (Luke 12:19)
13. Do garden work
14. Wild rest stop
15. Operatic highlight
16. *Mange*, in Marshalltown
17. Land measure
18. "Let them be for signs, and for ____, and for day, and years" (Genesis 1:14)
20. Pine
21. Exclamation of pain
22. Item to do
24. Newsman Phillips
27. Laughing sound
28. Moisture
31. Holds the deed to
32. "We have also a more ____ word of prophecy" (2 Peter 1:19)
33. Forest female
34. "If God ____ for us, who can be against us?" (Romans 8:31)
36. "We pray you in Christ's ____, be ye reconciled to God" (2 Corinthians 5:20)
37. "They wandered in deserts, and in mountains, and in ____ " (Hebrews 11:38)
39. ____ of the Chaldees
40. Late actor Ames
42. Survived in water
47. Kind of scale
48. "Ye ____ bought with a price" (1 Corinthians 6:20)
49. Tabu, to toddler

50. Greek letter (pl.)
51. Nothing
52. Oaf; bully
53. Black, for one
54. Kind of glass
55. Sea bird

DOWN

1. "The gathering together of the waters called he ____ " (Genesis 1:10)
2. "The devil threw him down and ____ him" (Luke 9:42)
3. "The churches of ____ salute you" (1 Corinthians 16:19)
4. "Produce your cause...bring forth your strong ____, saith the King of Jacob" (Isaiah 41:21)
5. There's partner
6. Sunday entree
7. "____ not I, but Christ liveth in me" (Galatians 2:20)
8. "The Lord is not ____ concerning his promise" (2 Peter 3:9)
9. Every
10. Soggy ground
11. Anger
19. "____ no man any thing, but to love" (Romans 13:8)
20. King of Judah; son of Abijam
23. Exclamation of delight
24. Earth
25. When this many are gathered together, the Lord is present
26. Christians worship the ____ true God
28. "A word spoken in ____ season, how good is it" (Proverbs 15:23)
29. Historical period
30. Unite

32. "How shall we sing the Lord's song in a ____ land?" (Psalm 137:4)
34. ___-oni, Rachel's youngest
35. Printer's measure
36. "A Boy Named ____" (J. Cash hit)
37. KJV verb
38. Airport runway
40. Recently, with "of"
41. Showing no favoritism (Fr.)
43. Call on for help
44. "Behold, I stand at the ____" (Revelation 3:20)

45. ____ Church, Virginia (site of 1864 battle)
46. Well ____
47. *Charlotte's* ____ (E.B. White classic)
48. Reply (abbr.)
   by Evelyn Boyington

ACROSS

1. "Call me not Naomi, call me ____" (Ruth 1:20)
5. Bunch of bubbles
9. Paramedic's report (abbr.)
12. "The slaughter of Midian at the rock of ____" (Isaiah 10:26)
13. "Every ____ word that men shall speak, they shall give account" (Matthew 12:36)
14. There's the ___
15. "She...began to ____ his feet with tears" (Luke 7:38)
16. Burden
17. Compass dir.
18. "Let us build us a city and ____, whose top may reach unto heaven" (Genesis 11:4)
20. Lets off fumes
22. Ship to ___
24. Team _____, Olympics competitor
25. Attitude
26. Has ___
29. "It shall be even given thee to the ____ of the kingdom" (Esther 5:3)
33. Creative concept
35. "I will send a ____ , saying, Go, find the arrows" (1 Samuel 20:21)
36. Golden calf, for one
37. More is ___
38. Telegram word
40. United
41. Ram's mate
43. Captured, in a way
45. Lion's portion
48. "What is the chaff to the ___?" (Jeremiah 23:28)

50. Require effort
51. "He himself stayed in ____ for a season" (Acts 19:22)
53. Become bored
56. Linking verb
57. ____ stop
58. "Whatsoever shall be given you in that ____, that speak ye" (Mark 13:11)
59. Affirmative
60. Overeat, almost
61. Dagger

DOWN

1. Weekend job, for many
2. Son of Jether (1 Chronicles 7:38)
3. Gives new life, as the Lord
4. "Him shall the people curse, nations shall ____ him" (Proverbs 24:24)
5. Rank's partner
6. Scent
7. In the manner of
8. "Thy kingdom is divided, and given to the ____ and the Persians" (Daniel 5:28)
9. Three (Ger.)
10. Fire
11. Fortas and others
19. Where one surfs
21. Mother, hello (abbr.)
22. "Strengthen their mast, they could not spread the ____" (Isaiah 33:23)
23. "____ us from the face of him that sitteth on the throne" (Revelation 6:16)
24. Cancel; annul
27. In addition

28. Partake
30. "Ye have received the Spirit of ____, whereby we cry, Abba, Father" (Romans 8:15)
31. Single
32. "Then all the disciples forsook him, and ____" (Matthew 26:56)
34. Tribe of Israel (var.)
39. ____millennialism
42. Becomes useless, with "out"
44. Vows
45. "None can ____ his hand" (Daniel 4:35)
46. Unclean animal (Leviticus 11:6)
47. Cutting tools
48. Knew; learned (arch.)
49. "____ the evil" (Amos 5:15)
52. Aegean, for one
54. Regret
55. Poetic contraction
by Evelyn Boyington

ACROSS

1. Woolly ones
5. Under the weather
8. Mull over
12. Imply
13. Feminine Israeli name
14. Covenant
15. Make null
16. Attila, for one
17. Zone
18. "As newborn babes, ____ the sincere milk of the word" (1 Peter 2:2)
20. "____ is all, and in all" (Colossians 3:11)
22. Cable, for one
23. Hairpin curve
24. "In thy fear will I ____ toward thy holy temple" (Psalm 5:7)
28. Temporary dwellings
32. "For Adam was first formed, then ____" (1 Timothy 2:13)
33. Gratuity
35. Vowel trio
36. "To be a reproach and a proverb, a ____ and a curse" (Jeremiah 24:9)
39. "The dragon shalt thou ____ under feet" (Psalm 91:13)
42. ____ drum
44. "Ye ____ of your father the devil" (John 8:44)
45. Graven image, perhaps
48. Mental pictures
52. Hope
53. Donkey
55. Disreputable establishment
56. Sheltered side
57. "A faithful witness will not ____" (Proverbs 14:5)
58. Appliance
59. "The day of the Lord is ____" (Joel 3:14)
60. Sra, in Sarasota
61. Left

DOWN

1. Son of Gera, the second judge of Israel (Judges 3:15)
2. "Woe to them that are mighty to drink ____" (Isaiah 5:22)
3. "The Creator of the ____ of the earth, fainteth not" (Isaiah 40:28)
4. Group of philosophers who met Paul at Athens (Acts 17:18)
5. "They that do such things shall not ____ the kingdom of God" (Galatians 5:21)
6. President Hoover's wife, familiarly
7. Masculine name
8. Rough; earthy
9. Mata ____
10. Summers, in Nice
11. Reporter's question
19. Stadium sound
21. Honolulu's time zone
24. ____ paint
25. Eggs
26. Father of Serug (Genesis 11:20)
27. "To him was given the key of the bottomless ____" (Revelation 9:1)
29. Snooze
30. Up to that point (var.)
31. Feminine nickname
34. The children of the Proverbs 31 woman call her blessed, and the husband ____ her
37. "They are all delivered unto death, to the ____ parts of the earth" (Ezekiel 31:14)

38. Greek letter
40. "The isles shall wait upon me, and on mine _____ shall they trust" (Isaiah 51:5)
41. Bucolic spot
43. King's bailiwick
45. _____ song
46. Mosaic piece
47. On a steamer
49. "_____ unto the Lord the glory due unto his name" (Psalm 96:8)
50. Tied
51. Dispatched
54. Title of respect
by Evelyn Boyington

ACROSS

1. Cleo's killer
4. Asa or Ahab
8. Perfect
12. "They cast ____, that is, the lot, before Haman" (Esther 3:7)
13. One who sold his birthright
14. "As he saith also in ____, I will call them my people" (Romans 9:25)
15. Where one uses a wood
16. "Six ____ shalt thou labour and do all thy work" (Exodus 20:9)
17. Reporter's question
18. "There shall come a ____ out of Jacob and a Sceptre shall rise" (Numbers 24:17)
20. Word's partner
21. "Stretch out the ____ that is in thy hand toward Ai" (Joshua 8:18)
23. Greek letter
25. To exhibit exhaustion
26. Burdened one
27. Golden State (abbr.)
29. Godfrey, to friends
30. "The word is nigh thee, even in thy mouth, and in thy ____" (Romans 10:8)
31. "For the Father...hath committed all judgment unto the ____" (John 5:22)
32. Bible div.
33. "Ye shall be baptized with the Holy Ghost not many days ____" (Acts 1:5)
34. KJV verb
35. Out of (arch.)
36. Says "whoa"
37. "I am the ____ vine" (John 15:1)
38. "Nadab and Abihu...offered strange ____ before the Lord" (Leviticus 10:1)
39. Hurries
40. Speed
42. Compass dir.
45. Opposed to aweather
46. "In ____ there was a voice heard, lamentation" (Matthew 2:18)
47. Iowa college
48. Kind of hall
49. Memo part
50. Before

DOWN

1. "A bishop the must be...____ to teach" (1 Timothy 3:2)
2. Betty White role on "Mary Tyler Moore" TV show
3. "God is...a very ____ help in trouble" (Psalm 46:1)
4. "Arabia, and all the princes of ____...in these were thy merchants" (Ezekiel 27:21)
5. Danube tributary
6. Negative vote
7. Masculine nickname
8. American social reformer Julia
9. Son of Nun of the tribe of Ephraim (Numbers 13:8)
10. "I am instructed...both to abound and to suffer ____" (Philippians 4:12)
11. Poetic contraction
19. Make lace
20. KJV verb
21. Measure of length
22. Say adieu
23. "____ hither thy finger, and behold my hands" (John 20:27)

24. Tortoise's opponent
26. "My people are ____ to back sliding from me" (Hosea 11:7)
27. Pasture youngster
28. They head for the hills
30. Now's partner
31. "Let the lying lips be put to ____" (Psalm 31:18)
33. Provides shelter
34. "We do not ____ after the flesh" (2 Corinthians 10:3)
35. Loosens
36. "So ____ gave Solomon cedar trees and fir trees" (1 Kings 5:10)
37. Game piece
38. "His ____ went throughout all Syria" (Matthew 4:24)
39. Son of Noah
40. Every third (comb. form)
41. "____ thou not the bread of him that hath an evil eye" (Proverbs 23:6)
43. Conjunction
44. Shoe width
by Evelyn Boyington

ACROSS

1. Atlas and Apennines (abbr.)
4. "Is there no ____ in Gilead?" (Jeremiah 8:22)
8. Son of Omri; notoriously evil king
12. Gershwin
13. Great Lake
14. KJV verb
15. Complete collections
17. "Thou shalt not plow with an ox and an ____ together" (Deuteronomy 22:10)
18. Curtain or horse
19. Canines, for example
21. Stage direction
23. Legal object
25. Chemical suffix
26. Certain physician (abbr.)
28. "The yoke shall be destroyed because of the ____" (Isaiah 10:27)
32. ____ ear
33. "Whatsoever a man soweth, that shall he also ____" (Galatians 6:7)
34. Energy unit
35. Mad at
36. "They ____ my path, they set forward my calamity" (Job 30:13)
37. "There were set there six ____ of stone" (John 2:6)
39. Elder (abbr.)
40. "The everlasting ____, the Lord" (Isaiah 40:28)
41. One fleet of foot in the forest
42. Grand ____ auto
44. "Let them praise his name in the ____" (Psalm 149:3)
48. "____ went before the ark" (2 Samuel 6:4)

50. Linking verb
52. "____ my lips"
53. Works like a gem
54. Steadfast
56. KJV grain
57. Aid's partner
58. Saline drop
59. "When we came to the ____, that we opened our sacks" (Genesis 43:21)

DOWN

1. "There went up a ____ from the earth and watered" (Genesis 2:6)
2. Birch or ginkgo
3. Make contented
4. "____ it ever so humble..."
5. Son of Jether (1 Chronicles 7:38)
6. Feminine name
7. "A thorn in the flesh, the ____ of Satan" (2 Corinthians 12:7)
8. "____ in me, and I in you" (John 15:4)
9. Animal not to be eaten (Deuteronomy 14:7)
10. Hubbub
11. Actor Cross
16. Sunset, for one
20. Coop dowager
22. Participle suffix
24. Hardly fickle
26. Gossip, literally (colloq.)
27. Addition column
28. "God is thy refuge, and underneath are the everlasting ____" (Deuteronomy 33:27)
29. "Thou art ____, O Lord" (Psalm 119:151)
30. Paddle
31. NYC subway

32. "Is any thing _____ hard for the Lord?" (Genesis 18:14)
35. Asparagus unit
37. Sorrow
38. "The staff of his shoulder, the _____ of his oppressor" (Isaiah 9:4)
40. "The Holy _____ shall come upon thee" (Luke 1:35)
42. _____ and again
43. Colorfast
45. Father of Salathiel (Luke 3:27)
46. "Whosoever slayeth _____, vengeance shall be taken on him" (Genesis 4:15)

47. Idyllic spot
48. Exclamation
49. Where the action is
51. Baseball stat.
55. Son of Judah (1 Chronicles 2:3)
by Evelyn Boyington

377

ACROSS

1. Sign of the end times (Matthew 24:6)
5. "Fear God and ____ his commandments" (Ecclesiastes 12:13)
9. Trucker's "motel"
12. "He [Isaac] called the name of the well ____" (Genesis 26:20)
13. Exclamation
14. Tint
15. Sinks
17. "I was afraid, and went and hid thy ____" (Matthew 25:25)
19. ____ and the Thummin (Exodus 28:30)
20. "My servant ____ at home sick" (Matthew 8:6)
21. Puts an end to
23. Parts of capitols
25. Charade
26. In the near future (arch.)
28. "Buy the truth and ____ it not" (Proverbs 23:23)
31. Preposition
32. Church part (pl.)
34. That is (abbr.)
35. "Ye may rejoice, and that I may be the ____ sorrowful" (Philippians 2:28)
38. Nuisance
39. Promise Keepers attendees
40. "Ye shall receive ____, after that the Holy Ghost is come" (Acts 1:8)
42. "____ your ways and your doings" (Jeremiah 7:3)
44. "There ____ from heaven a great light" (Acts 22:6)
46. Actor Thicke
47. Unleashed

49. "Those who by reason of use have their ____ exercised to discern" (Hebrews 5:14)
52. Holiday, for one
53. Choose's cohort
55. Settle in a cozy spot
56. French pronoun
57. "Thou hadst cast me...in the midst of the ____" (Jonah 2:3)
58. "The poison of ____ is under their lips" (Romans 3:13)

DOWN

1. Entanglement
2. Good king of Judah
3. Consequence
4. Avoid
5. Abyssinian weight
6. Chicago transport (abbr.)
7. "In the day you ____ thereof, then your eyes shall be opened" (Genesis 3:5)
8. "Sing unto the Lord with...the voice of a ____" (Psalm 98:5)
9. "Hast thou not...curdled me like ____" (Job 10:10)
10. Orpah, to Obed
11. House, in Hebrew
16. Hebrew month
18. "Behold, thou [Samson] hast mocked me [Delilah], and told me ____" (Judges 16:10)
21. Greet
22. Teen trauma
23. Capital of Delaware
24. Singles
27. Back of the neck
29. Property claim
30. Let borrow
33. Not fresh

36. Forks' cohorts
37. "As my beloved _____ I warn you" (1 Corinthians 4:14)
39. Monthly occurrence
41. Mourns
43. "Our fathers did eat _____ in the desert" (John 6:31)
44. Skirt feature
45. Practice and practice and practice
46. Queries
48. "To live is Christ and to _____ is gain" (Philippians 1:21)
50. Extra sense (abbr.)
51. Byways (abbr.)
54. About (abbr.)

by Evelyn Boyington

ACROSS

1. Buys (tickets) for later profit
7. "Believe on the Lord Jesus Christ, and thou shalt be ____" (Acts 16:31)
12. "An inheritance may be gotten ____ at the beginning" (Proverbs 20:21)
14. John, on Patmos
15. Luc, to Lisette
16. Kind of shot or shirt
17. Napa Valley sight (pl.)
18. Depilatory brand
20. "The ____ of sin is death" (Romans 6:23)
22. Note on the diatonic scale
23. Mete out
25. Bleed, as madras
26. Body of water (Fr.)
27. "Lo, I see four men ____, walking in the midst of the fire" (Daniel 3:25)
29. Horse hair
30. Aircraft authority
32. "Remember how ____ my time is" (Psalm 89:47)
34. 1/1000 of an inch (pl.)
35. Has strong feelings about
37. Ocean (abbr.)
38. Solidify
39. "Who hath...____ out heaven with the span" (Isaiah 40:12)
43. Borders VA and MD
44. Sewing fundamentals
46. "____ thyself, and come down from the cross" (Mark 15:30)
47. Interjection
48. Conjunction
49. Shoe size
51. Sue ____, honey brand
52. Traversed by *les bateaux mouches*
54. RSVP request
56. Ash and aspen
57. Wears; dons

DOWN

1. Columnist Alexander
2. "It is easier for a ____ to go through the eye of a needle" (Matthew 19:24)
3. Father of Seraiah (1 Chronicles 4:35)
4. Army officer (abbr.)
5. Pothole's cousin
6. Whole bunch
7. "I will serve thee ____ years for Rachel" (Genesis 29:18)
8. Alignment between countries
9. French export, to the French
10. Earth or air, for example
11. "Master...do for us whatsoever we shall ____" (Mark 10:35)
13. "Receive my sayings; and the ____ of thy life shall be many" (Proverbs 4:10)
19. Road trip expenses, sometimes
21. "That he was gone to be ____ with a man that is a sinner" (Luke 19:7)
24. As well
26. "Neither shalt thou ____ the corners of thy beard" (Leviticus 19:27)
28. Further; additional
29. Husband of Zipporah
30. He doesn't want to be called for a balk
31. "Love worketh no ____ to his neighbour" (Romans 13:10)
33. Haw's partner
34. "Thou ____ him a little lower than the angels" (Hebrews 2:7)

36. Change
38. Stations (Fr.)
40. Bible mount near Nazareth
41. Occurrence
42. "Ye have put off the old man with his ____" (Colossians 3:9)
44. Exhausted, with "in"
45. Understands
50. Particularly (abbr.)
53. Common abbr.
55. River in Italy
   by Evelyn Boyington

ACROSS

1. Revolutionary hero Nathan
5. Step made by faith
9. Age of Methuselah when he had a son: one hundred eighty-____ (Genesis 5:25)
10. Aerie dweller
12. This may include "or else"
13. Most faithful
15. "There stood before the river a ____ which had two horns" (Daniel 8:3)
16. Treasured, in a way
18. Assess
19. Herdsman of Tekoia whom God called to be a prophet
21. Rod and ____
23. Bishopric
24. Noted Quaker family, and others
26. Chooses
28. At odds (abbr.)
30. Songdom's "gal"
31. "The way of man is ____ and strange" (Proverbs 21:8)
35. Is diminished
39. "Go, sell the ____, and pay thy debt" (2 Kings 4:7)
40. He went searching for his father's lost donkeys
42. Neap, for one
43. "Incline not my heart to any ____ thing" (Psalm 141:4)
45. Sesquicentennial segment
47. Mature
48. Stern
50. Like- ____ (kindred spirit)
52. "The angels shall...____ the wicked from among the just" (Matthew 13:49)
53. Ezekiel saw a valley that was full of ___

54. Takes no action
55. "There shall come forth a rod out of the ____ of Jesse" (Isaiah 11:1)

DOWN

1. Mount on the northeastern boundary of Palestine (Joshua 12:1)
2. Roadway (abbr.)
3. Seep
4. Door direction
5. Colossians and Philippians, familiarly
6. What one lends
7. "The words of ___ the son of Jakeh, even the prophecy" (Proverbs 30:1)
8. "Do I seek to ____ men?" (Galatians 1:10)
9. "Let them be confounded and put to ____" (Psalm 35:4)
11. Fragrant compound
12. Sand, for one
14. Wooden pegs
17. Vitality
20. Twentieth-century English novelist
22. "His ____ also shall not wither" (Psalm 1:3)
25. LaCosta, and others
27. Apartment
29. "He had offered up ____ and supplications with strong crying" (Hebrews 5:7)
31. Those opposed
32. Splits
33. Mount of ___
34. ____ date
36. "Thou shalt also be...a royal ____ in the hand of thy God" (Isaiah 62:3)

37. "These things, saith he which hath the sharp sword with two ____" (Revelation 2:12)
38. ____ money
41. "Two ____ of the first year for a sacrifice of peace" (Leviticus 23:19)
44. Israel's high priest had to descend from this tribe
46. Lose control
49. Soak flax
51. Compass dir.

by Evelyn Boyington

ACROSS

1. Cartographer's creation
4. Had a stroke
8. Captain Hook's henchman
12. Mother of Hezekiah (2 Kings 18:2)
13. "The king arose, and ____ his garments" (2 Samuel 13:31)
14. "I ____ you!"
15. "My money is ___; and lo, it is even in my sack" (Genesis 42:28)
17. Deserve
18. Mar, in a way
19. "Beware of the scribes, which love...the chief ____ in the synagogues" (Mark 12:38,39)
21. English breakfast, for one
23. Keeps away from
26. Cathedral feature
29. "The vine languisheth, all the merry hearted do ____" (Isaiah 24:7)
32. Norma ____ (Sally Field role)
33. "He that hath clean hands and a ____ heart" (Psalm 24:4)
34. Worldwide workers group (abbr.)
35. Fantasy (Fr.)
36. Time for *les grandes vacances*
37. College building
38. "Thou hast been in ____ the garden of God" (Ezekiel 28:13)
39. "Evening ____" (former TV show)
41. Part of a circle (abbr.)
43. Tithe fraction
46. Park ____ (neighborhood in Brooklyn, NY)
50. ____ Canal
52. "____ his marvellous works...his wonders" (1 Chronicles 16:12)
54. Circuit
55. Mouths
56. On; upon (prefix)
57. ____ room
58. Blemish
59. Actress Sandra

DOWN

1. ____ Hill, where Paul spoke in Athens
2. Assist
3. City on the Arno River
4. "The ____ that smote the image became a great mountain" (Daniel 2:35)
5. "The words of his mouth were smoother than butter, but ____ was in his heart" (Psalm 55:21)
6. Mythological god of war
7. Babylonian conqueror
8. "Smite...and destroy all the children of ____" (Numbers 24:17)
9. "The children of Israel...cannot be ____ nor numbered" (Hosea 1:10)
10. "Men have not heard, nor perceived by the ____" (Isaiah 64:4)
11. Sea bird
16. "Ye pay ____ of mint and anise" (Matthew 23:23)
20. Furniture wood
22. "They...were forbidden of the Holy Ghost to preach the word in ____" (Acts 16:6)
24. Church part
25. Observed
26. Mirrors
27. Orpah's sister-in-law
28. "From the beginning of the ____ God made them male and female" (Mark 10:6)

30. _____ at ease
31. "They should not worship devils and idols of _____" (Revelation 9:20)
35. King's domain
37. Little red one
40. "Thou hast laid me in the lowest pit...in the _____" (Psalm 88:6)
42. To cause to be (suffix, Brit.)
44. "Doth he thank that servant...? I _____ not" (Luke 17:9)
45. Wife of Zeus
47. Grandfather of David
48. Cartoon character LePew
49. Pennsylvania city

50. Small-town America street
51. _____ v. Wade
53. "They _____ my path, they set forward my calamity" (Job 30:13)

by Evelyn Boyington

ACROSS

1. Wrath
4. Send out
8. "They made a calf...and offered sacrifice unto the ____" (Acts 7:41)
12. From or to a distance (prefix)
13. "He maketh the storm a ____" (Psalm 107:29)
14. Bog
15. He thought Hannah had been drinking
16. Bold alternative
17. Disobey a road sign
18. "Do good to them that ____ you" (Matthew 5:44)
20. Lady of Spain, perhaps (abbr.)
21. "In thee, O Lord, do I put my ____" (Psalm 71:1)
23. "____ God in the day of visitation" (1 Peter 2:12)
27. Clarifying abbr.
28. From here one has a bird's-eye view
30. Ripped apart (arch.)
31. Feminine name
33. "There is a ____, the streams whereof shall make glad" (Psalm 46:4)
35. Little lamb's cry
36. Land measure
38. AKA Cephas
40. Title of respect (abbr.)
41. What Demetrius the silversmith made (Acts 19:24)
43. Children of the vindicated Job: ____ sons and three daughters
44. Number of pieces of silver belonging to the woman in the parable of the lost coin
45. Cash cow (abbr.)

46. Isle of ____, in the English Channel
49. Arafat's assoc.
50. Not a lot
53. Buffalo's lake
54. ____ *Window* (Hitchcock film)
55. Before
56. Coffin
57. "____ it even to the foundation thereof" (Psalm 137:7)
58. Tribe of Israel

DOWN

1. Believer in (suffix)
2. Cousin, e.g.
3. U.S. statesman Root
4. "I will ____ you abroad among the nations" (Nethemiah 1:8)
5. Actor Alan
6. "They angered him... so that it went ____ with Moses" (Psalm 106:32)
7. Britain's John Major, once (abbr.)
8. "That I may ____ unto you some spiritual gift" (Romans 1:11)
9. "I must ____ in this land" (Deuteronomy 4:22)
10. Mine find
11. What Fred Astaire did?
17. Hit's inits.
19. Good king of Judah
20. Storm hazard
21. Son of Japheth (Genesis 10:2)
22. Toothbrush brand
23. "What ____?"
24. The Great ____ ____ (name for God)
25. "For he knoweth our ___; he remembereth that we are dust" (Psalm 103:14)

26. Pine
29. What sour grapes do, hopefully
32. To blunder
34. "I will ____ health unto thee" (Jeremiah 30:17)
37. One or the other
39. Jerky movement during sleep (abbr.)
42. "I will spread my ____ upon them" (Hosea 7:12)
45. Exclamation of pity
46. Sticky trap
47. Son of Bela (1 Chronicles 7:7)
48. Give (Scot.)
49. Legume

50. "I have ____ you with milk" (1 Corinthians 3:2)
51. Tide competitor
52. Benign skin tumor
54. B & O, e.g.
by Evelyn Boyington

ACROSS

1. "The ____ trees of the wheels were joined to the base" (1 Kings 7:32)
5. Ingredient in some cereals
9. Father of Kish (1 Samuel 9:1)
10. "____ up a child in the way he should go" (Proverbs 22:6)
12. Achieve success (colloq.)
13. "Mount Sion, which is ____" (Deuteronomy 4:48)
15. Fuss
16. Let go, not so nicely
18. Greek letter
19. Utility org. for noncity dwellers
20. Main rooms of ancient Roman house
22. Poetic contraction
23. Support one's alma mater
25. Job requirements
27. Stack or rack
29. "Ye shall go out with joy and be ____ forth with peace" (Isaiah 55:12)
30. Side and back, to name two
34. Narrow, deep pass
38. The style of (suffix)
39. Accustomed oneself, with "into"
41. Son of Benjamin (Genesis 46:21)
42. Push, and even shove
43. Inhabitant, e.g. (abbr.)
44. "Ye shall be hated of all ____" (Matthew 10:22)
45. Hope for all generations: Jesus has ____ from the dead!
48. Saturated with liquid, with "up"
51. "Laying up in ____ for themselves a good foundation" (1 Timothy 6:19)
52. "For we which have believed do ____ into rest" (Hebrews 4:3)
53. Taken to court
54. "Call ye upon him while he is ____" (Isaiah 55:6)

DOWN

1. Europe, in particular, to Americans
2. Hours in the day, to a centurion
3. O.T. book
4. "For Jacob my servant's sake, and Israel mine ____" (Isaiah 45:4)
5. Brother of Caleb (Joshua 15:17)
6. Linking verb
7. Black liquid
8. Tribe of Israel
9. Actress Eve
11. "But I will shew thee that which is ____ in the scripture" (Daniel 10:21)
12. River in Switzerland
14. Fashion designer Byron
17. Son of Benjamin (Genesis 46:21)
20. "Now it is high time to ____… now is our salvation nearer" (Romans 13:11)
21. "____ you ways and your doings" (Jeremiah 7:3)
24. Exclamation of surprise
26. Fuss
28. Ached
30. Watery animal fluid (pl.)
31. Alexander and others
32. Forgives; pardons
33. Compass dir.
35. "The third part of an hin of oil to ____ with the fine flour" (Ezekiel 46:14)
36. "Be of good ___; I have overcome the world" (John 16:33)

37. "Naphtali is a ____ let loose"
    (Genesis 49:21)
40. Industrial center in Germany
46. French coin
47. Before
49. "As the body is ____, and hath
    many members"
    (1 Corinthians 12:12)
50. School org.
    by Evelyn Boyington

ACROSS

1. Sinful
4. "And the Spirit and the ____ say, Come" (Revelation 22:17)
9. Word in many ranch names
12. On the outside (prefix)
13. To let slacken
14. Put on ____ (postpone)
15. Rebelled against
17. Convalesced
19. Friendly and Flintstone
21. "Shall I come unto you with a ____, or in love" (1 Corinthians 4:21)
22. "I give unto you power to ____ on serpents" (Luke 10:19)
24. "The labour of the righteous ____ to life" (Proverbs 10:16)
28. Actor William
29. Ms. Moreno
30. "As it was in the days of ____" (Luke 17:26)
31. Product safety inits.
32. "There was a rainbow...in sight like unto an ____" (Revelation 4:3)
35. Western state (abbr.)
36. NYC opera house
38. "Ye shall eat neither bread nor parched corn, nor green ____" (Leviticus 23:14)
39. Protest
41. Kind of alphabet
43. Dispatches
44. Requirement for college (abbr.)
45. Provides sketchy information
47. Spice rack spice
50. Like a mule, supposedly
53. Miner's pay dirt
54. "Neither let us ____ Christ, as some of them" (1 Corinthians 10:9)
56. Actor Louis
57. ____ & breakfast
58. "Foxes have ____" (Luke 9:58)
59. Oolong, for one

DOWN

1. "I remember thee upon my ____" (Psalm 63:6)
2. Mirror
3. "Who maketh thee to ____ from another?" (1 Corinthians 4:7)
4. To be fruitful
5. Comedian Foxx
6. Within; toward (prefix)
7. "Mine eye also is ____ by reason of sorrow" (Job 17:7)
8. "The ____ God is thy refuge" (Deuteronomy 33:27)
9. Implored (arch.)
10. Team's "winningest" pitcher
11. ____ Sea
16. Consumed with anger
18. Where Cain dwelled: land of ____
20. "I was dumb with silence...and my sorrow was ____" (Psalm 39:2)
22. Tom of Ringling Bros. fame
23. "I will make thee ____ over many things" (Matthew 25:21)
25. Greek letters
26. Namely (2 words)
27. Gives new life, as Jesus Christ does
29. Camino ____
33. "My soul ____ for heaviness" (Psalm 119:28)

34. "They that will be rich fall...into many...lusts, which ____ men in destruction" (1 Timothy 6:9)
37. "When the ruler of the feast had ____ the water that was made wine" (John 2:9)
40. Say okay
42. "____ ____ [2 words] with you, saith the Lord" (Haggai 1:13)
43. Book divisions
46. On cowboy's saddle checklist
47. ____ Hill, San Francisco
48. Office or function (suffix)

49. Neon competitor
51. Grain
52. KJV assent
55. Metric measure (abbr.)
by Evelyn Boyington

ACROSS

1. Horned mammal, often mentioned in the Bible
4. Son of (Hebrew)
7. ____ of Man
10. Tizzy
11. Compass pt.
12. One from Tarsus
14. "The younger son...____ his substance with riotous living" (Luke 15:13)
16. "Aaron and ____ stayed up his hands" (Exodus 17:12)
17. Exclamation of relief
19. Many moons
20. Mother ____
21. Jeanne d'Arc, for one (abbr.)
22. Hive dweller
24. "Exalt him that is ____" (Ezekiel 21:26)
25. To dam up
26. Simile syntax
27. "____ thou on my right hand" (Mark 12:36)
28. Legume
29. ____ eagle (skating stunt)
32. Almost
35. Cereal grain
36. Baseball great Drysdale
37. That is (abbr.)
38. "What do ye, loosing the ____" (Mark 11:5)
40. "Ye are grown ____ as the heifer at grass" (Jeremiah 50:11)
41. Appeal
43. Hole-making device
44. Put down
45. Nemesis, certainly
46. Exist
47. Outward appearance
48. "Do I seek to ____men?" (Galatians 1:10)
51. "____ thyself now with majesty and excellency" (Job 40:10)
53. ____ Dolorosa
54. "All the rivers ____ unto the sea" (Ecclesiastes 1:7)
55. Consumed
56. "Go to the ____, thou sluggard" (Proverbs 6:6)
57. Mamie Eisenhower, ____ Dowd

DOWN

1. Unrefined
2. Michigan town near Grand Rapids
3. Brother of Miriam
4. Has ____
5. Kind of game
6. Quadrant in D.C.
7. "All the women...in wisdom ____ goats' hair" (Exodus 35:26)
8. Paddle
9. Greek letter
13. Better than never
15. Big ____: circus site
16. "____ thee two tables of stone" (Exodus 34:1)
18. It gets let down
20. Kind of plate
21. "We have seen his ____ in the east" (Matthew 2:2)
22. "And there ____ light" (Genesis 1:3)
23. Slithering one
24. Put a ____ on it
25. Galilee, for one
27. Made a lap
28. Do a scribe's work

30. Bagel's basic kin
31. "And he said unto me, Take it, and ____ it up" (Revelation 10:9)
32. Slangy negative
33. "I speak the truth in Christ and ____ not" (1 Timothy 2:7)
34. Yes, to King James
36. "The ____ of the Lord is at hand" (Joel 1:15)
38. NYC sight
39. "One ____ five hundred pence, and the other fifty" (Luke 7:41)
40. ____ East
41. "Annabel Lee" poet

42. "Go ye and ____ what that meaneth" (Matthew 9:13)
44. Word in Valley Girl's vocabulary
45. Slipper, for example
47. Form of legislation
48. Bobby, for one
49. Feminine nickname
50. Compass pt.
52. Apiece (abbr.)
53. One of the thirteen colonies (abbr.)

by Evelyn Boyington

ACROSS

1. ____ Colonies, in eastern Iowa
6. Balmy weekend sky sight (pl.)
11. "I will bring the third part through the fire and will ____ them" (Zechariah 13:9)
13. Reason for saying "excuse me"
14. Popular NYC art museum, for short
15. Org. that includes Braves but not Indians
16. Pacific state (abbr.)
17. Pitcher's stat.
18. Mulberry, for one (abbr.)
19. Recover from the attic? (2 words)
22. Masculine nickname
23. "And ____ were the more added to the Lord" (Acts 5:14)
25. Prohibits
27. Compass pt.
28. Site of Miami University
31. Door sign
32. "Open ___ "
33. Pictured on highway sign
34. Sporty Ford model
37. Mimic
38. "Ye became ____ of us and of the Lord" (1 Thessalonians 1:6)
41. Hospital abbr.
43. Desired deeply
44. Kind of M.D.
46. Bygone automobile
48. Article
49. Sound of hesitation
50. Library section (abbr.)
51. "Thou shalt heap coals of fire upon his head, and the Lord shall ____ thee" (Proverbs 25:22)
53. Missouri and Ohio
55. Mohair measure
56. "The way of an ____ in the air" (Proverbs 30:19)

DOWN

1. "Underneath are the everlasting ____" (Deuteronomy 33:27)
2. Track competition
3. Astern
4. Metal in a 5-ct. piece
5. Abolish
6. Butter, for one
7. Common abbr.
8. Summer wear, for short
9. Old Testament scribe
10. "____ the law among my disciples" (Isaiah 8:16)
12. Feminine nickname
13. More pointed than push
19. "There is one lawgiver, who is able to save and to ____ " (James 4:12)
20. "Abram had dwelt ____ years in the land" (Genesis 16:3)
21. "A ____ man soweth strife" (Proverbs 16:28)
23. Lawyer's homework
24. "King Solomon made a navy of ____ " (1 Kings 9:26)
25. "Arise, take up thy ____, and go" (Matthew 9:6)
26. Let go (colloq.)
29. Chemical suffix
30. Poetic contraction
34. Pituitary, for one
35. Rocky hill
36. Land ____
39. "Now ____ a parable of the fig tree" (Matthew 24:32)
40. Strange
41. Answers incorrectly

42. Exude fumes
44. "That ____" (one-time TV sitcom)
45. Assume a position
47. Assume a mortgage, for example
50. "Let his children be continually vagabonds, and ____" (Psalm 109:10)
52. "I have given into thy hand the king of ____" (Joshua 8:1)
54. Site of Jamestown (abbr.)
   by Evelyn Boyington

ACROSS

1. Poetic contraction
4. "The ____ of the mountains is his pasture" (Job 39:8)
9. ____ fried
12. Linking verb
13. "The ____ of Egypt shall be moved" (Isaiah 19:1)
14. Inlet
15. "Behold a man gluttonous...a ____ of publicans and sinners" (Matthew 11:19)
17. "Charity...is not ____ provoked, thinketh no evil" (1 Corinthians 13:4, 5)
19. Joke
20. Brownish gray
21. Liturgical season that coincides with spring
23. ____ sum (Chinese dumplings)
24. Man, for example
27. Printer's measures
28. "Every ____ that a man doeth is without the body" (1 Corinthians 6:18)
29. "When thou prayest, ____ into thy closet" (Matthew 6:6)
30. ____ out (tennis term)
31. "The ____ went before, the players on instruments followed" (Psalm 68:25)
33. Movie rating
34. "Pay that which thou hast ____" (Ecclesiastes 5:4)
36. Singing syllable
37. About
38. Pitcher
39. James Herriot, for short
40. Driven group
41. "But ____ foolish questions, and genealogies" (Titus 3:9)

43. Blue
44. "Pharaoh was wroth...against the chief of the ____" (Genesis 40:2)
46. "The wicked shall be ____ in darkness" (1 Samuel 2:9)
49. Be in debt
50. "Aeneas, which had kept his bed ____ years" (Acts 9:33)
52. Years and years
53. Skin tumor
54. Grown-up gadgets, collectively
55. Ran into

DOWN

1. Boor
2. Stumble
3. Royal eras
4. American humorist Lardner
5. "____ to your faith virtue" (2 Peter 1:5)
6. Negative
7. Shine like the sun
8. More hirsute son of Isaac
9. "Jesus, made an high ____ for ever" (Hebrews 6:20)
10. Fare poorly
11. Negative, old style
16. Sup
18. Twirls
20. Got goosebumps
21. Make a getaway
22. "He shall surely ____ her to be his wife" (Exodus 22:16)
23. Noise level
25. Disdained individual, in Bible times
26. Energy unit
28. Caesar
29. TV series
31. "If any man ____ me, let him follow me" (John 12:26)

32. "Where wilt thou that we prepare for thee to ____ the passover?" (Matthew 26:17)
35. "O Lucifer...which didst ____ the nations" (Isaiah 14:12)
37. "I will ____ them from death" (Hosea 13:14)
39. Call on
40. Masculine nickname
42. Swedish coin
43. Tends to tots, tersely
44. Half a canine call
45. Reverence
46. Less than, with "of"

47. "As it was in the days of ____" (Luke 17:26)
48. Terminator, in a way (abbr.)
51. Matthew 28:19 verb
by Evelyn Boyington

ACROSS

1. "And falling into a place where two ____ met, they ran the ship aground" (Acts 27:41)
5. Father of Adoniram (1 Kings 4:6)
9. Linking verb
12. Yen
13. "I will fasten him as a ____ in a sure place" (Isaiah 22:23)
14. "La ____" (Debussy composition)
15. Tear
16. "And David saith, Let their table be made a...____" (Romans 11:9)
17. Certain vegetable serving
18. Extraordinary, in a way
20. "She layeth her ____ to the spindle" (Proverbs 31:19)
22. "If ye be reproached for the name of Christ, ____ are ye" (1 Peter 4:14)
24. Flap
25. Like a New York minute (abbr.)
26. At ___
29. Watch ___
33. Is supine
35. Cotton ___
36. Genus of the lily family
37. "My father did ____ you with a heavy yoke" (1 Kings 12:11)
38. Remove bobby pins
40. ____ the line
41. Poetic before
43. Rethink and revise
45. "He will not always ____: neither will he keep his anger" (Psalm 103:9)
48. It's sometimes glaring
50. "Thy word have I ____ in mine heart" (Psalm 119:11)
51. Kind of light or line

53. Tribe of Israel
56. Natural combination of minerals
57. Kilmer subject
58. And others (abbr.)
59. Pod dweller
60. "O ____ out thy light and thy truth" (Psalm 43:3)
61. Synagogue

DOWN

1. Polite title
2. Greek letter
3. "Behold, now is the ____ time; behold, now is the day of salvation" (2 Corinthians 6:2)
4. "We thy people and ____ of thy pasture" (Psalm 79:13)
5. Kind of hero
6. "John ____ witness of him" (John 1:15)
7. Circle part (abbr.)
8. Wave or ray
9. So be it
10. "They could not ____ the writing" (Daniel 5:8)
11. Solomon writes that whoever refuses reproof ___
19. Pastrami on ____ (deli order)
21. "____ Father, all things are possible" (Mark 14:36)
22. "I...have the keys of ____ and of death" (Revelation 1:18)
23. Continent
24. Mind the store
27. Marked by chills
28. "Where ____ abounded, grace did much more" (Romans 5:20)
30. "The law of the Medes and Persians, which ____ not" (Daniel 6:8)
31. High time

32. "A prophet mighty in ____ and word" (Luke 24:19)
34. Kind of money
39. Boathouse sight
42. Musical notations
44. Underground workers
45. Kind of house
46. "The labourer is worthy of his ____" (Luke 10:7)
47. Notion
48. "All the trees of ____, the choice and best of Lebanon" (Ezekiel 31:16)
49. "A bruised ____ shall he not break" (Matthew 12:20)

52. Wrath
54. Hebrew letter
55. Under the weather

by Evelyn Boyington

ACROSS

1. "What ____ I am afraid, I will trust in thee" (Psalm 56:3)
5. "They cast ____, that is, the lot, before Haman" (Esther 3:7)
8. It's not exactly red
12. In the near future (arch.)
13. Gobbled up
14. First two words in Key's composition
15. "Help thou mine ____" (Mark 9:24)
17. *Au* ____ (teenaged helper)
18. Relieve
19. Filled with evil desires, as a heart
21. Synonym for scow
24. Toward the sheltered side
25. "____ them that have the rule over you" (Hebrews 13:17)
26. "Thou hast ____ me when I was in distress" (Psalm 4:1)
30. Legal object
31. Michael, for one
32. Poem
33. "Yea, I ____ unto you, and... none of you that convinced Job" (Job 32:12)
35. Zone
36. Beverages
37. Squander
38. Cyrus was the king of ____ (Ezra 3:7)
41. One who hisses
42. Skirt feature
43. "Be sober, be ____" (1 Peter 5:8)
48. Melita, for one
49. Natural mineral
50. Day before (pl.)
51. Samuel, to some
52. See ____

53. Want no more

DOWN

1. Greek letter
2. Holiday, for one
3. Multitude
4. Strength
5. Receipt word
6. Western Native American
7. What the watchful waiter did?
8. Mines found on Cyprus
9. Dweller in the land of Seir, the country of Edom (Genesis 32:3)
10. Depilatory brand
11. Seaport in Lebanon
16. Recline
20. Repast
21. Fierce wind of the Adriatic
22. Aid's ally
23. What's left
24. Heavenly beings (Fr.)
26. Earnest attempt
27. Blood and guts
28. Utopia
29. "If we be ____ with Christ...we shall also live with him" (Romans 6:8)
31. Girl's nickname
34. Resurrection day
35. "A word fitly spoken is like ____ of gold" (Proverbs 25:11)
37. Supplemental income (abbr.)
38. Greek letters
39. Word in a threat
40. Stir up
41. Long in the tooth
44. Anger
45. Actress Gardner
46. Fish trap
47. Double this for (perhaps) fatal flier

by Evelyn Boyington

ACROSS

1. Mentor to Samuel
4. "Sir, we would see ____" (John 12:21)
9. Judicial sentence
12. Benign skin tumor
13. City of Hadad (Genesis 36:35)
14. "Out of whose womb came the ___?" (Job 38:29)
15. Apiece (abbr.)
16. Sign
17. ____ of Melchisedec (Hebrews 7:11)
19. "I was ____ in iniquity" (Psalm 51:5)
21. Ask what might have been
22. French possessive pronoun
23. Said goodnight
27. Without a nom or a nom de plume (abbr.)
29. "Simon Peter...went into the sepulchre, and seeth the ____ clothes" (John 20:6)
30. Bible language (abbr.)
31. ___-oni (Rachel's son)
32. Grace
33. Function
34. Son of Judah (Genesis 38:6)
35. Already sold
36. Played a tuba?
37. "Men of low degree...and men of high degree...are altogether ____ than vanity" (Psalm 62:9)
39. One one-thousandth of an inch
40. Ancient Hebrew liquid measure
41. "Dost thou still ____ thine integrity?" (Job 2:9)
44. "I lay in Sion a chief corner ____" (1 Peter 2:6)
46. "Ye ____ men with burdens grievous" (Luke 11:46)

47. Concerning
48. French possessive pronoun
49. "A man's wisdom maketh his face to ____" (Ecclesiastes 8:1)
51. Parts of a yr.
52. Actor Morita
53. Pursues, as the truth
54. "Go to the ____, thou sluggard" (Proverbs 6:6)

DOWN

1. Jacob gave Esau 200 ____ and 20 rams (Genesis 32:13-14)
2. Mother of Dinah
3. Hoosier state (abbr.)
4. Son of Zebedee, and disciple of Jesus
5. Tied
6. "Be ye angry, and ____ not" (Ephesians 4:26)
7. State of Salt Lake (abbr.)
8. "For the bed is ____ than that a man can stretch himself on it" (Isaiah 28:20)
9. New Jersey college
10. Fast point, in tennis
11. ____ your instructions
16. ____ sesame
18. "The ____ of that house was great" (Luke 6:49)
20. Son of Manasseh, king of Judah (2 Kings 21:18)
23. Ohio, for one
24. "John also was baptizing in ____" (John 3:23)
25. "Woe to them that are at ____ in Zion" (Amos 6:1)
26. Popular female fictional detective
27. Brother of Seth
28. Father of Salathiel (Luke 3:27)

29. Gennesaret, for one
32. "Let your soul delight itself in
    ____" (Isaiah 55:2)
33. Father of Arah
    (1 Chronicles 7:39)
35. Willowy
36. "If ye ____ and devour one
    another, take heed"
    (Galatians 5:15)
38. Holy ___
39. Overtakers of Babylon
41. Sergeant, for example
42. ____ horse
43. Aerie
44. Brand of automobile oil

45. Orange Pekoe, for example
46. "The highways ____ waste, the
    wayfaring man ceaseth"
    (Isaiah 33:8)
50. Pronoun
51. Sturbridge state (abbr.)
    by Evelyn Boyington

ANSWERS

Puzzle 1

Puzzle 2

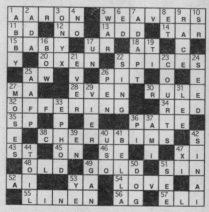

Puzzle 3

Puzzle 4

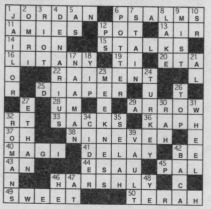

Puzzle 5

Puzzle 6

Puzzle 7

Puzzle 8

Puzzle 9

Puzzle 10

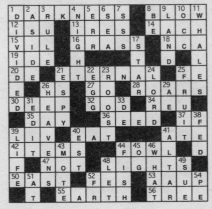

Puzzle 11

```
C H I N S   P O L A R
N A A M A H   A B A T E S
O N   P I E R C E D   M P
I A N   L A I T Y   V I I
S A U L   R M S   C E N T
E N G I N E S   B A N D S
    G O O D   R A I D
B L E N D   T E R R O R S
R A T S   S O N   O R E O
A N   E A T E N   A U
I D   A L L O W E D   D R
N E E D L E   E R O D E S
  D R E A M   D O N O R
```

Puzzle 12

```
N U N   H O R N E T   Y E
A S A   O N   E A S T E R
Y O K E   L A S T   E
      E   M Y   A N N A
L Y D I A   S T R O N G
B E   L I F E   T R E E
S A V E D   V O W
    I   V I P E R S   S
S I N A I   L E N T I L S
O R E   N T   I E
N O   P A W S   D O N E
G N A S H I N G   R E D
S Y R I A N   O N I O N S
```

Puzzle 13

```
        S I N G
    D E V O U R
  S I T   V E I L
  C E E   M I S G A B
S A E   S E C T   M E T
P U R P O S E   S E V E N
E S   E R S   B A N   A A
D E F O E   D O C T O R S
  D I P   W A L K   A M T
    G L O R I A   I K E
    E N A N   S T S
      O T T E R S
        H Y P O
```

Puzzle 14

```
H A R M   A B B E   L A P
O L A Y   F E A R   E R R
D O N S   R A R E   S E A
S E T H   A R E   S T A Y
      E R I   S S H
H E A P E D   T H E I R S
O A T H S   E E R I E
G R E E T S   R E P E N T
      R O T   I T S
L O R D   R U N   K E Y S
A V E   C U R S   I S E T
V E E   I N G E   N A T E
A R K   A G E D   S U I T
```

Puzzle 15

```
F I T   L O R D   H A R M
L E E S   X   E A   I
A   M E   R E A P   A N
M U P P I M   D   L I F E
E   T A M E   Y   A
    R A N S O M   C   A R M
A   B A G   C   T   B   I
G O   T E A R S   A L A S
O   B E   I   D I E   E
N   E   T   B E A R   O R
Y   G   E   E R R   L A Y
  G   A M A S A I   A T
E R   B A R   C A P H
```

Puzzle 16

```
        F A N   S A G
  A S I D E   P I N T S
  F I R S T S A M U E L
N I L   T   N A P
O R E   S H E B A   T I E
D E N   L   M   B   D N A
    T R E E   A N E W
B A N   E   F   E   E B B
A M I   P R I O R   L E E
T A G   S   L A D
  S H E E P H E R D E R
  S T A R E   G O U R D
    T A N   O W E
```

Puzzle 17

Puzzle 18

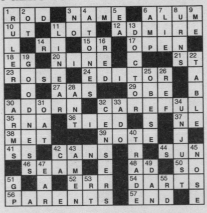

Puzzle 19

Puzzle 20

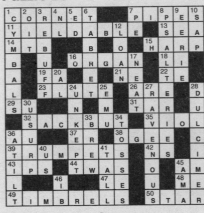

Puzzle 21

Puzzle 22

Puzzle 23

Puzzle 24

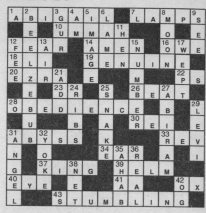

Puzzle 25

Puzzle 26

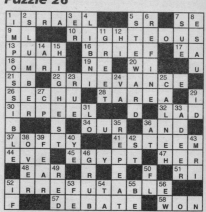

Puzzle 27

Puzzle 28

Puzzle 29

Puzzle 30

Puzzle 31

Puzzle 32

Puzzle 33

Puzzle 34

Puzzle 35

```
H I D   P E E P   H O M O
A D O   E V E S   A M O S
M E R A R I   S C H E M E
      H I L T   R A I S E
B A S I L   U S E S
A G A R   P I T A   A C T
B E W A R E   A M A S A I
Y E S   A R M Y   R E N D
      A G E S   A R R A Y
A F O R E   H A L O
D I V I D E   T O W E R S
A V E S   B E E N   R I G
M E R E   B A R E   N E T
```

Puzzle 36

```
F I N I N G P O T     I D
I D A   I   E   A H   N I
R E   F L E S H H O O K S
E A T     M T   R O A S T
P     M A U L     T F   A
A W L   I   E L M S     F
N E   U   E   P A     O F F
S P I N D L E   T E     E
    T   M I L L S T O N E
P   N A P   I     O N   L A
L O A N   E   A C   D
O   I   B R I C K K I L N
W I N E P R E S S   N E O
```

Puzzle 37

```
L O N G S U F F E R I N G
A   L O O N   A L B S
C   D A S H I K I   G P
R M S   P A   R E   J O Y
I E   A   Y A S   E   O R
M E   C H   O H   D O
A K   T R U T H   N M
T N   K S T   O X   E A
I E   Y   G S A N   S N
O S   F L   D A   S I
N S   S L A V I S H   A
  S C A R   E K E S   C
R I G H T E O U S N E S S
```

Puzzle 38

```
C H R Y S O P R O S U S
H   U R A S E   N A B A L
A F B   P E A K Y   O R E
L E I   P E R   X   A D E
C E E   H   L A   T I
E D S   I R   J P   N O
D I   R E   J A S P E R
O N E N E S S   C   L
N G   E   T U   I V O R Y
Y   A W E   R E N E W   O
    A G A T E   A U
B E R Y L   E T H   B E T
D I A M O N D   B A T H
```

Puzzle 39

```
M E O W   W A S T   J A R
A R A H   A B I A   E M U
N A K E D N E S S   R A T
    L E T T   T R U T H
S H A P E S   S E A S
P A L   M A D C A P
A R A D   L E D   E L I M
  A B A S E D   E N E
    A R A B   H E L M E T
B A S E R   S E M I
A L T   D E C A P O L I S
N S E   I G A L   N E R I
D O R   S O N S   S T A R
```

Puzzle 40

```
A P T   G A T E S     A T
I R I   A B I D A   A D O
J O   A D I N O   E L I S
A P P H I A   M E L O N S
  H E A T H   R U N
D E R B E   H E L E P H
I C E   O B A   A O
M Y S T E R Y   E M I M S
    H E R   W H I T
    A R   A H I S H A R
I N C R E A S E   T I R E
T O O   T H E R E   E E N
S E W   H I R E D   L A D
```

Puzzle 41

F	R	Y	I	N	G	P	A	N	A R C
	M	O	O		D	I	S	H	R
A	W	E		B	O		H		A U
G	A	C	A	L	F		B	O	W L S
O	T	U	S	E	T	H	W		E E
N	E	P	A	T			P	R	
R	O	S	S	N		P	L	A	T E
S	P	D		R	E	P	L	A	N
P	O	E	T	S		V	I	A	M E
O	T	E		K	E	T	T	L	E
O	A	R	B	O	R	T		N	U N
N	A	V	A	L		H	E	O	R A
S	I	G	H	S		F	O	R	K S

Puzzle 42

R	A	P	T		H	I	S		S E E R
A	L	S	O		E	R	I		A S I A
M	A	I	M		W	A	S		R A N G
		A	N	E		E	N	D	
B	E	T	T	E	R		R	A	I S E D
E	R	R	O	R	S		A	N	S W E R
A	I	E						O	R E
S	T	E	A	D	Y		G	L	O R I A
T	E	S	T	E	E		R	A	I N E D
		T	E	A			A	W	L
O	N	C	E		R	E	P		E R O S
L	A	I	N		L	E	E		R I D E
D	Y	E	D		Y	E	S		S P E W

Puzzle 43

E	L	I	J	A	H	A	B	I	J A H
A	A	R	O	N		A	B	A	S E O
R		U	C	A	L	A	R		W E
T	O	H	H		N	A	P		E
H	F	E		A	N	A	K	I	M N
Q	U	I	B	B	L	E		E	U G
U	N	E	I	T	H	E	R	S	H E
A	B	I	D	A	H	G	I	L	E A D
K	S		S	O	U	L	S		R I
E	C	H	O	U	N	A	S	K	E D
H	B	I	G	T	H	A		E	
M	A	L	A	C	H	I	H	E	A R T
A	R	L	E	L	A		G	M	O

Puzzle 44

B	E	G	I	N	N	I	N	G	D A Y
E	D	O	M		L	O	R	D	R E
G	E	A	B	E	L	A			K L
I	N	G	E	L		A	V	I	D L
N	E	N	M	I	T	Y		A	D O
N	O	D		S	T		A	V	O W
I	N	A	G	A	I	N		I	M
N	A	K	E	D	A	R	C	D	I M
G	M	V	I	C	E	I	I	N	E
S	E	T	H		S	O	L	I	D
B	A	A	H	E	B	A		S	O L
O	V	U	L	E	E	A	V	E	N E
W	L	A	R	G	E	E	E	L	Y

Puzzle 45

F	R	O	G	S	C	A	B	S	I S
P	E	R	U	T	I	E	R	O	R O
O	B	E	I	S	A	N	C	E	J O N
	L	A	T	E		A	L	O	N G
P	E	S	T	L	E	E	S	U	
O	N	E	W	A	T	E	R	S	
R	O	P	E	F	A	T	S	N	O B
S	U	N	D	E	R		E	R	E
L	E	D	T	A	B	R	E	T	
F	A	C	E	S	L	A	V	A	
A	S	H	E	M	U	L	A	T	I O N
T	A	R	R	A	T	E	H	O	N E
E	S	E	T	O	E	S	S	N	O W

Puzzle 46

B	A	M	B	I	D	O	N	O	R
M	L	E	E	S	E	R	I	N	M
O	W	L	E	R	A	S	E	E	V E
G	A	N	A	V	E	S		I	T
U	R	I	S	E	R	S	A	L	E
L	E	N	T	I	L	T	I	L	L E D
D	A	T		L	O	G			
R	H	I	N	O	S	A	L	T	A R S
H	E	A	D	E	L	H	E	E	L
Y	E	A	V	O	I	D	N	I	
M	D	S	L	E	P	E	R	P	E N
E	P	E	E	R	N	O	S	E	G
D	A	N	C	E	S	P	O	R	T

Puzzle 47

| A N T | | D A T U M | | | B S |

Across/grid answers:
- ANT, DATUM, BS
- JAH, ARISE, SAA
- AH, JUICE, ELAM
- HAGABA, REVILE
- MIV, S, LED
- HADAD, DIRECT
- ONE, ROT, OH
- RIOTING, SEIZE
- NON, GINS
- OF, DANDLED
- DECLARED, SALA
- IRA, NEEDS, NOR
- MEN, TIRIA, DIE

Puzzle 48

- CHAMELEON, DOG
- U, SUM, S, BEAR
- CAPSULATE, IRA
- KISS, FROGS, S
- O, EL, TIN, MRS
- WHALES, C, E, EH
- ID, FISHES, FO
- CPD, TNT, STEEP
- PELICAN, HARP
- MOROSE, OO
- US, VT, A, VIPER
- L, DE, IDEA, AR
- E, DRAGON, SWAN

Puzzle 49

- HAP, ADAM, SLOW
- ARE, LATE, TALI
- MIGHTY, STAVES
- EASE, ERASE
- KEDAR, ADAR
- LEER, ATER, SRA
- ARETAS, ASAHEL
- NYM, FEAR, RENT
- BORN, SINES
- ENTER, DICE
- BERATE, MOLTEN
- ERES, DARN, IRE
- DIET, PILE, PER

Puzzle 50

- APPLE, PAGEBOY
- LOAN, ORANGE
- MON, DAMSELS, A
- OLIVE, LA, BB
- N, C, FIG, RUTH
- DA, REIGN, O
- C, CE, AM, EKER
- CHESTNUT, NOR
- AD, OT, E, ONE
- LAZE, WETS, W, S
- I, E, LA, H, T, NUT
- MULBERRY, B, F
- EZ, LODE, LEMON

Puzzle 51

- LAZARUS, WINE
- O, EN, TALENT, L
- SAND, MID, PRE
- T, AS, PANDA, EA
- SON, VIRGINS, V
- HI, MINION, OE
- ELM, NET, G, WON
- E, A, EDAM, NEW
- PENNY, N, TARES
- TA, SHOT, SH
- MET, RA, AWED, A
- CANDLE, E, ILL
- ROCK, PRODIGAL

Puzzle 52

- NEW, ACTS, ORBS
- O, ADO, ORDAIN
- I, RV, AT, EDGE
- SE, EACH, A, RN
- EVEN, HELPER, E
- E, GO, EVE, W
- ANGEL, CAREFUL
- BTU, DIAL, R, NY
- LINE, MANY, D
- ED, SKIP, A, SON
- EASE, HOST, NA
- AS, PRO, TOTEM
- PSALTER, YEN, E

Puzzle 53

1 N	2 O	3 W		4 E	5 G	6 G	7 S		8 P	9 R	10 A	11 Y
12 A	D	A		13 P	E	L	E		14 H	A	L	O
15 N	O	R		16 N	A	E		17 A	M	E	N	
18 A	R	19 M	20 A	G	E	D	21 D	O	N		
		22 H	A	S		23 S	I	U		24 S	25 E
26 L	27 O	28 T		29 D	30 I	D		31 L	32 E	A	P	T
33 O	B	O	E		34 S	35 I	36 T		37 L	I	O	N
38 S	A	T	A	39 N		40 E	R	41 A		42 M	T	A
43 E	L		44 S	O	45 L		46 A	S	47 S		
		48 T	H	E	O	49 P	H	I	L	50 U	51 S	52
53 N	54 O	55 N	E		56 A	B	P		57 A	R	E
58 E	W	E	R		59 D	E	E	60 D		61 M	I	A
62 T	E	E	N		63 A	D	D	S		64 P	M	S

Puzzle 54

Puzzle 55

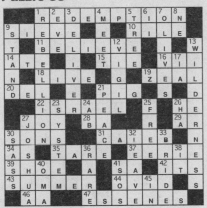

Puzzle 56

Puzzle 57

1 A	2 S	3 A		4 C	5 U	6 R	7 E	8 S		9 D	10 A	11 Y
12 N	E	T	13 H	A	N	E	E	L		14 I	C	E
15 Y	E		16 O	V	A	L		17 A	18 U	N	T	S
		19 F	U	E	L		20 G	Y	N	E		
21 D	22 R	E	S	S		23 K	N	E	A	D	24 E	25 D
26 R	A	T	E		27 H	E	A	T	S		28 N	E
29 O	N	E		30 N	O	R	T	H		31 O	D	E
32 O	G		33 H	I	R	E	S		34 A	P	E	D
35 P	E	36 L	I	C	A	N		37 S	L	E	D	S
		38 A	D	A	M		39 C	A	I	N		
40 W	41 O	M	E	N		42 P	O	L	E		43 O	44 A
45 H	I	P		46 O	47 B	T	A	I	N	I	N	G
49 A	L	S		50 R	E	A	L	M		51 N	O	E

Puzzle 58

1 F	2 E	3 L	4 L	5 O		6 W	7 S	8 H	9 I	P		10 C
11 O	R	I	O	N		12 L	O	V	E		13 P	O
R		14 N	O		15 O	N		A		16 E	N	
17 B	18 R	19 A	G		20 A	W	E		21 C	22 A	R	T
23 E	O	N		24 A		S		25 E	L	S	E	
26 A	Y		27 C	H	28 A	29 S	T	E		30 P	E	N
31 R	A	32 C	A		33 J	O	Y		34 A	V	35 T
36 A	L	A	R		37 A	U		38 S	H	39 E	M
N		40 H	N		41 A		42 E	R	E
43 C	44 A	45 I	N		46 D	47 O	R		48 L	E	N
49 E	N	I	G	M	A		50 B	51 A	52 L	M		T
			H		53 E	N	T	E	R		54 R
55 H	U	M	I	L	I	T	Y		56 S	T	A	R

Puzzle 59

```
S A L V A T I O N . . O P T
A M . I D A . P U C K E R . .
M E A S U R E . M R . N A . .
U N T I L . A B B A . . N M .
E . O T T E R . E Z R A . . .
L O N . G L O R Y . . N T . .
. V E R I L Y . S . I T E . .
G E M . N O . . . S . . . . .
R E I G N S . E P H . T . . .
C N N . P E . S E M I . . . .
B O T T L E . S H A R I F . .
I M . R O A R . L I L Y . . .
B E G O T T E N . M T . . . .
```

Puzzle 60

```
J A C O B . M O S E S . S
J O V I A L . P H I L I P
O S . D T . S S . M N . M E
N E W . S A U L S . . A P T
A P E S . I L L . F R E E .
H H . L A . T . M L . R R .
. N A T H A N A E L . . . .
S J . P E . N . R E . E M .
I O N S . H A Y . T A L E .
L S S . T O T E D . C I A .
A H . H A . E . E T . S T .
S U P E R B . S M I T H Y .
A A R O N . H O S E A . . .
```

Puzzle 61

```
C H I N S . P O L A R
N A A M A H . A B A T E S
O N . P I E R C E D . M P
I A N . L A I T Y . V I I
S A U L . R M S . C E N T
E N G I N E S . B A N D S
. G O O D . R A I D . . .
B L E N D . T E R R O R S
R A T S . S O N . O R E O
A N . E A T E N . A U . .
I D . A L L O W E D . D R
N E E D L E . E R O D E S
. D R E A M . D O N O R .
```

Puzzle 62

```
N U N . H O R N E T . Y E
A S A . O N . E A S T E R
Y O K E . L A S T . E . .
. E M Y . T . . A N N A .
L Y D I A . S T R O N G .
B E . L I F E . T R E E .
S A V E D . V O W . . S .
. I . V I P E R S . . . .
S I N A I . L E N T I L S
O R E . N T . . . I E . .
N O . P A W S . D O N E .
G N A S H I N G . R E D .
S Y R I A N . O N I O N S
```

Puzzle 63

```
. . . S I N G
. D E V O U R .
. S I T . V E I L
C E E . M I S G A B
S A E . S E C T . M E T
P U R P O S E . S E V E N
E S . E R S . B A N . A A
D E F O E . D O C T O R S
. D I P . W A L K . A M T
. G L O R I A . I K E .
. . E N A N . S T S .
. . . O T T E R S .
. . . . H Y P O .
```

Puzzle 64

```
H A R M . A B B E . L A P
O L A Y . F E A R . E R R
D O N S . R A R E . S E A
S E T H . A R E . S T A Y
. . . E R I . S S H . . .
H E A P E D . T H E I R S
O A T H S . . . E E R I E
G R E E T S . R E P E N T
. . . R O T . I T S . . .
L O R D . R U N . K E Y S
A V E . C U R S . I S E T
V E E . I N G E . N A T E
A R K . A G E D . S U I T
```

Puzzle 65

FIT · LORD · HARM
LEES · X · EA · AN
ME · REAP
MUPPIM · D · LIFE
TAME · Y · A
RANSOM · ARM
BAG · C · T · B · I
GO · TEARS · ALAS
BE · I · DIE · E
T · BEAR · OR
Y · G · E · ERR · LAY
G · AMASAI · AT
ER · BAR · CAPH

Puzzle 66

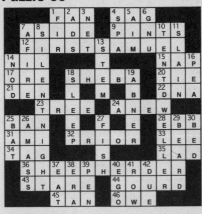

FAN · SAG
ASIDE · PINTS
FIRST SAMUEL
NIL · T · NAP
ORE · SHEBA · TIE
DEN · L · M · B · DNA
TREE · ANEW
BAN · E · F · E · EBB
AMI · PRIOR · LEE
TAG · S · LAD
SHEEPHERDER
STARE · GOURD
TAN · OWE

Puzzle 67

JUBAL · JABAL
UE · I · SU · RO
LEA · R · HUNTING
YARDAGE · ERASE
SER · APT · IR
STRAW · HARP · BA
WINE · NAY
D · F · FARMING · E
BLUE · DO · C
ARG · G · NIMROD · DC
BALLOON · REA
ESI · AGATHA · I
LS · SCH · ORGAN

Puzzle 68

ROD · NAME · ALUM
UT · LOT · ADMIRE
L · RI · OR · OPEN
FG · NINE · C · ST
ROSE · EDITOR · A
O · AAS · OBE · B
ADORN · CAREFUL
RNA · TIED · S · NE
MET · NOTE · J
SS · CANS · R · SUN
SEAM · E · AD · SO
G · A · ERR · DARTS
PARENTS · END

Puzzle 69

SEA · DUST · JUST
INN · ESAU · UPON
NEGEB · VR · NT
ESTHER · AR
SILAS · E · HEAL
ASU · BITE · PIE
AM · SNARED · ERA
N · J · AGED · SN · F
GLORY · LET
REBA · E · REV · AN
YE · VOTE · VE · ME
KEEP · RAINBOW
PSALTERY · EST

Puzzle 70

CORNET · PIPES
YIELDABLE · SEA
MTB · B · O · HARP
B · U · ORGAN · LI
A · FA · E · NE · TE
L · FLUTE · ARE · D
SU · N · M · TAR · U
SACKBUT · VIOL
AU · ER · OGEE · E
TRUMPETS · NSI
IPS · TWAS · O · AM
L · I · LE · U · ME
TIMBRELS · STAR

Puzzle 71

Puzzle 72

Puzzle 73

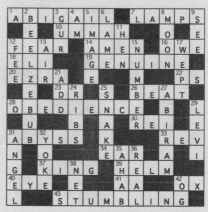

Puzzle 74

Puzzle 75

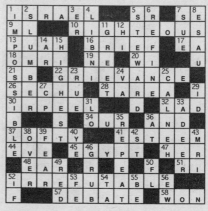

Puzzle 76

Puzzle 77

Puzzle 78

Puzzle 79

Puzzle 80

Puzzle 81

Puzzle 82

Puzzle 83

```
. . . L A B A N S . . . K C .
A D O N I R A M . . E O S . .
S O . I N . H A M . R M C . .
S U M M E R . R A B B A H . .
. B E . A I . T I E . . . . .
A L L . O N . L E A H S . . .
S E E . E T A M . H O T . . .
A D A M S . Y E . I R . . . .
. . . E R E . E D . A S . . .
H I N N O M . T O P H E T . .
E B B . M I L . O O . M R . .
L O A . N A C R E . E I . . .
P S . . S P A S M . N G . . .
```

Puzzle 84

```
S O M E T I M E S . . U A W .
E R A S U R E . H O S E A . .
E E . T N . T H E R E . I . .
K . S E E K . U . . D . T . .
I V E . S O U G H T . W I . .
N E E D . A N . D I V A N . .
G E K . . B K . M . . I G . .
. E M . S E E K E S T . . . .
U N T I M E L Y . . P E D . .
N . H G . A I . W A I T . . .
I T . H I R E D . . R H G . .
T E N T . C F . E L I . O . .
E A S Y . H . W A I T E D . .
```

Puzzle 85

```
H I D . P E E P . H O M O . .
A D O . E V E S . A M O S . .
M E R A R I . S C H E M E . .
. . H I L T . R A I S E . . .
B A S I L . U S E S . . . . .
A G A R . P I T A . A C T . .
B E W A R E . A M A S A I . .
Y E S . A R M Y . R E N D . .
. . A G E S . A R R A Y . . .
A F O R E . H A L O . . . . .
D I V I D E . T O W E R S . .
A V E S . B E E N . R I G . .
M E R E . B A R E . N E T . .
```

Puzzle 86

```
F I N I N G P O T . . . I D .
I D A . I . E A H . N I . . .
R E . F L E S H H O O K S . .
E A T . M T . R O A S T . . .
P . M A U L . . T F . A . . .
A W L . I . E L M S . . F . .
N F . U . E . P A . O F F . .
S P I N D L E . T E . E . . .
. . T . M I L L S T O N E . .
P . N A P . I . O N . L A . .
L O A N . E . A C . D . . . .
O . I . B R I C K K L I N . .
W I N E P R E S S . N E O . .
```

Puzzle 87

```
L O N G S U F F E R I N G . .
A . L O O N . A L B S . . . .
C . D A S H I K I . . G P . .
R M S . P A R E . J O Y . . .
I E . A . Y A S . E . O R . .
M E . C H . B . O H . D O . .
A K . T R U T H . N M . . . .
T N . K S T . O X . E A . . .
I E . Y . G S A N . S N . . .
O S . . F L . D A . S I . . .
N S . S L A V I S H . A . . .
. . S C A R . E K E S . C . .
R I G H T E O U S N E S S . .
```

Puzzle 88

```
C H R Y S O P R O S U S . . .
H . U R A S E . N A B A L . .
A F B . P E A K Y . O R E . .
L E I . P E R . X . A D E . .
C E E . H . L A . T I . . . .
E D S . I R . J P . N O . . .
D I . R E . J A S P E R . . .
O N E N E S S . C L . . . . .
N G . E . T U . I V O R Y . .
Y . A W E . R E N E W . O . .
. B . A G A T E . . A U . . .
B E R Y L . E T H . B E T . .
D I A M O N D . B A T H . . .
```

Puzzle 89

1 M	2 E	3 O	4 W		5 W	6 A	7 S	8 T		9 J	10 A	11 R
12 A	R	A	H		13 A	B	I	A		14 E	M	U
15 N	A	K	E	16 D	N	E	S	S		17 R	A	T
			18 L	E	T	T		19 T	20 R	U	T	H
21 S	22 H	23 A	P	E	S		24 S	E	A	S		
25 P	A	L		26 M	A	D	C	A	P		27 P	
28 A	R	A	D	29	30 L	E	D		31 E	L	I	32 M
	33 A	B	A	S	E	D		35 E	N	E		
	36 A	R	A	B		37 H	38 E	39 L	M	E	T	
40 B	41 A	S	E	R		42 S	E	M	I			
43 A	L	T		44 D	45 E	C	A	P	46 O	47 L	48 I	S
49 N	S	E		50 I	G	A	L		51 N	E	R	I
52 D	O	R		53 S	O	N	S		54 S	T	A	R

Puzzle 90

1 A	2 P	3 T		4 G	5 A	6 T	7 E	8 S			9 A	10 T
11 I	R	I		12 A	B	I	D	A		13 A	D	O
14 J	O		15 A	D	I	N	O		16 E	L	I	S
17 A	P	18 P	H	I	A		19 M	20 E	L	O	N	S
	21 H	E	A	T	H			22 R	U	N		
23 D	E	R	B	E		24 H	E	L	E	P	25 H	26
27 I	C	E		28 O	29 B	A			30 A	O		
31 M	Y	S	32 T	E	R	Y		34 E	M	I	M	S
	37 H	E	R				38 W	H	I	T		
			39 A	R		40 A	H	I	S	H	A	R
43 I	44 N	45 C	R	E	A	S	E			47 T	I	R	E
48 T	O	O		49 T	H	E	R	E		50	51 E	E	N
52 S	E	W		53 H	I	R	E	D		54 L	A	D

Puzzle 91

1 F	R	2 Y	3 I	4 N	G	5 P	A	6 N		7 A	R	8 C
L		9 M	O	O		10 D	I	S	11 H		R	
12 A	13 W	E		14 B	15 O		H		16 A	U		
17 G	A		18 C	19 A	L	F		20 B	O	W	L	S
21 O	T		22 U	S	E	T	23 H		W		24 E	E
25 N	E		26 P	A	T		A		27 P	R		
	28 R	29 O	S	S		30 N		31 P	L	A	T	33 E
34 S	P	D		35 R	E	P	L	A	N	T		T
37 P	O	E	T	S	38	39 V	I	A		40 M	E	
41 O	T		E		42 K	E	T	T	L	E	43 R	
	44 A	45 R	B	O	R		T			46 N	47 U	N
48 N	A	V	A	L		50 H	E		51 O	R	A	
52 S	I	G	H	S		53 F	O	R	K	S		

Puzzle 92

1 R	2 A	3 P	4 T		5 H	6 I	7 S		8 S	9 E	10 E	11 R
12 A	L	S	O		13 E	R	I		14 A	S	I	A
15 M	A	I	M		16 W	A	S		17 R	A	N	G
		18 A	N	19 E		20 E	N	21 D				
22 B	23 E	T	T	E	24 R		25 R	A	I	26 S	27 E	28 D
29 E	R	R	O	R	S		30 A	N	S	W	E	R
31 A	I	E						32 O	R	E		
33 S	T	E	A	D	Y		34 G	35 L	36 O	37 R	38 I	39 A
40 T	E	S	T	E	E		41 R	A	I	N	E	D
		42 T	E	A		43 A	W	L				
44 O	45 N	46 C	E		47 R	48 E	P		49 E	50 R	51 O	52 S
53 L	A	I	N		54 L	E	E		55 R	I	D	E
56 D	Y	E	D		57 Y	E	S		58 S	P	E	W

Puzzle 93

1 E	2 L	3 I	4 J	A	H		6 A	7 B	8 I	J	9 A	10 H
11 A	A	R	O	N		12 A	B	A	S	E		O
R		13 U	C	A	L		14 A	R		15 W	E	
16 T	O		17 H	H		18 N	A	P	19		20 E	
H		21 F	E		22 A	N	A	K	I	M		N
25 Q	U	I	B	26 B	L	E		27 E	U		G
	28 N	E	I	T	H	29 E	30 R		31 S	H	32 E
33 A	B	I	D	A	H		34 G	I	L	E	A	D
		35 S	O	U	L	36 S				37 R	I	
38 E	39 C	H	O		40 U	N	A	S	K	E	D	
	H		42 B	43 I	G	T	H	A		E		
44 M	A	L	A	C	H	I		45 H	46 E	47 A	R	48 T
49 A	R		50 L	E		51 L	A		52 G	M		O

Puzzle 94

1 B	2 E	3 G	4 I	N	N	I	N	G		8 D	9 A	10 Y
11 E	D	O	M		12 L	O	R	D			13 R	E
14 G	E		15 A	16 B	E	L		A		18 K	L	
19 I	N		20 G	E	L		21 A	V	22 I	D		L
N		23 E	N	M	I	24 T	Y		25 A	D	26 O	
27 N	28 O	D			29 S	T		30 A	V	O	W	
31 I	N		32 A	G	A	I	33 N		34 I	M		
35 N	A	36 K	E	D		37 A	R	C		38 D	I	39 M
40 G	M		41 V	I		42 C	E		43	44 N	E	
		45 S	E	T	H	46		47 S	O	L	I	D
49 B	50 A	A		51 H	E	52 B	A		53 S	O	L	
54 O	V	U	L	E		56 E	A	V	E		57 N	E
W		59 L	A	R	G	E		60 E	E	L		Y

Puzzle 95

```
F R O G . . S C A B . . S I S
P E R U . . T I E R . . O R O
O B E I S A N C E . . . J O N
. . . L A T E . . A L O N G .
P E S T L E . . E S U . . . .
O N E . . W A T E R S . . . .
R O P E . . F A T . . S N O B
. . S U N D E R . . . E R E .
. . . . E D . T A B R E T . .
F A C E S . . L A V A . . . .
A S H . . E M U L A T I O N .
T A R . . R A T E . . H O N E
E S E . . T O E S . . S N O W
```

Puzzle 96

```
. B A M B I . . D O N O R .
M . L E E S . . E R I N . M
O W L . E R A S E . . E V E
G A . . N A V E S . . . S .
U R I S . E . R . . S A L E
L E N T I L . . T I L L E D
. . D A T . . . . L O G . .
R H I N O S . . A L T A R S
H E A D . E . L . . H E E L
Y E . . A V O I D . . . N .
M D S . L E P E R . . P E N
E . P E E R . . N O S E . G
. D A N C E . . S P O R T .
```

Puzzle 97

```
A N T . D A T U M . . B S .
J A H . A R I S E . . S A A
A H . J U I C E . E L A M .
H A G A B A . R E V I L E .
. M I V . S . . L E D . . .
H A D A D . . D I R E C T .
O N E . R O T . . . O H . .
R I O T I N G . . S E I Z E
. . N O N . . G I N S . . .
. . . O F . D A N D L E D .
D E C L A R E D . . S A L A
I R A . N E E D S . . N O R
M E N . T I R I A . . D I E
```

Puzzle 98

```
C H A M E L E O N . . D O G
U . S U M . S . . . . B E A R
C A P S U L A T E . . I R A
K I S S . . F R O G S . . S
O . E L . . T I N . . M R S
W H A L E S . C . E . . E H
. I D . F I S H E S . . F O
C P D . . T N T . . S T E E P
. P E L I C A N . . H A R P
M O R O S E . O O . . . E
U S . V T . . A . . V I P E R
L . D E . I D E A . . A R
E . D R A G O N . . S W A N
```

Puzzle 99

```
H A P . A D A M . S L O W
A R E . L A T E . T A L I
M I G H T Y . S T A V E S
. E A S E . . E R A S E .
K E D A R . A D A R . . .
L E E R . A T E R . S R A
A R E T A S . A S A H E L
N Y M . F E A R . R E N T
. B O R N . . S I N E S .
E N T E R . D I C E . . .
B E R A T E . M O L T E N
E R E S . D A R N . I R E
D I E T . P I L E . P E R
```

Puzzle 100

```
A P P L E . . P A G E B O Y
L O A N . . O R A N G E . .
M O N . D A M S E L S . . A
O L I V E . . L A . . B B .
N . C . F I G . . R U T H .
D A . I . R E I G N . . O .
. C . C E . A M . . E K E R
C H E S T N U T . . N O R .
. A D . O T . E . . O N E .
L A Z E . W E T S . W . S .
I . E . L A . H T . N U T .
M U L B E R R Y . . B . F .
E Z . L O D E . . L E M O N
```

Puzzle 101

W	O	R	L	D	S		S	G

Across/Down answers:
WORLDS · SG · ARIA · ABI · ILKS · SATIATED · MAST · EST · HOS · MASH · INCENSED · IF · STEAL · GO · CO · RABBI · BY · AR · SALA · WEPT · HEAP · TOPHETH · MULE · WEAR · DAMNABLE · TARE · EXO · LAITY · OR · WEN · ALPHA · EE

Puzzle 102

EHI · ORPAH · ME · HEN · ROUSE · SAY · UZ · TABLE · HIDE · DEBATE · RUINED · KEROS · SEA · WISER · KELITA · EAT · ABS · OR · THIRSTY · HUKOK · RIE · TIRE · BE · SINGING · CONSIDER · ELON · ORE · NEBAT · ASA · LOW · GNASH · HEW

Puzzle 103

RTE · KISHI · HO · ARA · OTHER · JAM · SO · WHEEL · GATE · HUPHAM · MANNER · BOATS · PAN · SLOTH · ATTAIN · EER · IRS · CO · ASENATH · OWNER · ROB · ABIA · TI · ANANIAS · BREEDING · DOST · EAR · ARELI · TIE · EWE · NAMES · HAP

Puzzle 104

QUAKE · TEACH · SUPPER · HASHEM · HE · TERRORS · LO · EN · PEARS · KI · DCC · TEN · WAS · SHELAH · SPIRIT · AIR · USE · JASPER · ELASAH · THE · ATE · HAS · IS · SA · HOSTS · IS · OR · GODHEAD · ME · NATURE · ELIDAD · HORNS · MADON

Puzzle 105

SIAHA · ALOOF · CITIES · HANNAH · AS · MET · YE · IE · LEAVENED · ERR · ARBA · AMA · EYED · HAIL · TATTLERS · SUAH · EPI · EPHER · HAB · AHASAI · SORER · SUIT · TITHE · TO · ER · BASHAN · HE · DANIEL · AGABUS · HONEY · NEIEL

Puzzle 106

HINES · HEAPS · BOTTLE · OWNETH · OR · HANDLED · AI · AR · MAIDS · IR · ROM · AGE · ARA · DRIETH · NAHASH · DRS · PAR · SEED · STROKE · BAT · AHA · NON · AM · SMOTE · HO · RI · SANDALS · AS · STALE · NAHATH · SALAD · SHETH

Puzzle 107

```
K I N G L Y   J A A K A N
I T   N E E D E T H   S O
  S E A T   I S A I A H
  D T S   S I D O N
U Z   A H A   A S
S E P H A R   H A G A B A
E P H E R   T I D A L
S H I M M A   B E N O N I
T I   H A I   A M
  I S A   S T R A W
S N U B   A T O N E S
O P   C L O S E S T   H E
G A T H E R   R E S T E D
```

Puzzle 108

```
  H O N O R   S T E P S
B E N O N I   H O P E T H
U Z   R E S H E P H   A I
K I   S E A L S   R R
K O A   S I A   A R A
I N F A N T   H E R E S H
  O R O   R A N
R O O T E D   S I M O N S
A R T   R O E   N E H
H A   H O B A H   T O
A T   S O P A T E R   H E
B O W E L S   E R I T E S
  R E A D Y   D E B I R
```

Puzzle 109

```
A M   V I S I T   A N
A R A N   O T H N I   H O
P A R A D I S E   W E T
O H   M I C   A C   A R E
  D E M E T R I U S
O N E   S O   E R   S A
B E N O   O L I V E S
A R   I S S   N   O A K
  S L I M E   P A W S
R I E   A I   E Z   O F
I R A   N A H A M A N I
B I T H Y N I A   O M E R
  S E E I N G   N E D
```

Puzzle 110

```
  S O L E S   O Z I A S
K O H A T H   N E R I A H
E D   M A A S I A I   P E
N O   M A H O L   H E
A M I   P E N   O I L
N A M E T H   S T A I R S
  N A H   O W L
S E A R E D   S P E E C H
A S H   E S T   D O E
T H   F A I R S   O R
A T   D A L A I A H   L O
N O T I C E   F L O W E D
  N I G E R   E A R E D
```

Puzzle 111

```
  H O   U R I E L
J O N A   N I S R O C H
E M E R A L D S   L O T
W E   A R E   U S   A S H
  C H A S T E N E D
K I R   S O   O H   H A
A M Y L   S W I P E S
F P   I A   D A   O A K
  J E R A H   E B E R
A H A   M M   P E   D O
S U R   E I G H T E E N
P R E T E N S E   A L S O
  B I D D E N   H I T
```

Puzzle 112

```
      A L B S
    E X C E E D
  A R E   S A I D
  D U E   A T T I R E
A E R   E N O S   E A T
S P A R R O W   S A R A H
I E   E I N   F P M   L I
A N G L E   T R U S T E D
D E I   H E E D   O N E
  R E P E N T   A R T
    D E A D   I A N
      T R E N C H
      T R E E
```

Puzzle 113

```
            I R A S
      T E M P T S
    W A R     P A C O
    V I N   V E R I L Y
W O N   K I A S   I E R
E T E R N A L   A V A I L
A I   E E L   O N E   D A
K N I F E   A N O T H E R
  G T O   I R A N   A R K
    O R I S O N   A L S
      M A S U   H G T
        L U N G E R
          E D O M
```

Puzzle 114

```
B E E R S H E B A   N E   G A D
E   M   A   L A   M A L T A   A
T A M A R   A C A   A     L O D
H   A   D A M A S C U S   A G E
E   U I     E A T   R       R
S   S U S A   L I D   H A I   B
      C A Y   O       A T E
A M   P E   C A N A     Y
  O P H E L I   I R O N   R O
  L I D   A R A B I A     E
A D U L L A M   O E L I     B
  I   M A   M A L   N I L E
H E A P   A G E E     N   T
E   P I   I     J U D A H
N   S I O N   M A D   A   I E
S E E   B U S Y   I S R A E L
```

Puzzle 115

```
M I R A C L E   A R K     M
  A C H A R   B E   V A
    H U B   A B A S E
I C H A B O D   A C H I M
  A I   U E   H A N D
T A L C   R E S T   V
  E L U Z   R I V E R S
    R O S E E   O R P H A N
  S W   L L A M A     C A
S H E L O M I   S O   H I
  E D I T   R I   T E L
A M   V E X   O P H E L
    R E S I D U E   N
```

Puzzle 116

```
S T A R     B U Y S     M A
H O P E   D E P O T     L
A P P L E   T O U R     L
R   L I P S   N   I T I S
    Y E A H     P O L E
E N D   A B E L   M I T
N E T   M O N E Y   E
  S H A D E   O N E   S T
S T O R Y   J U D A H   H
  R O E   E G   R I P E
T U N E D   S H E L T E R
A S R   B U   C Y C L E
N A Y   P E S T O   H T
```

Puzzle 117

```
D E F I L E   A B S E N T
A N   L O V E   X   A
S T A F F   N E R   A R M
H E N   I C O N I U M   E
  R O S E   G   I
H   R A C E   K N E E
  N A Y   I   K E E P
A C T S   E L A   Y   I S
V L   I   C   A S K
E N T E R   C H A R I T Y
N   E   I   B A A L
  C O P Y   A D   S H E D
    T E R   H   S O
```

Puzzle 118

```
M   T R A N S F O R M E D
O N E   G A T E   E A T
R   L E A V E N   D R A M
T E L   P E A C E   A M I
A D   E   D E B T     L
L I P S   F   D E E P   K
  F   N O R   R A I N
E Y E S   R E I   R E A P
L   A   M A J E S T Y
O M R I   E S E K   Y   A
N   N E R O   R     B C
  F A T   N A O M I   T
    S A D   N E S T S
```

Puzzle 119

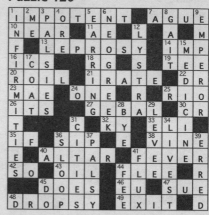

E	D	O	M	I	T	E	S		A	C	T	S	S
P		A	N		G	N	A	S	H			O	
H	A	T	T	I	E		O		S	O	U	L	
O		H		Q	C	U	P		O		I		
D		C	U	T		T	O		S	A	T		
	U	Z	I		E		W	O	E		A		
T	I		T	I	T	H	E		U	R			
O	N	O		Y	E	R		C	R	Y			
N	U	N		I	R	A		F	I				
G			R	N		F	A	C	E				
U	P		G	E	R	A		I		L	B		
E		Y		A		L	E	F	T		U		
S	H	E	E	P			H				Z		

Puzzle 120

I	M	P	O	T	E	N	T		A	G	U	E	E
N	E	A	R		A	E		L		A	M		
F		L	E	P	R	O	S	Y		I	M	P	
I	C	S		R	G	S		T	E	E			
R	O	I	L		I	R	A	T	E		D	R	
M	A	E		O	N	E		R		R	I	O	
I	T	S		G	E	B	A	L		C	R		
T		C		K	Y		E	L	I				
I	F		S	I	P		E		V	I	N	E	
E		A	L	T	A	R		F	E	V	E	R	
S	O		O	I	L		F	L	E	E		R	
D	O	E	S		E	U		S	U	E			
D	R	O	P	S	Y		E	X	I	T	D		

Puzzle 121

L	E	V	I	A	T	H	A	N		D	O	G
A	W	A	R	E		O		S	O	L	O	
B	E		O	R		R	A	M		N		A
	N	A	U	S	E	A		K	I	T		
C	I		T		E	D	S		E	N		
B	A	D	G	E	R		E	S	P	Y		B
A	M		I		A	S		A		A		
D	E	E	R		W	E		B		H	E	N
E	L		D	A		M	A		I			
S		L	I	O	N		H	A	R	T	S	
T	A	M	E		X	I		F	E		H	
D		S	E	E		I	D	A		C	E	
F	O	X		U	N	I	C	O	R	N	D	

Puzzle 122

L	O	P		E	L	I	E	L		S	O	D
A	B	I		M	A	T	T	E		H	A	Y
M	A		A	P	S	E		B	R	A	K	E
P	L	A	N	T	S		S	A	U	L		
	W	A	Y		A	P	O	S	T	L	E	
E	D	E	N		T	R	U	T	H		E	D
L	O	D		M	O	R	E	H		B	A	G
A	R		M	E	D	A	D		L	I	F	E
N	A	M	E	D	A	Y		P	O	T		
	I	D	L	Y		P	A	R	E	N	T	
T	H	R	E	E		P	A	I	D		O	R
E	A	T		Y	E	A	R	N		D	O	E
A	S	H		S	A	T	E	S		O	N	E

Puzzle 123

S	O	B		P	I	P	E		S	W	A	T
O	R	A		A	T	E	R		P	A	V	E
P	E	R		R	E	A	R		E	R	I	E
	N	O	A	M		A	M	E	N	D	S	
S	T	A	I	D		E	N	I	D			
T	A	B	L	E		A	D	D		G	O	A
A	L	A	S		I	T	S		S	L	I	P
Y	E	S		N	N	E		H	E	E	L	S
	J	O	H	N		E	R	A	S	E		
A	D	H	E	R	E		K	E	E	N		
M	I	A	S		R	A	I	D		I	R	E
E	C	R	U		I	D	L	E		N	O	N
N	E	T	S		T	E	N	D		G	O	D

Puzzle 124

C	A		S	E	B	A		S	H	A	M	E
U	R		S	T	E	M		L	I	N	E	N
R	E	S		A	T		W	O	R	D		
B	A	T	T	L	E		A	W	E		A	I
S		A	R		A	S		S	A	N	D	
	R	E	T	E	S	T		T	H	E	E	
T	E		O	N	S	E	T		M	A		
O	B	E	D		M	E	D	I	U	M		
M	E	N	E		I	S		S	O	R	T	
E	D		S	A	T		D	E	E	P	E	R
T	I	N	Y		R	A		S	P	A		
S	H	A	R	E		H	O	R	N		A	D
S	T	R	E	W		A	P	S	E		Y	E

Puzzle 125

```
D A M . H O R S E . B I D
O B E Y . G A L L . U T E
M E L E E . H A Z E R I M
. . T A L L . Y A R N S .
G R I S L E D . B A T . .
R A N T . A R B A S . B Y
E G G . A V O I D . B E E
W E . C R E W S . B L E W
. M A R . N O T I O N S .
. D A V I D . N E T S . .
F O R E V E R . N E S T S
E R R . E B E R . S O R E
W A Y . S T O W S . M A T
```

Puzzle 126

```
B A R A K . H A G G I A H
L . O D E S . S E E T H E
A H . D E E P . M E . E A
R I M . P L O W S . F A R
E N O S . A T E . D A R K
. . D A T A . E . H I T E
C . B E G I N N I N G . N
O H . R E T . . S E R F .
N O O N . P A W . D O E R
C R Y . C I T E S . W E E
E N . G O . E S A U . T I
D E S E R T . T U R N . N
E T E R N A L . L I O N S
```

Puzzle 127

```
R E P . A B E A M . S T A
O E R . S E R V E . P A W
B R O T H E R . S P I N E
. . P E E P . T S A R . .
G A H A R . F A I R E S T
A H E M . G E R A . T O .
A L T . E L I A S . J A W
S A . T O S H . T U R N .
H I G H E S T . N E S T S
. . H E R S . G O A T . .
S T E R N . S O R R O W S
E O N . A N I A M . N O E
W E T . L O R D S . E N E
```

Puzzle 128

```
E T C H . T I S . O B O E
N R A . P A S T E . A L L
D I S T A L . U G A N D A
. C H A L C E D O N Y . M
. K E N . N . . T A P . .
A S S . A G A T E . N A G
I T . D I A M O N D . N O
M E N . D R E G S . B A G
. R I O . L . . L A T . .
N . C H R Y S O L Y T E .
A T E M P O . P U E B L O
N I L . H Y R A X . O A R
O N Y X . O I L . L Y S E
```

Puzzle 129

```
S H Y . D A S H . S P O T
L E E . A C H E . N O A H
I A . D I N E . D A I R Y
P R A I S E . H I P S . .
. W R Y . B E S P E A K .
S U E T . M E R C Y . S I
O L D . B A A L S . G I N
A N . V E N U S . B R A D
P A T I E N T . G E E . .
. O R C A . P R A Y E R .
F A I T H . C A E N . D O
L U L U . L O V E . W E D
T O E . O P E N . O N E .
```

Puzzle 130

```
S U S A . C R A B . R U N
S P E D . Z O B A . O N E
E S A U . A B E L . A D O
. L O R E . A A R O N .
A M I T Y . S A X . .
J E R . S A L E M . M I O
A D A M . B I T . B O T H
R E N . B E T H L E H E M
. O U T . . A T O M S
C H U R N . S A S H .
H A G . D E E P . A C T S
I L L . L O N E . N O A H
P L Y . E N D S . Y O R E
```

Puzzle 131

R	E	A	M		C	O	W		H	O	P	E
I	D	D	O		O	R	O		E	N	O	S
D	E	A	R		R	A	N		W	E	R	E
			T	I	P		D	I	E			
L	A	B	A	N	S		E	N	R	A	G	E
S	T	E	R	N	E		R	E	S	C	U	E
	R	A							H	A		
R	I	S	E	U	P		T	E	M	A	N	S
N	A	T	U	R	E		A	R	E	N	O	T
			R	U	N		B	E	D			
U	N	D	O		U	A	R		D	O	R	A
R	E	A	P		R	T	E		L	E	A	H
I	R	M	A		Y	E	T		E	R	M	A

Puzzle 132

B	A	N	C		F	I	R		E	B	E	D
B	R	I	O		U	R	E		L	O	V	E
B	O	N	N		R	A	N		E	D	E	N
N	E	C	R	O	M	A	N	C	E	R		
			E	A	R		M	O	T			
L	I	M	I	T		F	E	D		W	O	N
E	R	A	T		R	E	D		V	I	N	E
T	A	R		H	E	M		F	I	N	E	R
			S	E	M		S	I	N			
A	S	T	R	O	L	O	G	E	R	S		
A	S	E	A		V	A	N		G	O	A	D
T	I	L	L		E	R	G		A	D	I	N
T	A	L	L		D	D	S		R	E	L	A

Puzzle 133

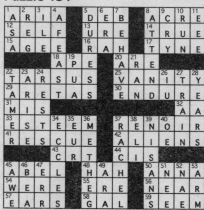

		C	A	B	S	
	S	A	M	E	C	H
G	I	N		W	H	I	T
M	O	N		P	A	I	N	E	D
S	O	N		W	A	R	N		M	E	R
P	R	E	S	A	G	E		S	P	O	I	L
I	T		T	I	E		S	H	E		V	I
N	A	B	A	L		C	H	A	R	G	E	R
L	E	V		C	H	O	W		E	R	A
N	E	P	H	E	W		P	E	S
E	P	E	E		A	I	R
D	E	S	E	R	T
R	E	N	T

Puzzle 134

A	R	I	A		D	E	B		A	C	R	E
S	E	L	F		U	R	E		T	R	U	E
A	G	E	E		R	A	H		T	Y	N	E
			A	P	E		A	R	E			
T	A	R	S	U	S		V	A	N	I	T	Y
A	R	E	T	A	S		E	N	D	U	R	E
M	I	S								A	A	
E	S	T	E	E	M		R	E	N	O	I	R
R	E	S	C	U	E		A	L	I	E	N	S
			C	R	T		C	I	S			
A	B	E	L		H	A	H		A	N	N	A
W	E	R	E		E	R	E		N	E	A	R
E	A	R	S		G	A	L		S	E	E	M

Puzzle 135

A	L	A	S		P	P	D		N	O	A	H
S	A	R	A		A	L	E		A	N	T	I
A	M	A	T		O	S		B	A	T	S	
	P	H	I	L	I	P	P	I	A	N	S	
		S	O	D		A	L	L				
S	W	I	F	T		M	I	L		A	R	I
M	A	N	Y		B	A	R		A	S	I	A
U	S	E		A	R	T		K	N	E	E	L
		P	S	I		S	E	A				
I	N	H	A	B	I	T	A	N	T	S		
I	D	E	O		E	R	A		I	O	T	A
L	O	R	N		R	A	Y		A	L	A	N
A	L	O	E		Y	E	S		S	A	Y	S

Puzzle 136

A	C	T		S	E	T			P	E	N	
S	A	H		L	A	O		E	L	A	N	
P	R	E	D	E	S	T	I	N	A	T	E	
S	T	R	I	P	E		S	O	T			
		E	N	T		S	O	L	O	M	O	N
C	A	F	E		P	A	L	S		O	L	E
A	G	O	D		L	U	D		A	R	E	A
M	A	R		G	A	T	E		S	T	O	P
P	R	E	S	A	G	E		S	E	A		
			L	I	I		S	E	A	L	E	D
P	R	I	N	C	I	P	A	L	I	T	Y	
A	I	D	S		S	A	T		T	R	E	
N	A	E		M	T	S			Y	E	S	

Puzzle 137

A	N	E	W		A	S	P		N	E	T	S
T	E	R	I		M	I	L		E	L	O	I
T	E	E	D		E	R	A		P	I	R	N
			O	W	N		N	I	H			
S	H	E	W	E	D		K	E	E	P	E	R
C	O	A	S	T	S		S	O	W	E	T	H
O	R	G							T	H	E	
R	E	L	I	E	D		A	E	N	E	A	S
E	M	E	R	G	E		S	M	Y	R	N	A
		E	O	N			S	E	M			
M	U	N		I	R	E		P	Y	R	E	
A	R	B	A		E	A	R		H	A	I	R
D	I	S	H		D	E	T		M	E	N	

Puzzle 138

T	A	P		A	R	A	M		S	A	S	E
E	S	A		L	A	T	U		I	G	O	R
R	I	T		T	I	E	R		N	O	N	E
M	A	R	V	E	L		M	E	A			
		I	E	R		J	U	N	I	P	E	R
S	E	A	T		T	A	R	O		R	A	E
E	R	R		S	A	K	E	S		O	S	E
L	A	C		A	X	E	D		U	S	E	D
A	T	H	A	I	A	H		A	N	E		
			A	L	T		G	U	I	L	T	Y
E	B	E	R		I	B	A	R		Y	E	A
V	E	T	O		O	O	L	A		T	A	R
E	D	E	N		N	O	E	L		E	R	N

Puzzle 139

E	T	C		L	A	I	C		S	A	M	E
B	A	L		A	N	N	O		T	R	U	E
E	R	E		B	O	O	N		R	I	D	E
R	E	A	S	O	N		S	I	A			
		N	E	R		B	U	L	W	A	R	K
E	R	T		F	A	M	E		B	E	E	
R	A	W		S	O	R	E	S		U	N	E
A	M	A		A	R	E	S		K	N	O	P
S	A	Y	I	N	G	S		B	I	D		
			M	D	I		M	E	R	A	R	I
A	S	I	A		V	E	E	R		N	O	D
F	L	A	G		E	P	E	E		C	O	D
T	Y	N	E		N	I	T	A		E	T	O

Puzzle 140

G	S	A		S	T	A		P	A	I	N	
L	A	S	T		Y	E	N		A	B	L	E
I	D	E	A		R	E	O		I	B	E	X
B	A	R	B		I	N	T	E	R	E	S	T
			I	R	A		H	R				
T	E	N	T	H		J	E	S	U	R	U	N
A	D	A	H		O	R		N	Y	R	O	
J	O	N	A	D	A	B		S	C	E	N	T
			O	T		P	O	T				
T	O	G	E	T	H	E	R		I	S	N	T
A	L	I	A		E	P	I		O	K	E	
L	I	E	S		N	E	Z		N	O	B	S
C	O	R	E		S	E	E			W	O	E

Puzzle 141

A	L	L		C	O	A	L		B	A	J	A
W	O	E		O	N	C	E		O	N	A	M
E	S	T	A	T	E		B	E	S	I	D	E
		L	E	S	T		N	O	M	E		
D	O	D	O	S		R	O	O	M			
E	V	E	N		B	A	N	C		L	A	D
B	E	N	E	A	R		T	H	R	O	N	E
T	R	Y		M	A	N	O		A	S	T	A
			S	A	Y	S		E	N	T	E	R
T	E	M	A	N		C	O	C	K			
A	R	E	T	A	S		B	O	S	S	E	S
L	A	L	A		A	B	E	L		I	R	A
E	N		N		M	E	D	E		R	E	D

Puzzle 142

C	A	D		D	O	R		I	R	A	D	
A	R	I	B		E	V	E		M	O	L	E
P	E	A	U		M	U	M		R	U	I	N
T	A	L	L		A	M	O	R	I	T	E	S
			W	A	S		V	E				
W	O	M	A	N		H	A	V	I	L	A	H
E	D	A	R		O	I	L		M	E	D	E
S	A	C	K	B	U	T		L	A	V	E	R
			E	T		S	A	G				
C	A	S	T	A	W	A	Y		I	V	A	N
O	M	E	R		A	I	R		N	E	B	O
M	E	N	U		R	O	I		E	R	L	E
A	N	T	E		D	E	A			Y	E	S

Puzzle 143

1 A	2 B	3 B	4 A	■	5 O	6 W	7 N	8 S	■	9 A	10 D	11 O
12 B	A	A	L	■	13 F	E	E	T	■	14 B	I	N
15 E	T	E	S	■	16 T	E	A	R	■	17 O	D	E
18 T	H	R	O	19 N	E	■	20 R	E	21 A	D	Y	■
■	■	22 E	N	G	■	24 E	N	E	M	25 Y		
■	26 A	27 F	T	■	28 L	E	T	■	30 U	R		
31 B	A	R	■	32 F	O	R	■	33 S	34 I	S		
35 H	E	■	36 E	37 B	E	R	■	38 B	E	N		
39 A	N	40 G	E	R	■	41 Y	42 E	A				
■	43 E	N	D	O	44 R	■	45 N	A	46 T	47 H	48 A	49 N
50 F	F	A	■	51 K	A	52 L	E	■	53 H	A	L	E
54 R	I	T	■	55 E	D	O	M	■	56 I	R	M	A
57 I	T	S	■	58 N	O	S	Y	■	59 S	E	A	L

Puzzle 144

1 A	2 R	3 T	■	4 R	5 A	6 F	■	7 S	8 A	9 R	10 A
11 S	O	U	12 L	■	13 A	V	A	■	14 P	L	E	B
15 A	B	B	A	■	16 N	E	S	■	17 A	L	E	E
■	18 W	19 I	T	C	H	C	R	A	F	T		
■	21 H	A	Y	E	S	■	23 I	O	E			
24 L	O	V	E	R	■	25 B	O	W	■	26 T	27 H	28 E
29 O	M	E	R	■	30 T	I	N	■	31 S	H	O	W
32 P	E	R	■	33 S	I	T	■	34 S	H	I	N	E
■	■	35 T	I	M	■	36 R	A	I	S	E		
37 B	38 E	39 F	O	R	40 E	T	I	M	E			
41 A	N	E	W	■	42 W	A	S	■	43 L	44 E	45 N	46 D
47 C	O	T	E	■	48 A	R	E	■	49 D	O	E	R
50 A	S	E	R	■	51 S	O	N	■	52 S	O	Y	

Puzzle 145

1 A	2 G	3 A	4 G	■	5 S	6 I	7 S	■	8 A	9 B	10 B	11 E
12 M	I	L	A	■	13 H	A	P	■	14 L	A	E	L
15 P	E	E	R	■	16 A	M	A	■	17 A	N	T	S
18 R	E	M	E	19 M	B	R	A	N	C	E		
■	21 E	R	E	■	22 R	I	D					
23 A	L	O	N	G	■	26 F	O	R	■	27 R	28 A	29 T
30 F	E	L	T	■	31 N	E	W	■	32 J	O	S	E
33 T	E	D	■	34 M	O	W	■	35 T	U	B	A	L
■	36 A	R	I	■	37 H	E	N					
38 M	39 I	N	I	S	T	E	R	40 I	N	41 G		
43 S	O	N	G	■	44 O	A	R	■	45 P	I	N	E
47 H	A	R	E	■	48 M	I	O	■	49 E	L	A	M
50 E	B	E	R	■	51 E	L	D	■	52 R	E	T	S

Puzzle 146

1 R	2 E	3 A	4 D	■	5 R	6 E	7 D	■	8 P	9 A	10 L	11 E
12 A	L	I	A	■	13 O	R	E	■	14 A	G	A	R
15 M	A	N	Y	■	16 M	A	S	■	17 I	R	I	S
18 S	H	U	S	19 H	■	20 P	A	L	A	C	E	
■	■	22 T	I	N	■	23 A	I	S				
24 N	25 E	26 B	A	T	■	27 T	I	D	■	28 R	29 A	30 N
31 A	D	A	R	■	32 U	A	R	■	33 M	O	V	E
34 M	E	S	■	35 A	N	N	■	36 S	O	B	E	R
■	■	37 E	R	G	■	38 C	O	T				
39 M	40 O	41 U	N	T	O	F	O	L	I	43 V	44 E	45 S
46 E	R	R	S	■	47 D	A	R	■	48 O	A	T	H
49 R	A	G	U	■	50 L	I	D	■	51 N	I	N	A
■	52 N	E	E	■	53 Y	R	S	■	54 S	N	A	G

Puzzle 147

1 L	2 O	3 Y	■	4 A	5 S	6 S	■	7 C	8 I	9 S
10 A	P	E	■	11 L	A	M	■	12 S	A	R	A
13 M	E	R	14 C	I	F	U	15 L	■	16 R	A	W
17 P	L	E	A	S	E	■	18 O	A	T		
■	20 F	R	A	■	21 C	O	V	E	R	22 E	23 D
25 B	L	U	E	■	27 M	U	S	E	■	28 E	V	E
29 L	A	S	S	■	30 O	R	E	■	31 B	E	L
32 U	T	E	■	33 D	R	E	D	■	34 H	E	R	E
35 R	E	D	36 N	E	S	S	■	37 S	E	L	
■	■	38 E	E	E	■	39 S	C	A	L	40 D	41 S
42 S	43 U	P	P	L	44 I	C	A	T	I	O	N
45 I	R	A	S	■	46 D	A	R	■	47 O	N	O
48 R	E	L	■	49 A	T	E	■	50 N	E	W	

Puzzle 148

1 I	2 D	3 A	■	4 C	5 L	6 A	7 P	■	8 S	9 T	10 S
11 R	E	B	■	12 D	E	V	I	L	■	13 Y	E	A
14 A	R	I	■	15 U	N	I	■	16 E	17 A	R	L	Y
■	18 L	19 E	N	T	■	20 L	A	N	I		
■	21 L	E	V	■	22 D	I	S	T	A	23 N	24 T
25 C	O	N	E	■	26 N	A	V	E	S	■	27 O	H
28 A	W	E	■	29 A	R	E	■	30 R	O	E	
31 N	E	■	32 L	33 A	B	A	N	■	34 D	E	N	Y
35 A	R	36 T	E	M	A	S	■	37 O	N	E	
■	38 H	E	A	L	■	39 B	40 A	R	E		
41 A	42 M	I	S	S	■	43 C	I	S	■	44 W	45 A	46 N
47 W	I	N	■	48 A	49 H	I	R	A	■	50 E	N	E
51 L	O	G	■	52 S	A	I	D	■	53 D	E	W	

Puzzle 149

L	A	R	A		H	A		C		J	A	W
O	M	E	R		A	L	M	A		U	S	A
G	I	V	E	P	L	A	C	E		S	I	R
		L	I	V			S	A	T	A	N	
F	A	M	I	N	E		R	A	N	I		
A	L	A		S	T	R	I	F	E			
D	O	G	S		E	E	E		M	I	R	E
	E	N	A	B	L	E		E	N	E		
	I	T	E	M		W	A	N	D	E	R	
R	E	F		W		F	I	L	E			
A	L	I		A	V	E	N	G	E	N	O	T
N	O	E		R	A	N	G		D	A	R	E
D	I	D		E	N	D	S		S	T	A	R

Puzzle 150

O	F	F		A	L	L		F	O	O	T
T	R	E	S		D	O	A		O	M	R	I
T	A	T	A		O	N	T		A	N	C	E
O	M	E	R		P	E	C	U	L	I	A	R
	E	A	T		H	E					
C	A	M	P	S		L	E	A	D	E	R	S
P	L	A	T		H	O	T		E	R	I	E
L	E	B	A	N	O	N		A	C	R	E	S
	O	W		A	W	L					
R	E	M	E	M	B	E	R		A	G	E	D
I	R	A	D		E	S	O		R	A	V	E
D	A	R	E		I	T	S		E	V	E	N
E	N	A	N		T	H	E		E	L	S	

Puzzle 151

W	A	S	T		W	A	D	S		A	R	E
A	S	E	R		A	B	I	A		M	E	R
S	P	R	E	A	D	I	N	G	S		F	A
	A	R	I	D			E	T	T	E	S	
S	H	A	D	E		E	N		A	E	R	
L	A	P		L	O	S	E		T	R	E	E
O	B	T	A	I	N		S	T	E	R	N	S
G	I	F	T		C	A	S	H		O	C	T
	T	O	T	T	E	R		A	G	R	E	E
M	A	R	A	H		R	A	R	E			
A	B		I	R	R	I	G	A	T	I	O	N
S	L	Y		E	A	V	E		U	L	A	N
T	E	R		E	W	E	S		P	E	R	E

Puzzle 152

S	U	P		H	O	L	E	S		S	O	N
T	R	A		E	V	E	N	T		T	W	O
E	N	T	E	R	E	D		A	M	E	N	D
	I	R	O	N			S	T	A	R		
S	H	E	R	D		J	O	U	R	N	E	Y
H	E	N	S		H	O	O	E	Y		R	E
E	A	T		C	O	I	N	S		E	R	A
M	R		V	A	I	N		A	V	E	R	
	T	H	I	R	S	T		S	H	E	D	S
	A	B	E	T		B	E	A	N			
T	H	I	E	F		G	R	A	Z	I	N	G
O	A	R		U	R	I	E	L		N	E	E
P	L	Y		L	A	N	D	S		G	O	T

Puzzle 153

L	I	T		E	R	I	C		D	R	O	P
E	R	A		K	O	O	L		A	C	R	E
T	A	B	R	E	T		A	R	M		G	A
	L	A	D		C	I	D		M	A	R	
O	B	E	Y		G	Y	M		B	A	N	S
N	E	T		S	U	M		R	E	D		
E	D		T	I	M	B	R	E	L		S	A
	E	A	T		A	I	L		H	A	D	
S	O	N	G		E	L	M		M	A	D	E
O	L	D		W	A	S		P	A	L		
R	I		A	I	R		T	I	T	T	L	E
E	V	E	R		E	V	E	N		E	A	R
S	E	A	T		D	I	N	E		D	Y	E

Puzzle 154

B	A	R	S		G	L	A	S	S		D	O
E		H	A	I	L		D	I	E		E	X
E	N		P	R	A	Y		R	E	A	P	
N	O	T		E	D	E	N		D	R	O	P
	S	O	S		L	E	D		E	R	R	
B	E	S	T		P	L	E	A	D		T	I
E		S	E	A	L		D	Y	E	D		D
A	S		P	I	E	T	Y		N	A	M	E
S	T	E		R	A	W		S	U	E		
T	O	L	D		T	I	R	E		B	A	T
	D	I	E	T		N	E	A	R		N	O
A	G		F	A	D		E	R	A	S		R
W	Y		Y	I	E	L	D		M	A	D	E

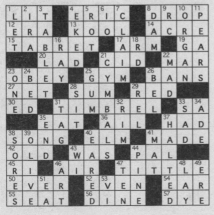

Puzzle 155

	H	A	I	R	S		R	A	G	E	S	
S	U	N	S	E	T		E	V	A	D	E	S
P	S	T		P	U	R	S	E		S	A	P
O	H		P	O	U	R			M	I		
R	A	S	E		O	I	L		B	A	A	L
T	I	M	B	E	R		T	A	L	E	N	T
	E	O	N				R	E	S			
S	T	A	N	D	S		R	E	S	O	R	T
V	E	R	Y		U	S	E		S	P	U	R
E	N		P	R	I	S	M			N	E	
N	O	R		A	E	R	I	E		I	N	N
S	N	A	I	L	S		D	A	N	C	E	D
	S	W	E	E	T		E	L	D	E	R	

Puzzle 156

O	W	E		W	H	E	A	T		T	A	U
W	E	N		H	E	A	V	I	N	E	S	S
N	A	T	I	O	N	S		E	A	S	E	
	R	E	D			S	T	R	A	W		
F	I	R	E	S		A	N		O	S	A	
O	N		A	L	A	R	M	S		A	W	S
C	E	N	S	E	R		A	W	A	K	E	S
U	S	O		E	I	T	H	E	R		E	N
S	S	W		P	E	R		R	O	O	T	S
			I	S	L	A	M		D	A	N	
A	R	A	M			D	E	S	I	R	E	S
H	A	P	P	I	N	E	S	S		S	A	
A	N	T		N	U	R	S	E		E	S	O

Puzzle 157

A	R	E		S	E	E	R	S		M	A	N
P	A	T		T	E	N	E	T		E	R	E
T	H	E	L	O	R	D	L	I	V	E	T	H
	R	E	P				R	O	T			
H	A	N	G	S		A	R	I	S	E	S	
A	L	A	S		C	I	T	E	D		X	I
M	I	L		O	I	L	E	D		S	I	N
A	V		E	N	T	E	R		B	A	L	K
N	E	A	T	L	Y		S	A	V	E	S	
	B	U	Y				A	I				
P	R	A	I	S	E	T	H	E	L	O	R	D
H	A	S		O	D	O	U	R		U	T	E
I	N	E		N	O	T	E	S		R	E	W

Puzzle 158

B	E	E		T	O	G	S		P	A	R	T
A	S	A		A	L	O	E		I	L	A	I
Y	E	S		N	I	L	E		A	I	M	S
	K	I	N	G	O	F	K	I	N	G	S	
	E	E	L	S		I	R	O	N			
W	A	S	T	E		G	N	U		E	A	
A	N	T	S		T	A	G		D	O	W	N
N	Y		W	H	Y		T	O	W	E	D	
		S	T	A	R		S	H	O	E		
	L	O	R	D	O	F	L	O	R	D	S	
H	I	R	E		N	A	U	M		H	U	T
A	N	T	E		E	Z	R	A		I	R	E
M	E	S	S		S	E	S		M	E	N	

Puzzle 159

M	A	R		C	H	O	P		R	A	R	E
E	R	E		H	A	R	E		E	R	I	E
T	E	D		O	R	E	N		M	E	D	E
	E	A	S	T		N	O	I	S	E	S	
T	H	E	M	E		P	I	N	T			
W	O	M	E	N		L	E	E		F	E	D
O	M	E	N		H	A	S		R	A	L	E
S	E	R		D	E	N		F	A	L	S	E
	M	O	A	T			E	N	T	E	R	
R	E	P	E	N	T		R	A	T	E		
E	V	E	R		H	O	U	R		R	E	D
N	E	A	R		E	L	S	E		E	R	R
O	N	L	Y		N	E	E	D		D	A	Y

Puzzle 160

	N	A	I	L	S		B	R	E	E	D	
L	E	A	V	E	N		R	E	N	T	E	D
E	A	R		S	A	R	A	I		A	L	E
A	R		T	R	A	I	N			U	B	
V	E	I	L		E	N	D		M	L	X	I
E	R	R	O	R	S		S	L	A	Y	E	R
		O	A	T				A	R	D		
B	A	N	D	E	D		L	Y	S	I	A	S
L	E	S	S		E	R	A		H	A	L	T
E	N		D	A	I	S	Y			I	A	
S	E	A		A	L	P	H	A		P	E	N
S	A	D	D	L	E		E	R	R	A	N	D
	S	E	V	E	R		S	N	I	T	S	

Puzzle 161

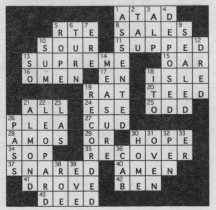

ARE RISES HAS
MAD URKEL ABE
ET ASSYRIA BE
NEEDS VISED
POET HELP
ELI TRUER IDA
TIS ASA ROW
APT SMART ICE
LAMP DEBT
THERE RESIN
RE TARRIED SO
ORE RAILS ALA
WEN STALE NEH

Puzzle 162

DAWN AER ROPE
ARIA BEE EDEN
NEST ILL CORE
SHIED ALARM
ONE TEN
ATONES EATING
WON NEO
LOOSED BASKET
TOE USE
MORNS RALED
MOPE INN LAIR
ALEE ROE ESAU
PENT END RELS

Puzzle 163

SAM GETS RIDE
AGE LAIC ENON
FATHER ABASED
ERRED RACE
ITEMS SHREW
SUCH ETAT TEF
TN BLAME RN
ADE ETRE BO S
ROUSE ENDOR
NERI ERASE
SPIRIT DANCES
ENCE CAIN LEA
T ED HISS EMU

Puzzle 164

ERS TASKS MAD
SAP ALEPH ADO
SWALLOW EATEN
RIOT SALT
CARON SERPENT
ANON HARES OR
LOW COVER ABE
ED SAVE ABLE
BEETLES CRIES
NELL ROAD
THEME NUMBERS
IAM SHEEP TIE
STY TOADS HOT

Puzzle 165

ATAD
RTE SALES
SOUR SUPPED
SUPREME OAR
OMEN EN ISLE
RAT TEED
ALL ESE ODD
PLEA CUD
AMOS OR HOPE
SOP RECOVER
SNARED AMEN
DROVE BEN
DEED

Puzzle 166

ROB HALF OHM
ENOS OLEO BOA
ACRE ETERNITY
LENT MI
ASIDE SLAVE
LEG CELL GEL
ASA ENDED RIM
HAI TEAR ELS
RUNNY RHYME
OED OMER
STEWARDS SEMI
EER RAIL SNIP
EYE SWAY TRE

Puzzle 167

```
C A V E   F L O W
B A T O N   L I G H T
S I N E W   S U P   Y E T
A S E   N U T S   N O
L O   C A S E   S T O P
E N D   A M A   L I O N S
R A G E   N O N E
S H A R E   D E N   S E W
H U G E   P A T E   M E
O N   S I R S   S T I R
E T E   H E N   S H A M E
S A D O C   H A U L S
R O D E   T Y R E
```

Puzzle 168

```
G I L D   H E L P   S T E
A R E A   P L E A   P E A
P E A R L   M E R   L A T
K I D   S T A I R S
S L E E P E R   N E T
T O R N   T A M E R   H O
U S E   S E N O R   M A N
B E   B A R G E   L A T E
C A N   E S C A P E S
B R A N D S   A W
E A R   A L L   L Y D I A
A R E   L A I R   E O N S
R E D   S P I N   R E N E
```

Puzzle 169

```
A N G E   A D A M   A R M
R O L L   P A R A   C O O
T R O D   E M I R   R E O
R E A D S   C H E S T
T H I R D   S H E
R I O   S E A T   A M O S
E L U L   D Y E   L I V E
E L S E   G E M S   N E E
A T E   T H I N K
S H A P E   F L E E S
O E R   A R I A   A T A D
R A M   C O S T   R E B A
T R Y   H O T E   T R I G
```

Puzzle 170

```
B E L   S H E B A   D A Y
A P E   P A N E L   R I E
S I N N E R S   M A I D S
T I N E   L O V E
S P I L T   V E N I S O N
M U L E   B I N D S   M A
E L S   L A N D S   H E M
A S   S O R E S   S A G E
R E D U C E S   P A P A S
O N U S   H E L P
L E E K S   M E N T I O N
A N S   T R A I N   E R E
G E T   S O R R Y   R E D
```

Puzzle 171

```
P S A L M S   T H A R A
R E S I D E S   R A G E S
A L T   S A T   I R O N S
M A I L   L O V E D   D E
S H R E W   R I D   T E N
N A M E S   D I R T
P E D R O   I D O L S
E R E S   U N T I E
S E L   P R E   A S H E R
H P   M A N S E   T A L E
K A M E L   T A R   I D E
O R A T E   S T I R R E D
L E P E R   S A T Y R S
```

Puzzle 172

```
L A M B   A B E L   T E A
A R E A   R A V E   R A W
W E A K   T R E A S U R E
S E T S   S P E N D
C R U D E   B E T A
A I R   A T A D   S P A T
I C E   R A R E R   R U E
N E S T   L A N A   E N D
I N C   T E S T S
O P H N I   B E D S
P L E A S U R E   G U L F
E E R   A S I A   E R I E
N A B   N E A R   D E E D
```

Puzzle 173

T	S	P		A	L	O	N	E	S	P	A

```
T S P   A L O N E     S P A
O I L S     O P E N     H A S
S T O L E     T A S T E T H
      W A R     T I E R S
T R I V I A L     G A D
R E N E     L I O N S     A T
E N G     A M A S S     O D E
E T     C H A R T     A N O N
      A H A     S E A L E S T
    G R A Z E     O M I T
M O O R I N G     T A H O E
E R S     A V E R     S A R I
N E E     H Y E N A     T A N
```

Puzzle 174

```
J A Y     A S P     H E M
O W E     N E T     E N O S
Y E L L O W     D I D     H A
      P I N     M A R     S O S
L A S T     M A N     B A T H
O G     B E D     P E N
G O L D E N     D I G G E D
      E Y E     H O T     A R
D I N E     W A G     D U T Y
A R T     T A P     S I P
M A     F I R     T E M P E R
      M E A N     B E N     E L F
      D R Y     E N D     R I D
```

Puzzle 175

```
F I R     L A M P     L E S S
A C E     I D O L     I R O N
R E M O V E     A R E     L O
      A W E     A N T     D E W
R A I L     A P T     E A S Y
U R N     S I P     C A Y
N M     T E L L E S T     H O
      L O W     I R A     F E W
S H O E     S E E     L A M E
H I T     S A D     W E T
A R     A R K     M I G H T Y
D E A R     E D E N     E W E
E D I T     S O N G     R O T
```

Puzzle 176

```
M I S S     B E A R     E R E
A R C H     E L S E     R O W
A S H E R     P L E A S E
      O R E O     E A S E S
P R O D U C T     A R E
O I L     C R O S S     L B
L O     G U I L E     A I
E T     C A R E D     A T E
      H U R     D E L I V E R
S T O R M     R I S E
A S L E E P     T A R A H
G A D     N A M E     A S I A
E R S     T W I N     C E L T
```

Puzzle 177

```
      O W L S     S L A P
    T R I A L     T A M E D
G R A N D E     A D O R A M
O A T     D E N Y     S I N E
A L O E     P A I R     S C I
L A R G E     G N A S H E R
      G A P     G I N
B L E S S E S     N O B L E
L U R     T O U R     W E E D
E T R E     P R A Y     E V E
W E A S E L     H E A V E N
    S N A K E     A L T E R
      D U E S     B L T S
```

Puzzle 178

```
S I R S     A C R E     O W L
P O E T     R O A D     P O E
A N N A     E M S     N E E D
      E G G     B E G I N
S W E A R     D O T     A S
C L I     D A M     D R O V E
L I N E     M A D     E V E R
A N G R Y     R U E     E R E
P G     R E D     E N T R Y
      B O A R D     S E C
S E E R     E A T     R O B E
A W L     B A R E     A M O S
Y E T     E D E N     H E A T
```

Puzzle 179

T	A	M	A		R	O	M	E		W	A	R
E	L	A	M		A	N	E	M		E	L	I
N	A		E	D	G	E			R	E	A	P
	T	R	U	E		S	T	Y		B	E	
P	R	I	C	E		T	H	I	E	F		
L	A	T	E		S	H	A	M		O	D	D
A	S	H		S	P	A	R	E		R	O	E
N	E	E		T	I	N	E		A	G	U	E
	S	T	I	C	K		S	W	O	R	D	
S	H		A	R	E		M	E	A	T		
T	O	W	N		L	E	A	K		E	R	
O	A	R		A	R	I	A		E	A	S	E
P	R	Y		M	E	E	T		N	E	E	D

Puzzle 180

J	A	W		P	A	R	E		A	I	L	S
A	B	E		E	B	O	N		S	N	E	E
W	E	A	K	E	N	E	D		S	C	A	R
S	T	R	I	P	E		O	I	L			
	T	E	R		A	R	R	O	W	S		
D	I	N	E	D		A	R	E		S	E	E
A	R	E	S		O	L	D		C	E	R	T
T	O	I		A	W	L		R	I	D	E	S
E	N	G	A	G	E		B	E	T			
	H	I	E		A	M	E	R	C	E		
R	I	B	S		F	O	R	E	S	H	I	P
I	D	O	L		O	D	E	D		E	T	E
D	A	R	E		E	D	D	Y		A	Y	E

Puzzle 181

B	A	R		A	S	H	E	R		A	S	A
A	R	T		S	T	A	T	E		D	E	L
B	E		F	L	E	S	H	L	Y		E	A
E	A	G	L	E		I	R	O	N	S		
	E	Y	E	S		N	E	S	T			
D	A	N		P	L	E	A	D		H	E	M
A	R	E		A	R	M		N	O	E		
M	A	R		T	I	R	E	S		I	N	N
	A	N	O	N		S	I	D	E			
B	A	L	A	K		R	O	L	L	S		
A	M		P	E	O	P	L	E	S		A	A
T	O	W		N	I	S	A	N		P	I	N
S	K	Y		S	L	I	P	S		A	R	K

Puzzle 182

S	A	L	E		C	A	R	E		T	O	W
A	M	O	S		A	M	E	N		E	W	E
P	I		T	E	N	T			B	E	E	S
	P	A	R	E		P	S	I		S	T	
C	R	E	T	E		S	A	I	T	H		
R	A	R	E		T	H	I	N		A	H	A
I	C	I		T	H	A	N	K		P	A	N
B	E	L		O	I	L	S		S	P	I	T
	S	H	O	R	T		S	E	E	R	S	
O	H		O	L	D		B	E	E	N		
M	E	A	T		M	E	E	T		A	I	
E	R	R		O	P	E	N		H	E	I	R
R	O	E		W	O	N	T		E	A	R	S

Puzzle 183

S	T	A	R		T	R	Y		S	E	M	I
E	A	S	E		H	O	E		L	A	I	R
A	R	I	A		E	A	T		A	C	R	E
S	E	A	S	O	N	S		A	C	H	E	
	O	W		T	A	S	K					
S	T	O	N	E		H	A		D	E	W	
O	W	N	S		S	U	R	E				
D	O	E		B	E		S	T	E	A	D	
	D	E	N	S		U	R					
L	E	O	N		T	R	E	A	D	E	D	
W	A	G	E		A	R	E		N	O	N	O
E	T	A	S		N	I	L		G	O	O	N
B	E	L	T		S	P	Y		E	R	N	E

Puzzle 184

M	A	R	A		F	O	A	M		D	O	A
O	R	E	B		I	D	L	E		R	U	B
W	A	S	H		L	O	A	D		E	S	E
	T	O	W	E	R		E	M	I	T	S	
S	H	O	R	E		U	S	A				
A	I	R		B	E	E	N		H	A	L	F
I	D	E	A		L	A	D		I	D	O	L
L	E	S	S		S	T	O	P		O	N	E
	E	W	E		R	O	P	E	D			
S	H	A	R	E		W	H	E	A	T		
T	A	X		A	S	I	A		T	I	R	E
A	R	E		R	E	S	T		H	O	U	R
Y	E	S		S	A	T	E		S	N	E	E

Puzzle 185

E	W	E	S		I	L	L		C	H	E	W

Row 1: EWES · ILL · CHEW
Row 2: HINT · NOA · OATH
Row 3: UNDO · HUN · AREA
Row 4: DESIRE · CHRIST
Row 5: CAR · ESS
Row 6: WORSHIP · TENTS
Row 7: EVE · TIP · AIU
Row 8: TAUNT · TRAMPLE
Row 9: EAR · ARE
Row 10: STATUE · IMAGES
Row 11: WISH · ASS · DIVE
Row 12: ALEE · LIE · OVEN
Row 13: NEAR · MRS · WENT

Puzzle 186

Row 1: ASP · KING · HONE
Row 2: PUR · ESAU · OSEE
Row 3: TEE · DAYS · WHEN
Row 4: STAR · DEED
Row 5: SPEAR · RHO · A
Row 6: PANT · BEAST · CA
Row 7: ART · HEART · SON
Row 8: NT · HENCE · WILT
Row 9: FORTH · HALTS
Row 10: TRUE · FIRE
Row 11: HIES · TEAR · NNE
Row 12: ALEE · RAMA · COE
Row 13: MESS · ITEM · ERE

Puzzle 187

Row 1: MTS · BALM · AHAB
Row 2: IRA · ERIE · BADE
Row 3: SETS · ASS · IRON
Row 4: TEETH · ASIDE
Row 5: RES · ENE · DO
Row 6: ANOINTING · TIN
Row 7: REAP · ERG · SORE
Row 8: MAR · WATERPOTS
Row 9: SR · GOD · ROE
Row 10: THEFT · DANCE
Row 11: AHIO · ARE · READ
Row 12: HUMS · SURE · RIE
Row 13: ABET · TEAR · INN

Puzzle 188

Row 1: WARS · KEEP · CAB
Row 2: ESEK · ALAS · HUE
Row 3: BASINS · TALENT
Row 4: URIM · LIETH
Row 5: HALTS · DOMES
Row 6: ACT · ANON · SELL
Row 7: IN · NAVES · IE
Row 8: LESS · PEST · MEN
Row 9: POWER · AMEND
Row 10: SHONE · ALAN
Row 11: LOOSED · SENSES
Row 12: INN · PICK · NEST
Row 13: TES · SEAS · ASPS

Puzzle 189

Row 1: SCALPS · SAVED
Row 2: HASTILY · EXILE
Row 3: AMI · TEE · VINES
Row 4: NEET · WAGES · MI
Row 5: ALLOT · RUN · MER
Row 6: LOOSE · MANE
Row 7: PILOT · SHORT
Row 8: MILS · HATES
Row 9: ATL · GEL · METED
Row 10: DC · DARTS · SAVE
Row 11: EH · OR · EEE · BEE
Row 12: SEINE · RESPOND
Row 13: TREES · SPORTS

Puzzle 190

Row 1: HALE · LEAP
Row 2: SEVEN · EAGLE
Row 3: THREAT · TRUEST
Row 4: RAM · KEPT · RATE
Row 5: AMOS · REEL · SEE
Row 6: PENNS · PREFERS
Row 7: OPP · SAL
Row 8: FROWARD · FADES
Row 9: OIL · SAUL · TIDE
Row 10: EVIL · YEAR · AGE
Row 11: SEVERE · MINDED
Row 12: SEVER · BONES
Row 13: SITS · STEM

Puzzle 191

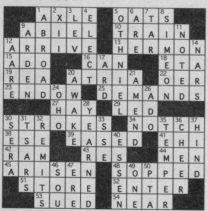

M	A	P		S	W	A	M		S	M	E	E
A	B	I		T	A	R	E		H	E	A	R
R	E	S	T	O	R	E	D		E	A	R	N
S	T	A	I	N		S	E	A	T	S		
		T	E	A		S	H	U	N	S		
A	R	C	H		S	I	G	H		R	A	E
P	U	R	E		I	L	O		R	E	V	E
E	T	E		H	A	L	L		E	D	E	N
S	H	A	D	E			D	I	A			
	T	E	N	T	H		S	L	O	P	E	
E	R	I	E		R	E	M	E	M	B	E	R
L	O	O	P		O	R	A		E	P	I	
M	E	N	S		W	A	R	T		D	E	E

Puzzle 192

I	R	E		S	H	I	P		I	D	O	L
T	E	L		C	A	L	M		M	I	R	E
E	L	I		A	L	L		S	P	E	E	D
		H	A	T	E		S	R	A			
T	R	U	S	T		G	L	O	R	I	F	Y
I	E		A	E	R	I	E		T	A	R	E
R	A	E		R	I	V	E	R		M	A	A
A	C	R	E		P	E	T	E	R		M	R
S	H	R	I	N	E	S		S	E	V	E	N
			T	E	N		A	T	M			
W	I	G	H	T		P	L	O		F	E	W
E	R	I	E		R	E	A	R		E	R	E
B	I	E	R		R	A	S	E		D	A	N

Puzzle 193

	A	X	L	E		O	A	T	S	
A	B	I	E	L		T	R	A	I	N
A	R	R	I	V	E		H	E	R	M	O	N
A	D	O		C	A	N		E	T	A
R	E	A		A	T	R	I	A		O	E	R
E	N	D	O	W		D	E	M	A	N	D	S
	H	A	Y		L	E	D	
S	T	R	O	K	E	S		N	O	T	C	H
E	S	E		E	A	S	E	D		E	H	I
R	A	M		R	E	S		M	E	N
A	R	I	S	E	N		S	O	P	P	E	D
	S	T	O	R	E		E	N	T	E	R
	S	U	E	D		N	E	A	R

Puzzle 194

	B	A	D		B	R	I	D	E		B	A	R
E	P	I		R	E	M	I	T		I	C	E
D	E	F	I	E	D		M	E	N	D	E	D
	F	R	E	D	S		R	O	D
T	R	E	A	D		T	E	N	D	E	T	H
H	U	R	T		R	I	T	A		N	O	E
U	L		E	M	E	R	A	L	D		W	A
M	E	T		E	A	R	S		R	A	I	L
B	R	A	I	L	L	E		P	O	S	T	S
	S	A	T		D	R	A	W	S
N	U	T	M	E	G		O	R	N	E	R	Y
O	R	E		T	E	M	P	T		N	Y	E
B	E	D		H	O	L	E	S		T	E	A

Puzzle 195

R	A	M		B	E	N		S	O	N
A	D	O		E	N	E		P	A	U	L
W	A	S	T	E	D		H	U	R		A	H
	E	O	N		H	E	N		S	T	E
W	A	S	P		L	O	W		S	T	E	M
A	S		S	I	T		P	E	A
S	P	R	E	A	D		N	E	A	R	L	Y
	O	A	T		D	O	N		I	E
C	O	L	T		F	A	T		P	L	E	A
A	W	L		L	A	Y		F	O	E
B	E		A	I	R		P	L	E	A	S	E
	D	E	C	K		V	I	A		R	U	N
	A	T	E		A	N	T		N	E	E

Puzzle 196

A	M	A	N	A			K	I	T	E	S
R	E	F	I	N	E		S	N	E	E	Z	E
M	E	T		N	L		H	I		E	R	A
S	T		D	U	S	T	O	F	F		A	L
	B	E	L	I	E	V	E	R	S	
B	A	R	S		E	N	E		O	H	I	O
E	X	I	T				W	I	D	E
D	E	E	R		G	T	O		A	P	E	R
	F	O	L	L	O	W	E	R	S	
E	R		Y	E	A	R	N	E	D		G	P
R	E	O		A	N		E	R		B	I	O
R	E	W	A	R	D		R	I	V	E	R	S
S	K	E	I	N			E	A	G	L	E

Puzzle 197

O	E	R		R	A	N	G	E		P	A	N
A	R	E		I	D	O	L	S		R	I	A
F	R	I	E	N	D		E	A	S	I	L	Y
		G	A	G		T	A	U	P	E		
L	E	N	T		D	I	M		I	S	L	E
E	N	S		S	I	N		E	N	T	E	R
A	D		S	I	N	G	E	R	S		P	G
V	O	W	E	D		L	A			R	E	
E	W	E	R		V	E	T		H	E	R	D
		A	V	O	I	D		S	A	D		
B	A	K	E	R	S		S	I	L	E	N	T
O	W	E		E	I	G	H	T		E	O	N
W	E	N			T	O	Y	S		M	E	T

Puzzle 198

S	E	A	S		A	B	D	A		A	R	E
I	T	C	H		N	A	I	L		M	E	R
R	A	C	E		T	R	A	P		E	A	R
		E	E	R	I	E		H	A	N	D	S
H	A	P	P	Y		T	A	B				
E	S	T		E	A	S	E		B	A	N	D
L	I	E	S		G	I	N		A	L	O	E
L	A	D	E		U	N	D	O		T	O	E
			E	R	E		A	M	E	N	D	
C	H	I	D	E		E	R	R	O	R		
H	I	D		S	I	D	E		L	E	V	I
O	R	E		T	R	E	E		E	T	A	L
P	E	A		S	E	N	D		S	H	U	L

Puzzle 199

T	I	M	E		P	U	R		C	E	N	T
A	N	O	N		A	T	E		O	S	A	Y
U	N	B	E	L	I	E	F		P	A	I	R
		R	I	D		I	M	P	U	R	E	
B	A	R	G	E		A	L	E	E			
O	B	E	Y		E	N	L	A	R	G	E	D
R	E	S		A	N	G	E	L		O	D	E
A	T	T	E	N	D	E	D		A	R	E	A
		A	D	E	S		S	P	E	N	D	
P	E	R	S	I	A		A	S	P			
S	L	I	T		V	I	G	I	L	A	N	T
I	S	L	E		O	R	E		E	V	E	S
S	E	E	R		R	E	D		S	A	T	E

Puzzle 200

E	L	I		J	E	S	U	S		R	A	P
W	E	N		A	V	I	T	H		I	C	E
E	A		O	M	E	N		O	R	D	E	R
S	H	A	P	E	N		R	U	E			
		M	E	S		R	E	T	I	R	E	D
A	N	O	N		L	I	N	E	N		A	R
B	E	N		F	A	V	O	R		U	S	E
E	R		T	A	K	E	N		B	L	E	W
L	I	G	H	T	E	R		M	I	L		
		H	I	N		R	E	T	A	I	N	
S	T	O	N	E		L	A	D	E		R	E
T	E	S		S	H	I	N	E		M	O	S
P	A	T		S	E	E	K	S		A	N	T

HEROES OF THE FAITH

This exciting biographical series explores the lives of famous Christian men and women throughout the ages. These trade paper books will inspire and encourage you to follow the example of these "Heroes of the Faith" who made Christ the center of their existence. 208 pages each. Only $3.97 each!

Gladys Aylward, Missionary to China
Sam Wellman

Brother Andrew, God's Undercover Agent
Alan Millwright

Corrie ten Boom, Heroine of Haarlem
Sam Wellman

William and Catherine Booth,
Founders of the Salvation Army
Helen Hosier

John Bunyan,
Author of The Pilgrim's Progress
Sam Wellman

William Carey, Father of Missions
Sam Wellman

Amy Carmichael, Abandoned to God
Sam Wellman

Fanny Crosby, the Hymn Writer
Bernard Ruffin

Frederick Douglass,
Abolitionist and Reformer
Rachael Phillips

Jonathan Edwards, the Great Awakener
Helen Hosier

Jim Elliot, Missionary to Ecuador
Susan Miller

Charles Finney, the Great Revivalist
Bonnie Harvey

Billy Graham, the Great Evangelist
Sam Wellman

C. S. Lewis, Author of Mere Christianity
Sam Wellman

Martin Luther, the Great Reformer
Dan Harmon

George Müller, Man of Faith
Bonnie Harvey

Eric Liddell, Olympian and Missionary
Ellen Caughey

David Livingstone,
Missionary and Explorer
Sam Wellman

George Washington Carver,
Inventor and Naturalist
Sam Wellman

D. L. Moody,
the American Evangelist
Bonnie Harvey

Samuel Morris,
the Apostle of Simple Faith
W. Terry Whalin

Mother Teresa,
Missionary of Charity
Sam Wellman

Watchman Nee, Man of Suffering
Bob Laurent

John Newton, Author of "Amazing Grace"
Anne Sandberg

Florence Nightingale, Lady with the Lamp
Sam Wellman

Mary Slessor, Queen of Calabar
Sam Wellman

Charles Spurgeon, the Great Orator
Dan Harmon

Hudson Taylor, Founder,
China Inland Mission
Vance Christie

Sojourner Truth, American Abolitionist
W. Terry Whalin

William Tyndale,
Bible Translator and Martyr
Bruce and Becky Durost Fish

John Wesley, the Great Methodist
Sam Wellman

George Whitefield, Pioneering Evangelist
Bruce and Becky Durost Fish

Available wherever books are sold.
Or order from:
Barbour Publishing, Inc.
P.O. Box 719
Uhrichsville, Ohio 44683
http://www.barbourbooks.com

If you order by mail, add $2.00 to your order for shipping.
Prices subject to change without notice.